MODERN INTRODUCTORY PHYSICS

Modern Introductory Physics

IRA M. FREEMAN

Associate Professor of Physics
Rutgers University

SECOND EDITION

McGRAW-HILL BOOK COMPANY, INC.

New York   Toronto   London

1957

PREFACE   *57982*

An increasing number of American colleges and universities are including one or more introductory science courses in the curricula of students majoring in other fields. This book was written primarily for a physics course of such type, addressed to undergraduates whose major is not science. It is not assumed that the student has previously studied physics, or even any other specialized science.

Anyone whose previous formal training has been devoted largely to the arts and humanities may well lack enthusiasm for beginning his study of science, and especially for beginning it with a branch having the unfortunate reputation of physics. The commonest reason for the existence of this feeling is, however, nothing more than our natural human distrust of the unfamiliar. As Bronowski[1] points out,

> Many people persuade themselves that they cannot understand mechanical things, or that they have no head for figures. These convictions make them feel enclosed and safe, and of course save them a great deal of trouble. But the reader who has a head for anything at all is pretty sure to have a head for whatever he really wants to put his mind to. His interest, say, in mathematics, has usually been killed by routine teaching, exactly as the literary interest of most scientists (and, for that matter, of most non-scientists) has been killed by the set book and the Shakespeare play. Few people would argue that those whose taste for poetry has not survived the School Certificate are fundamentally insensitive to poetry. Yet they cheerfully write off the large intellectual pleasures of science as if they belonged only to minds of a special cast. Science is not a special sense. It is as wide and literal as its name: knowledge.

As to the pertinency of studying science, very little need be said at this stage in history. The ingenious gadgets that surround us in ever-increasing numbers are showy and hard to ignore, but they are not science any more than a legal brief or a cake recipe is literature. Science is a major factor in our modern culture. It is something we must study and understand if only because it is

[1] Bronowski, J., "The Common Sense of Science," William Heinemann, Ltd., London, 1951.

v

drastically altering the world and the institutions with which today's students will have to cope. Specifically, a good case can be made for choosing physics as the branch of science to be studied. This point will be elaborated in Chapter 1.

In preparing this book, I have limited the number of topics treated, selecting from the vast and ever-growing body of material only those portions which I feel are intrinsically important and which help in a significant way in the attainment of some grasp of the scope, methods, aims, and conclusions of classical and modern physics. It is hoped that limitation of the subject matter will make available a reasonable amount of time for exploring the wider implications of this science and for examining its method of attacking problems. The text seeks to give adequate attention to the historical and philosophical aspects of the science, for I find that these are features that can most readily make the subject vital and meaningful for the nonscience student.

At the time the first edition of this book appeared, the idea of treating a restricted number of topics in depth was considered somewhat novel. It is gratifying to find that this approach has been well received, and is even being extended to courses intended for professional scientific training.

A number of teachers who used the earlier edition were kind enough to communicate suggestions for improving the usefulness of the book. In line with this advice, a new chapter on thermodynamics was incorporated into the text. In addition, the number and range of difficulty of the exercises have been extended and the lists of reading references have been enlarged considerably. Numerous other changes have been made, including the introduction of a few elementary trigonometric expressions. The Appendixes have been rounded out to include analytical deductions of a few significant relationships quoted in the text.

IRA M. FREEMAN

CONTENTS

Chapter 1

THE DEVELOPMENT OF SCIENCE

In the public mind, the sciences have a reputation for being inherently difficult and forbidding. If it were not for the technical applications influencing almost every phase of modern life, it is doubtful that there would exist even the casual interest usually encountered.

There is no denying the fact that the ideas and concepts of science are not generally light intellectual fare and that the attainment of even a reasonable mastery of a single specialized branch of the subject requires a lifetime of diligent application. On the other hand, there is nothing mysterious or difficult to grasp in the general way in which a scientist works. The primary characterizing feature of scientific activity is a very simple idea—that of attempting to arrive at objective knowledge and understanding without regard to personal prejudices or desires. The motive behind this activity is a craving for intellectual satisfaction; it is, more bluntly, curiosity.

The history of scientific thought is a long one. Like that of any other human enterprise it is marked by many tribulations, much groping, and frequent failures, as well as by superb triumphs and brilliant achievements. But there is an essential way in which scientific activity differs from other forms of endeavor: it is *sequential*. The bulk of verified knowledge is handed on from one generation of scientists to the next. This body of information may experience much modification and revision in the process; but the important point is that it continues to evolve as it grows. It is not possible to say this in a broad sense for any other branch of knowledge. To be sure, in such subjects as political history we have a continually increasing body of factual information. However, this type of growth differs importantly from the development of science in that the latter alone deserves to be termed *sequential*.

1

The saints of today are not necessarily more saintly than those of a thousand years ago; our artists are not necessarily greater than those of early Greece; they are likely to be inferior; and, of course, our men of science are not necessarily more intelligent than those of old; yet one thing is certain, their knowledge is at once more extensive and more accurate. The acquisition and systemization of positive knowledge is the only human activity that is truly cumulative and progressive.[1]

In order to appreciate the procedures that science has evolved for investigating nature, some consideration will now be given to the earlier history of the development of scientific thought. At this point only a very short and compact sketch will serve; in later chapters and in the references cited you will find some of the more important achievements discussed in greater detail.

THE ORIGINS OF SCIENCE

Science had its origin in some remote era when people began to show curiosity concerning their environment and to record what they saw. In time, reflection on these observations led to the idea that nature is knowable and dependable and that as a result predictions could be made which would give man a certain degree of control over his environment. This approach was a great advance over the belief in magic and supernatural forces with which primitive man tried to influence natural events. Thus the new way of viewing the universe was characterized by an implicit confidence in the idea that nature is uniform and orderly—that she operates according to "laws." This concept will be amplified below.

The actual birth of science took place in prehistoric times, probably in Egypt and Babylonia, more than 2000 years before the Christian era. Initially for the purpose of meeting practical needs, considerable amounts of astronomical information based on observation were accumulated by these peoples. But true progress in science did not begin until about the sixth century B.C., when the Greek civilization began to flourish. The next 500 years was the age of the great philosophers of antiquity—Thales, Pythagoras, Plato, Aristotle, Archimedes, and others.

It was Aristotle who laid the foundation for the scientific outlook on questions about nature. His influence in many fields, including politics, ethics, rhetoric, and metaphysics as well as science, was

[1] Sarton, George, "Introduction to the History of Science," Williams & Wilkins, Baltimore, 1927.

still in evidence twenty centuries after his time. One of Aristotle's greatest and more lasting contributions to knowledge was his promotion of the *inductive,* or *synthetic,* method of reasoning—the method of proceeding from particular facts to generalizations concerning them. He stated his thesis in this way:

We must not accept a general principle from logic only, but we must prove its applicability to each fact; for it is in facts that we must seek general principles, and these must always accord with facts, from which induction is the pathway to general laws.

However, in much of his work, Aristotle apparently failed to follow his own doctrine. Too often he showed himself willing to draw hasty inferences based on insufficient evidence and to cling to a previous conclusion in the face of new observations that contradicted it.

Of all the prominent Greek thinkers, Archimedes is notably one who may be classed as scientific in the modern sense. He discovered some of the basic laws governing mechanisms and floating bodies and brought them to bear on a variety of practical problems. To Archimedes we owe the first applications of mathematics to the description of nature. He was very far in advance of his time.

With the exception of the work of this man, Greek science, with its preference for "armchair philosophy" over experiment, had a certain sterility about it and left relatively few specific results of lasting value. But whatever the shortcomings of their science the Greeks did leave behind them two outstanding accomplishments contributing to future progress. They originated the concept of *pure science*—the quest after knowledge for its own sake—and they developed the use of *mathematical reasoning*—the first step toward exact science.

Roman civilization contributed little to the development of science. As far as this subject was concerned, the Romans were interested almost exclusively in its practical applications. They also built great libraries to preserve the results of Greek culture, but they added little that was new in scientific thought. By A.D. 500 the Roman Empire began to disintegrate, and the Arabian civilization that followed it did little more than maintain the Greek learning.

In this brief sketch perhaps only two names merit mention in the entire period from the Greeks to the Renaissance. One is that of

Claudius Ptolemy of Alexandria, who made original observations in optics. His greatest work was the collection of the known astronomical information of that time into an encyclopedic work called the *Almagest* (A.D. 139).

The other important name in science during this long period is that of the Arabian Alhazen (died 1038), who contributed to mathematics, astronomy, and especially to many phases of optics.

The ascendant intellectual influence during the Middle Ages was the Church. A fusion of the teachings of Aristotle and those of the Church, largely brought about by St. Thomas Aquinas in the thirteenth century, developed into the great movement known as Scholasticism, which dominated the important centers of learning in Europe.

The turbulent transitional period (the fourteenth to the sixteenth century) between medieval and modern times—the Renaissance—was a time of intense intellectual activity. Such men as Copernicus, Kepler, Galileo, and Newton completely freed science from the domination of Aristotelian thought and introduced the modern scientific outlook based on observation and experiment.

First in importance among the scientific achievements of the Renaissance was the advancement of the view that the sun, rather than the earth, is the center of our system of sun, moon, and planets. At the beginning of the sixteenth century the prevailing idea was that of an earth-centered universe, as described by Ptolemy. The Polish astronomer Nikolaus Copernicus saw that a much simpler interpretation of observed planetary motions could be obtained by assuming that the earth is merely one of the planets and that all of them move about the sun. In our present age of relatively great freedom of thought and expression it is hard to appreciate the courage required to advance an idea of this nature. A great wave of opposition and harsh criticism confronted Copernicus's views when, near the end of his life, he consented to their publication.[1]

Copernicus's *sun-centered* theory of the solar system was only qualitative. Johannes Kepler, a German astronomer, became interested in attempting to find a general mathematical description of the Copernican system. Utilizing the extensive and accurate ob-

---

[1] The manuscript, called "De orbium coelestium revolutionibus," was printed in 1543 after its author's death. In the same year appeared the first comprehensive treatise on anatomy by the Belgian physician Andreas Vesalius.

servations of planetary positions made by his teacher, the Danish astronomer Tycho Brahe, he puzzled over the problem for nearly a quarter of a century, to emerge finally (1618) with an empirical solution. In the form of three laws of planetary motion (page 89) he reduced all the complicated motions of the planets to ordered simplicity. More than half a century later, Newton was to make a momentous advance and actually *deduce* Kepler's laws by assuming the existence of a force called "gravitation."

The true spirit of modern scientific inquiry is generally admitted to have its first clear expression in the work of the gifted Italian Galileo Galilei. His recognition of observation and experiment as the basis of scientific work is the outstanding characteristic of the science of today. It is often said that he replaced the question "Why?" which Aristotle put to nature with "How?" Galileo's stormy personality and insistence on his way of thinking brought him into grave difficulties with the authority of the Church, and he was forced to deny formally his support of the Copernican ideas. Many references to Galileo's work will appear later in this book.

Newton was born in England in 1642 (Julian calendar), within a year of Galileo's death. While men such as Copernicus and Kepler had launched the scientific method, it remained for Newton to bring it to full development. Galileo had gone a great part of the way, but Newton completed the process by checking his theories by means of further experiments. Moreover, Newton's use of mathematics in shaping theory was much more profound and complete than that of his predecessors. With his keen insight and sound judgment he was able to lay the foundations of mechanics—and hence of most of physical science—as well as to make contributions of first importance in optics and in pure mathematics.

It is fair to say that Newton's genius for synthesizing and generalizing experience has rarely been equaled in the history of human thought. You will be in a better position to evaluate this statement after following the details of some of these accomplishments in subsequent chapters of this book.[1]

[1] Even a brief look at some of Newton's original writings will show the breadth of his interests and his mastery of scientific exposition. See, for example, "Principia mathematica," edited by F. Cajori (University of California Press, Berkeley, Calif., 1934) and "Opticks," edited by E. T. Whittaker (McGraw-Hill, New York, 1931).

WHAT SCIENTISTS DO

What is the general nature of the scientific approach to problems—the procedure anticipated by Aristotle and developed by Copernicus, Kepler, and especially Newton? The answer is implicitly contained in the history of scientific thought, even in the brief sketch given in the preceding paragraphs, but it may be well to detail and amplify some of its features.

Let it be said at the outset that there is no rigid "scientific method" for studying nature—no set procedure that is invariably followed in scientific investigation. It has been asserted that there are as many scientific methods as there are scientists! Moreover, the steps that lead to a scientific advance must vary with respect to the particular area or problem treated. A single, invariable formula simply does not exist.

With this caution in mind, let us put down, for purposes of discussion, a rather inclusive list of some features of the scientific enterprise:

1. *Delimitation of the problem.* Choice of a particular group of phenomena for attention at a given time.
2. *Collection* and careful recording of *observations* relating to the selected area.
3. *Correlation and systematization* of the observations, leading to *generalizations* (scientific laws).
4. *Construction of a hypothesis,* or theory, embracing all the evidence.
5. *Deductions from theory,* suggesting new observations.
6. *Testing* or differentiating between alternative hypotheses by means of *crucial experiments*.

A study of the history of scientific ideas will show that in some instances these steps are often used in quite other orders than the one given, and that in many cases some of them are omitted altogether. The familiar fact that a "flash of insight" can often forward the progress of scientific work implies the possibility of short-circuiting some of the stages outlined above. Scientific activity, like any other creative activity, is difficult to fit into a pattern. Ask any practitioner of science what scheme or pattern of thought he has followed in a particular investigation and he will be hard-pressed to give a definite answer. From Galileo to Einstein, the history of science is replete with instances of worthy ideas that did not originate, at least consciously, from the contemplation of nature, but in some much more obscure and intangible way.

The stubborn fact remains, however, that every natural science must make contact with the actual world of experience at some point or other. We can see how this works out by returning to an examination of the features listed above.

With regard to the first point, little need be said. For purely practical reasons, some restriction of attention must be enforced. The outlining of a suitable area of interest and the fixing of its boundaries are not always easy; but, at the start, some selection must be made according to one's best judgment and state of knowledge at the time.

With the second step, that of assembling observations, we come to the point that sharply differentiates Greek science from its modern counterpart. The former was an a priori science, based too often on speculation rather than on experience. It failed to recognize the fact that all natural science, if it is to deal with the universe as we can know it, must be founded on observation. The distinction is aptly stated by Andrade and Huxley:[1]

Science means finding out how things actually *do* happen, not laying down principles as to how they *ought* to happen.

In the above discussion the terms "observation" and "experiment" have been used almost interchangeably. The distinction is well expressed by Cajori (Ref. 14):

In observation the scientist simply takes notice of the phenomena nature happens to present to his unaided senses. In experimentation, the scientist creates new situations in nature and exacts a reply as to the consequences of these new situations.

In this sense we regard astronomy primarily as an observational science, where we must watch passively while the phenomena unfold. In physics or chemistry, for example, we can often "set the stage" for events to happen, and this constitutes experimentation. But in either case the important thing is the extraction of objective evidence from what is seen. This is by no means easy, for human

[1] "More Simple Science: The Earth and Man," p. 328, Harper, New York, 1936.

sense impressions often deceive (sensory illusions, hallucinations, etc.).

Another question to be faced in making observations is *how much* to look for. There are so many diverse aspects to even the simplest phenomenon that it would be impossible in practice to search out and record every one of them. Even after resolving to circumscribe the inquiry and arranging experimental conditions to rule out unwanted and secondary effect, questions often arise as to the pertinence of a given observation to the question at hand. If, say, the problem is that of determining how a stone moves when allowed to fall, should the color of the stone, the time of day, and the temperature of the air be recorded when the experiments are made? This is always a difficult question and, at the start of a new investigation, frequently impossible to answer. The selection of what are called *relevant observations* in a given problem depends to a great extent on the judgment of the investigator, and circumstances that are relevant to one problem may be irrelevant or trivial in another.

In many scientific investigations, particularly in physics, it is often possible to arrange matters so as to reduce what would otherwise be an unmanageable set of conditions. Galileo, in one phase of his work on the motion of a falling body, saw that the complicating effect of the resistance of the surrounding air might be made ineffective by using massive bodies for which air resistance was relatively negligible. It was not until much later that the more general problem of the fall of an object in a resisting medium was solved—and then only for objects of special shape moving at relatively low speeds. At the present time, much time and effort is being spent on experiments that will, it is hoped, make possible the extension of the solution to very high speeds; but the general problem is still unsolved.

There is one aspect of the question of making observations that is usually taken for granted, namely, that an observation made today may be expected again on another occasion when the same essential conditions prevail. This proposition, variously called the *constancy* (or "uniformity") *of nature* or the "orderliness of the universe," is absolutely essential if there is to be any science at all. According to W. H. Watson:[1]

[1] "On Understanding Physics," Macmillan, New York, 1938.

The Uniformity of Nature is not a hypothesis about the world at all—we are not prepared to substitute an alternative hypothesis—it is a statement concerning our method of representing nature.

Ernst Mach has said:[1]

All our efforts to mirror the world in thought would be futile if we found nothing permanent in the varied changes of things.

Other authorities have termed the proposition an article of faith, tolerated in science because it is in accord with experience. In any case, whether this principle is something inherent in and characteristic of nature itself or whether it is merely a creation of the mind, its *usefulness* to science is beyond question. It is science's answer to the ancient belief in capricious demons and deities—a motion that still survives in some of our superstitions of today.

Closely connected with any discussion of the uniformity of nature is the question, "What about a phenomenon that is observed only once?" The answer is that if close examination fails to reveal any mistake in observation the question must for the time being remain open. It is characteristic of the spirit of science that once-observed phenomena are not discredited but are viewed with suspended judgment.

If science were to stop with the mere amassing of data, it would be nothing more than an encyclopedia or a catalogue of isolated facts. We realize that this is not the case, and this brings us to another point—that of classification and generalization (page 6). There seems to be some natural craving of human intellect for synthesis. This may, in part, be connected with a desire to simplify our environment or at least to make it easier to grasp in its totality.

A generalization, arrived at by inductive reasoning, must be based on a large number of particular observations. Unlike a civil law there is no element of compulsion or obligation about a natural law. It has been said that the former is a *pre*scription, while the latter is a *de*scription—a concise statement of the behavior of nature with respect to a certain group of phenomena.[2] Galileo made such a synthesis, for example, when he announced that all stones fall at the same rate. Again, Kepler correlated Tycho's particular observations on the positions of the planets and arrived at three

[1] "Popular Scientific Lectures," Open Court, La Salle, Ill., 1895.
[2] Compare the quotation from Andrade and Huxley given on p. 7.

laws describing the motions of all the planets. Newton performed a further synthesis by combining Galileo's mechanical results, Kepler's laws of planetary motion, and additional observations on tides, comets, etc., into one magnificent generalization—the law of universal gravitation.

It is important to distinguish between a particular fact (observation) and a specific law. The differentiating factor is that of generality. A specific fact relates to one individual, while a law is a statement about an entire class of individuals. Thus the statements, "There are 16 ounces in a pound" and "The diameter of the earth is 8000 miles," are statements of particular fact; actually, both amount to matters of pure convention. On the other hand, such statements as "The total amount of energy in the universe is constant" or "The sum of the angles of a triangle is 180°" apply, respectively, to *any* energy transformation and to *any* triangle. They are true generalizations.[1]

A generalization, once attained, then serves as a short cut to experience. For instance, suppose the generalization is "A piece of iron will sink when placed in water." Having arrived at this conclusion a long time ago through seeing innumerable pieces of immersed iron sink to the bottom, we feel it is unnecessary to test this proposition further—that the next piece of iron we have occasion to place in water will go to the bottom. And yet there is no absolute guarantee that the very next time the experiment is tried it will work this way! We can never be completely sure; and a little reflection will show that all generalizations, being necessarily based on a finite number of cases, can at best be said to have a given *probability* of being true.

This probability, of course, increases rapidly with the number of cases at hand; and if a generalization has already been successful in encompassing a very large number of observations, it may for all practical purposes be assumed to be valid unless and until a contradictory observation turns up. In the example of the experiments on iron immersed in water, it is quite conceivable that a certain piece of iron, when placed under water, will slowly rise to

---

[1] The proposition about the triangle is not quite like the generalizations that constitute natural laws, for it is not based directly on experience but is deduced from certain geometrical *axioms* whose validity is assumed at the start. In mathematics, such sets of axioms take the place of observations in natural science. In this respect, mathematics is a sort of idealized science.

the surface instead of sinking. But examination of this object may show it to have a large cavity inside it, in which case harmony is at once restored, provided that we have a *theory* of flotation.

This brings us naturally to the next item listed on page 6—the setting up of a hypothesis. This may be characterized as a working guess as to how the generalizations are connected in a logical system. A good hypothesis suggests new experiments, and if the additional findings bear it out, the hypothesis is said to attain the status of a scientific theory.

Two quotations are appropriate here. In discussing the Copernican theory (page 4), Armitage[1] says:

We have first to understand what is meant by the "truth" of a scientific theory. In science we employ the word "truth" in a rather special sense, differing from its use in everyday life. In judging the truth of a theory we apply two main tests. On the one hand we expect a theory to be able to take hold of a mass of facts which seem isolated and meaningless and to bind them together into an intelligible system so that we can see the connections between them. On the other hand we expect a theory to be able to suggest lines of enquiry along which further investigations can be fruitfully made. These may lead to fresh discoveries resulting, perhaps, in the overthrow of the old theory and the setting up of a new one able to account for the new discoveries as well as for the facts previously known. For no theory in science is regarded as the final truth, only as a step, or as a useful tool, towards the attainment of a further measure of truth.

Herbert Dingle[2] adds:

A scientific statement must, directly or indirectly, express experience and be subject to the test of experience. If the expression is indirect, the connexion must be rational. These requirements have been satisfied by scientists with a consistency and purity of practice that is not even approximately equalled in any other large-scale human endeavour; that is why science has made such astonishing progress in so short a time.

The wave theory of light, to be discussed later in this book, is a splendid example of a successful scientific theory. Advanced originally as a working hypothesis to explain a limited number of laws, it suggested new phenomena to seek out. It turned out that the wave idea accounted for the additional facts in a more satisfactory way than did any other proposed scheme.

[1] Reference 7, at end of chapter.
[2] "The Scientific Adventure," Philosophical Library, New York, 1953.

The same striving for simplicity that makes the mind seek out generalizations also leads it to choose between alternative theories if they exist. Other things being equal, we usually prefer the simpler of two conceptual schemes. On this ground alone, the Copernican theory of the solar system (page 4) gained the ascendancy over the ideas of Ptolemy. A successful theory brings us a great measure of mental satisfaction. In terms of such a theory, we gain a feeling of understanding a given aspect of our environment, where by "understanding" we mean appreciation of the connections linking the phenomena to the more familiar facts of our experience.

If a discrepancy is found between a well-established theory and new experimental evidence, the first thing that should be done is to check the experimental conditions, various persons repeating the test if necessary in order to ensure the validity of the observation. If there is still a conflict, it is the theory that must yield. If the theory has been highly successful in explaining a large number of previous observations, it is extremely unlikely that it will have to be abandoned altogether. It may be possible to alter certain parts of it to bring the acquired information into harmony with what was known before.

The role of mathematics in science is a double one. It is both a tool and a medium of expression. The framework of natural laws leading to the establishment of a theory is usually, although not always, constructed with the help of mathematics acting as a sort of formalized logic. Once the theory is attained, it is often found that the best way to describe it is in terms of mathematical symbols. In many instances a mathematical formulation is not possible, and ordinary language must take the place of mathematics in both roles; but the rules of mathematics are far more rigid and its concepts much more precise than those of language (see Ref. 9), and the sciences that are able to avail themselves of mathematical formulation to a great extent are justly called *exact* sciences.

The foregoing sketch is regrettably brief and inadequate. It is felt, however, that the material of the remainder of this book is really in continuation of the present discussion since physics, to a greater extent than any other science, furnishes good examples of the principles outlined above. Consideration of some of the specific material of the following chapters in the light of these principles will prove more profitable than an extension of the general discussion at this point.

READING REFERENCES

For General Reading

1. Eddington, A. S.: "The Nature of the Physical World," Macmillan, New York, 1928.
2. Jeans, J. H.: "The Universe Around Us," 4th ed., Macmillan, New York, 1944. References 1 and 2 are representative expositions by two of the ablest modern interpreters of science. They are "heavy going" for popular treatments but should be read nevertheless for their general flavor.
3. Russell, Bertrand: "The Scientific Outlook," Norton, New York, 1931.
4. Crowther, J. G.: "The Social Relations of Science," Macmillan, New York, 1941. Besides treating the phase of the subject described by the title, this book presents a skillful account of the development of science.
5. Somerville, J.: "The Way of Science," Schuman, New York, 1953. A remarkably clear and simple exposition of how science developed and what it does.
6. Conant, J. B.: "Modern Science and Modern Man," Columbia University Press, New York, 1952. The content of four lectures delivered at Columbia University.
7. Armitage, A.: "The World of Copernicus," Mentor Books, New York, 1947.
8. Harsányi, Zsolt: "The Star Gazer," translated by Paul Tabor, Putnam, New York, 1939. A novelized life of Galileo. Extremely interesting and instructive for the picture it presents of the times during which Galileo lived.
9. Hayakawa, S. I.: "Language in Action," Harcourt, Brace, New York, 1941. Discusses some of the problems connected with the use of language in ordinary affairs and in science.

For Historical Reference

10. Anthony, H. D.: "Science and its Background," Macmillan, New York, 1948.
11. Butterfield, H.: "The Origins of Modern Science, 1300–1800," Macmillan, New York, 1951.
12. Taylor, F. S.: "A Short History of Science and Scientific Thought," Norton, New York, 1949.
13. Crew, H.: "The Rise of Modern Physics," Williams & Wilkins, Baltimore, 1935.
14. Cajori, F.: "A History of Physics," Macmillan, New York, 1929.
15. Cohen, M. R., and I. E. Drabkin: "A Source Book in Greek Science," McGraw-Hill, New York, 1948.

16. Moulton, F. R., and J. J. Schifferes: "The Autobiography of Science," Doubleday, New York, 1945. Excerpts from the most important original writings of many scientists. Brief biographies are also given in many instances.

Primarily for the Instructor

17. Frank, Philipp: "Between Physics and Philosophy," Harvard University Press, Cambridge, Mass., 1941.
18. Bridgman, P. W.: "The Nature of Physical Theory," Princeton University Press, Princeton, N.J., 1936.
19. Bronowski, J.: "The Common Sense of Science," Heinemann, London, 1951. Develops the idea that the layman's key to science is its unity with the arts.
20. Conant, J. B.: "On Understanding Science," Yale University Press, New Haven, 1947. Suggests a means of teaching the scientific method through selected examples taken from the history of science.
21. Hanson, N. R.: The History and Philosophy of Science in Undergraduate Physics, *Phys. Today*, Vol. 8, No. 8, p. 4, 1954.
22. Cohen, I. B.: A Sense of History in Science, *Am. Jour. Phys.*, Vol. 18, No. 6, pp. 343–359, 1950.

Chapter 2

PHYSICS AS AN EXACT SCIENCE

2·1 The Scope of Physics

The various sciences may be divided into two broad classes, physical and biological, the former dealing with inanimate matter and the latter with living things. Until about a century ago it was perfectly possible for one man to master the entire body of knowledge of science, and many outstanding workers in physics and chemistry were also competent physicians and biologists. Today, of course, the situation is decidedly different. The tremendous upswing of scientific activity and the attendant accumulation of information during the past few decades have forced scientists to specialize their activities to an ever-increasing degree, often with the regrettable result that a worker in one subbranch of a given field can know only in a general way what his colleague in a neighboring cubicle of the same subject is doing. Perhaps the situation will not always be so discouraging as it now seems, for it is possible that future discovery of broader generalizations will serve to unify science to a greater extent and reveal connections and correlations between entire fields whose details must now be studied separately.

A century ago there was no clear-cut division between the several branches of physical science as we know them today: physics, chemistry, astronomy, geology, meteorology, etc. Instead all were included in the term *natural philosophy*. Not long after the start of the last century, differentiation and splitting off began. Astronomy and chemistry developed methods and procedures of their own. At the same time the invention of new means of motive power such as the steam engine and the electric motor gave rise to the profession of engineering. Of the original content of natural philosophy there remained a number of seemingly miscellaneous topics—mechanics, heat, sound, electricity, magnetism, and light—and these came to be called, collectively, physics.

2·2 The Branches of Physics Are Related

The division of the subject of physics into the above branches is largely a matter of convenience. In reality the boundaries between the subdivisions are diffuse, and many interrelations exist, as you will find in the course of your study of the subject. Early in the nineteenth century, for example, it was found possible to interpret the basic phenomena of heat by means of purely mechanical considerations involving the motion of molecules. We now know that magnetism is caused by the motion of electricity. Again, in electricity the basic measurements resolve themselves into those of mechanical forces. The behavior of light, you will find, is interpretable largely as an electromagnetic phenomenon; and, most surprisingly, matter and energy are interchangeable.

Sound waves are merely mechanical waves of compression in the air; but, because of the unique and characteristic nature of the phenomena, sound deserves to be studied as a branch of physics distinct from the rest of mechanics. In the same way, differences in the original approach or in subsequent applications have indicated the compartmentalization existing in other areas. Because mechanics was one of the earliest scientific topics to attain reasonable development, its successes led investigators to accept it as a kind of model for their speculations about other phases of nature and to try to "explain" a variety of natural phenomena in terms of strictly mechanical principles. Thus, in addition to "mechanical" theories of sound and heat, there arose mechanical theories of light. These proved highly artificial and ultimately inadequate. Only comparatively recently has science recognized the fact that the construction of purely mechanical models of natural phenomena is not always possible. This point will be brought out in later chapters.

In recent years several theorists, notably Einstein, have set themselves the program of constructing a *unified field theory* which would relate the gravitational, mechanical, and electromagnetic attributes of matter. Thus far, only partial success has been realized.

2·3 Measurement of Length

Since physics is an exact science, it is necessary to be able to specify quantitatively the things talked about. This means that we must have some way of *measuring* the quantities under discussion. It is helpful, before plunging into the subject matter of physics itself, to consider what the process of measurement involves and how it can be carried out in particular cases.

There are many types of measurement, some of them extremely simple and direct, others very involved and making use of instruments of highly complex design. Let us first, however, ask ourselves, "What is the simplest and most fundamental kind of measurement one might be required to make?" If you think about this a little, the answer will invariably be, "The measurement of length"; for if you consider various measuring instruments found around the home—kitchen scale, tape measure, electric watt-hour meter, clock—the tape measure is obviously the simplest in principle.

Familiar as the process may be, it is nevertheless worth while to summarize briefly the exact procedure involved in this simplest kind of measurement. To begin with, if you ask several persons to tell you the length of a piece of rope, do not expect a single, unique answer even if each has taken the trouble to measure the rope with great care. You may get such diverse answers as 18 feet, 3 fathoms, and 5.5 meters—yet all the figures may be right. The point is that, in order to measure something, one must select a suitable *unit*.

The size of the unit is arbitrary, but it must be the *same kind* of quantity as the one to be measured. For example, in measuring a length, the unit itself must be a length. Conveniently, the unit may be marked off by scratches on a stick, or a number of units may be marked off on the stick in succession. The direct process of measuring the length then consists in laying off the unit in the familiar end-to-end fashion, starting at one end of the object to be measured and counting the number of times this can be done by the time the other end is reached. The result will in general not be an exact integral number of units, but will involve a fraction. Thus it may turn out to be 12⅜ units, or 7.824 units, etc.[1]

It is sometimes inconvenient or impossible to use the direct tapeline method of measuring length, and other means must then be used. For example, a surveyor can measure the distance to an inaccessible object by sighting on it from two different vantage points and then resorting to calculation. Nevertheless, fundamen-

---

[1] How far the subdivision of the unit need be carried is a matter for further discussion (p. 27).

tally he is still merely comparing the distance to be measured with the size of a selected unit.

2·4 Length Units

The system of measure used in civil affairs in all English-speaking countries is called the *English system,* and the fundamental length unit in this scheme is the yard. This is taken to be the straight-line distance, measured at 62°F, between the marks on a certain bronze bar kept in a vault at the Office of the Exchequer in London, and it is assumed that all goods sold by length are measured by means of a stick or tape that has been compared indirectly with the standard yard through the medium of copies preserved in bureaus of standards of the various countries.

For convenience in measuring lengths that differ greatly in order of size, secondary units are in use—among others the inch, foot, and mile. In measuring the dimensions of a book, for instance, the inch would be the most convenient unit, while in specifying the distance between two towns the mile would be indicated. The book might perfectly well be measured in miles, but the resulting number would be inconveniently small; similarly, quoting the distance between towns in inches would require an unduly large number.

The numerical factors relating one English unit of length to another are not connected in any logical way—they are arbitrary. One must commit to memory the fact that there are 12 inches in a foot, 3 feet in a yard, 5280 feet in a mile. These numbers bear no simple relation to each other, and computing the number of inches in, say, 27.16 miles is an arithmetical operation requiring some time and effort. It would be much simpler if we had a system of measurement where all conversion factors were *multiples of ten,* so that changing from one unit to another would be accomplished simply by moving the decimal point appropriately. Such a scheme is the *metric system,* devised at about the time of the French Revolution and now the accepted system of measure in all scientific work. The fundamental metric standard of length is called the *meter.*

It was the original intention of the commission responsible for the new system to make the standard length a given fraction of the earth's circumference, but later geodesic measurements showed the figure to be in error. In practice, however, the standard meter is the distance, measured at the temperature of melting ice, between two lines ruled on a certain bar of platinum alloy that is kept at the International Bureau of Weights and Measures in France. Copies of this bar are preserved in other countries; the U.S. Bureau of Standards has two.

Multiples and submultiples of the meter are related to it by powers of ten. The name of each is formed by attaching a distinguishing prefix to "-meter." Thus a *centi*meter is 0.01 meter; a *kilo*meter is 1000 meters. Table 2·1 lists the most frequently used metric length units together with their abbreviations and their relation to English units. You need not make a special effort to memorize the list, for you will soon remember the more common of these units and acquire a feeling for their size by actually using them.

Table 2·1 Metric Units of Length

1 *kilometer* (km)	= 1000 meters
1 *meter* (m)	*primary unit*
1 *decimeter* (dm)	= 0.1 meter
1 *centimeter* (cm)	= 0.01 meter
1 *millimeter* (mm)	= 0.001 meter

1 km = 0.621 mi   1 m = 39.37 in.   2.54 cm = 1 in.

It might be pointed out how the decimal basis of the metric system simplifies the conversion from one unit of length to another. Thus it is easy to change 0.013 km to centimeters: Inasmuch as there are 100 cm in a meter and 1000 m in a kilometer, there will be 100 × 1000, or 100,000, cm in a kilometer. Then 0.013 km will amount to 0.013 × 100,000, or (moving the decimal point five places to the right to multiply by 100,000), 1300 cm.

2·5 Measuring Areas and Volumes

Having discussed the determination of length (or distance), which is a one-dimensional space measurement, it is natural to speak next of the measurement of *area,* or surface, a two-dimensional space quantity. Just as before, an arbitrary unit is required —a unit that in this case is itself an area—and it is simplest and most convenient to choose a square area for this purpose. Moreover, we can avoid introducing anything really new by taking the side of the area unit equal to one of our previously selected length units. In the English system we use square inches, square feet, square miles, etc., and in the metric system square centimeters, square meters, etc. As abbreviations we use in.^{2}, cm^2, etc.

Suppose the area to be measured is that of a lake on a map (Fig. 2·1). We can imagine a unit area cut out of cardboard, placed on the map, traced around with a pencil, and then moved to an

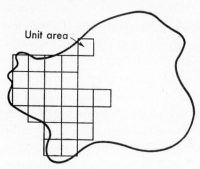

adjacent position, and this process repeated until the whole lake has been covered. Counting the number of times this can be done and making due allowance for the overlappings and deficiencies at the boundary, we then obtain a number for the area. Notice that the procedure is exactly comparable with what was done in measuring a length. Here, of course, both the

FIG. 2·1   Measuring an area.

thing to be measured and the unit are of two dimensions where formerly they were of one.

It should be mentioned that the primitive way of finding the area by laying squares side by side is not the one generally used in practical work. If the figure whose area is wanted is of simple geometric shape—circle, rectangle, triangle, etc.—the area may be computed from measurements of the lengths of various lines in it. There are also mechanical devices for finding the area of an irregular figure. A simple yet surprisingly accurate method is to cut the area out of cardboard, weigh the piece, and compare its weight with that of a one-unit square cut from the same sheet of cardboard. Try it.

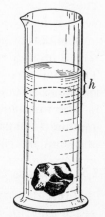

Our final space measurement is that in three dimensions—*volume,* or bulk. As you can see, this presents no new problems and runs quite parallel with the previous space-measurement processes. Here, as before, a unit is required. The unit is most conveniently taken to be a cube whose edge is equal to one of the length units already specified. We

FIG. 2·2   Finding the volume of an irregular solid.

may have cubic inches (in.³), cubic centimeters (cm³), and so on.[1]

A method of volume measurement analogous to the previous

---

[1] Sometimes the abbreviation *cc* is seen for cubic centimeters and *sq cm* for square centimeters, but cm³ and cm² are preferable, since they indicate at a glance the nature of the unit, that is, whether it is two- or three-dimensional.

direct procedures for determining length and area would probably be that of slicing the solid into unit cubes and totaling their number. A more feasible means often used for irregular solids (provided that they are impervious to water) consists in putting the solid into a cylindrical glass vessel containing water, noting the liquid levels before and after doing this, and then computing the volume of water displaced (Fig. 2·2).

2·6 Mass and Its Measurement

In the study of physics we are usually concerned with the behavior of definite portions of matter. How can we specify the amount of matter in a body? Obviously, space (volume) measurements are not enough, for everybody appreciates, at least in some intuitive sense, that there is more matter in a cubic foot of iron than in a cubic foot of cork. For the present we may characterize the *mass* of a body as the measure of the quantity of matter in it. It seems reasonable (think of the example of the iron and the cork) to compare the mass of two bodies simply by weighing them. Of course, this requires certain precautions; for example, if a spring scale is used, both bodies must be weighed at the same location.

The mass concept is not simple and will be discussed in greater detail later (page 90). At this time, however, we note that, while mass and weight are not identical concepts, one convenient means of comparing masses is by weighing.

The fundamental standard of mass in the metric system is the standard kilogram, a cylinder of platinum alloy kept at the International Bureau of Weights and Measures. The founders of the system intended the kilogram to be the mass of 1000 cubic centimeters of water, measured at the temperature at which it has its greatest density (page 23), thus referring the unit of mass to the space units through the choice of a standard substance.[1]

As in the case of length measurements, auxiliary units are chosen that differ from the primary unit by powers of ten. In Table 2·2 you will find listed the commonest mass units, their abbreviations, and their relation to English units.

---

[1] It turns out, however, that 1 kilogram of water at the above temperature occupies a volume of 1000.027 cm.[3] This volume has been given a special name, a *liter,* and 0.001 liter is called a *milliliter* (ml). For all but extremely refined measurements the milliliter and the cubic centimeter may be taken to be identical. One liter amounts to 1.057 liquid quarts.

Table 2·2   Metric Units of Mass

1 *metric ton*	= 1000 kilograms
1 *kilogram* (kg)	*primary unit*
1 *gram* (gm)	= 0.001 kg
1 *milligram* (mg)	= 0.001 gm

1 kg = 2.204 lb   453.6 gm = 1 lb   1 oz = 28.35 gm

2·7 Time and Its Measurement

Physics, particularly mechanics, is concerned not only with the masses of bodies but with their motions. The idea of motion involves the concept of *time,* and this is the next of the fundamental quantities we shall wish to know how to measure. Time is a difficult concept to define; the word may have one meaning to a psychologist, another to a historian, and still another to a physicist. It is obviously a different kind of thing from the quantities previously encountered and will require its own method of measurement. It is not much help to say that time is duration. Nevertheless, whatever our private ideas of the meaning of this quantity, it will perhaps be agreed that the time concept suggests something that flows at a constant rate. A suitable time measurer, then, would be a mechanism that moves at a constant rate. Such a mechanical device is called a "clock."

Much more uniform than any ordinary mechanical clockwork is the rotation of the earth on its axis, and it is this motion that serves to define our fundamental unit of time—the *second.* The time elapsing between one apparent passage of the sun across the meridian and the next such transit is called an "apparent solar day."

For several reasons this interval is not absolutely constant, and therefore the average of all solar days through the year—the *mean solar day*—is taken as our civil standard of time. For convenience the mean solar day is subdivided into 24 hours, each consisting of 60 minutes and each of these in turn of 60 seconds. Thus the primary time unit, the second, is defined as $\frac{1}{24}$ of $\frac{1}{60}$ of $\frac{1}{60}$, or 1/86,400, of a mean solar day.

Fortunately, the second is the primary time unit in both the English and the metric system. It is not usual to create auxiliary units differing from it by powers of ten, as is the case for length and mass.

2·8 Fundamental and Derived Units; Density

Up to this point we have settled upon methods of measurement for length, mass, and time and have chosen units for their measurement. These three quantities are *fundamental* in the sense that we shall find that most of the other quantities to be dealt with in physics can be specified readily in terms of various combinations of these three. This fact greatly simplifies the process of measurement. The advantages of such a situation will become apparent from the very first as we take up the study of mechanical quantities in the next chapter.

As an example of a quantity that is a combination of the fundamental units, refer again to an idea which was merely hinted at in Sec. 2·6. We commonly say that iron is "heavier" than cork. What does this mean? Certainly a 1-inch iron ball is not heavier than a bale of cork. If you think about it, the obvious conclusion is that the above expression tries to say simply that any piece of iron weighs much more than an *equal volume* of cork. How can all this be specified in an exact way? Apparently one method is to weigh, say, a cubic foot of the material in question. If this is done for iron, we find about 490 pounds for the weight. Then we may say that the density (more strictly, the *weight density*) of iron is 490 pounds per cubic foot, which may be written 490 lb/ft³. The density is a characteristic, not solely of the particular cube of iron we weighed, but of this kind of iron altogether; we should find that the same number would result if *any* piece of iron of this composition were weighed and we then divided its weight by its volume. In exact mathematical language, if we call the density of any substance D, the mass of any sample of it M, and the volume of the sample V, the definition of mass density is simply

$$D = \frac{M}{V} \qquad\qquad (2\cdot 1)$$

The derived quantity, density, is thus defined as a combination of a mass unit with a volume unit. The latter is simply the length unit L, cubed. In a shorthand notation we could write the dimensions of mass density as M/L^3. In a similar way, many other derived quantities to be introduced later will be defined as combinations of the three fundamental types of unit, L, M, and T (time).

We have been talking about density as measured in pounds per cubic foot, which would be an appropriate English unit for this quantity, but any other unit may be used for M and any for L. Thus grams per cubic centimeter, tons per cubic yard, or kilograms per cubic meter might be employed. The particular set of metric units that uses the centimeter for L, the gram for M, and the second for T as primary units is sometimes called the "centimeter-gram-second" (cgs) system, and this is the scheme most widely used in laboratory science today. A new formulation, based on the meter, kilogram, and second (mks), was officially sanctioned in 1935 by the International Committee on Weights and Measures and appears to have certain advantages. It has not yet attained universal use, but will undoubtedly gain acceptance to a greater extent.

2·9 The Denary Notation

In what follows we shall occasionally need to deal with numbers that are extremely large and others that are exceedingly small. The process of writing out such numbers and computing with them in the usual decimal form is troublesome and frequently leads to mistakes. There is, however, a convenient scheme for expressing numbers in terms of powers of ten, called the **denary** notation. The basic idea is simple, and a little practice makes the use of this system almost effortless, so that the few minutes required to learn it are well spent.

Expressed as a power of ten, 100 is merely 10^2, that is, "ten squared," or ten used as a factor twice. In the same way, 1000 may be written 10^3, or "ten cubed"—ten used as a factor three times over. Ten thousand becomes 10^4—"ten to the fourth (power)." Now suppose you are given a number like 4,700,000,000; how should you express it in powers of ten? This number is not merely a 1 followed by a certain number of zeros, and therefore it cannot be written simply as a power of ten standing alone. The 4 and the 7 will obviously have to be present in the final expression.

Let us provisionally reduce the size of the large given number by **dividing** it by ten repeatedly until it becomes a number between 1 and 10. This would mean, for the present example of 4,700,000,-000, dividing by 10 nine times over—that is, dividing by 10^9. To make things right and to leave the value of the number intact, we must now **multiply** it by 10^9. This sounds as if we were undoing what has just been accomplished; but the fact is that the multiplication by 10^9 is merely **indicated** in the final expression, and the result is written 4.7×10^9. "But," you ask, "what has been gained by this?" The answer is that in place of a long, clumsy string of digits we now have a compact expression which, moreover, tells at a glance that the number is of the *order of magnitude* of 10^9, or 1 billion. Furthermore, we propose to show that arithmetical calculations can be carried out with all the participating numbers in this form and that the results can be obtained also in denary form.

For numbers of moderate size—of the order of, say, one thousand—the ordinary decimal form may be retained. But consider the economy involved in writing the average distance from the earth to the sun as 9.3×10^7 mi in place of 93,000,000 mi or the number of vibrations per second of green light as 6×10^{14} in place of 600,000,000,000,000.

For very small numbers we make use of *negative* exponents of ten. A number with a negative power means the reciprocal of (one divided by) the number. Thus $10^{-1} = 1/10^1 = 0.1$; $10^{-2} = 1/10^2 = 0.01$; $10^{-3} = 0.001$; etc. The diameter of a molecule of hydrogen is about 0.000000024 cm; this may be written in denary form as

$$2.4 \times 10^{-8} \text{ cm}$$

a number which indicates at once that the diameter is of the order of a hundred-millionth of a centimeter.

2·10 Numerical Calculations

Direct computation in denary form is not difficult. You must know the rules for combining quantities having exponents; if these are not clearly in mind, turn now to page 476 for a brief review.

Assume that certain numbers have been found as a result of laboratory measurements and that when they are substituted into the appropriate mathematical relation the following calculation remains to be done:

$$\frac{(3.14)(5.60 \times 10^{-4})(7.10 \times 10^{12})}{(4.97 \times 10^7)(1.03 \times 10^{-5})^2}$$

The answer, in denary form, will consist of a number (conveniently, one between one and ten) and a certain power of ten. Let us find the power of ten first: Adding algebraically all the exponents in the numerator of the fraction, we get $-4 + 12 = 8$. Adding all those in the denominator gives us $7 + 2(-5) = -3$. Subtracting,

$8 - (-3) = 11$, so that, provisionally, the exponent part of the final result is 10^{11}.

Now we compute the purely numerical part. In any such calculation, do not plunge at once into laborious multiplication and division of all the numbers involved, but look carefully at the various quantities to see whether or not they have any common factors that can be canceled, thus simplifying the arithmetical work. This often proves to be the case. In the present example we can proceed as follows:

$$\frac{(3.14)\overset{0.80}{(\cancel{5.00}} \times 10^{-4})\overset{10}{(\cancel{7.10}} \times 10^{12})}{\underset{0.71}{(\cancel{4.97}} \times 10^7)(1.03 \times 10^{-5})^2}$$

Finally, with all numbers reduced as far as possible, we perform the multiplication and division and get 23.7 as the numerical result. Then the complete answer could be written 23.7×10^{11}; or, fixing the numerical part so that it is between one and ten, we write instead 2.37×10^{12} as the final result.

You will find that these operations speedily lose their first appearance of complexity after you have practiced on several examples.

2·11   Other Mathematical Questions; Precision of Measurement

While it is true that physics makes liberal use of the language and procedures of mathematics, an introductory study of the subject can be undertaken without drawing upon anything beyond arithmetic, simple algebra, and a few basic facts of geometry or trigonometry. The principles needed are reviewed in the Appendix, and you should study this before going on.

Another question of a mathematical nature which will be of interest as we proceed is that concerned with precision of measurement. This has to do with such practical matters as the determination of the reliability of the result of a given set of measurements, how far the result of a computation should be carried out, etc.

If a given quantity, such as the length of a room, is measured several times under similar conditions, the values obtained will not be identical. Experience shows that the best value to use for the quantity in question is the *average* of the several measurements— that is, the sum of the separate values divided by the number of measurements.

The reliability of this average may be estimated by taking the differences (neglecting algebraic sign) between each measurement and the average of the set and averaging all these *residuals.* For example, if the length of a table is measured in inches and the separate measurements turn out to be 48, 51, 47, 52, and 47 in., their average value is 49 in. The individual deviations from the average are 1, 2, 2, 3, 2 in., and the average residual is 2 in. The result of the series of measurements is written 49 ± 2 in. (Read: "49 plus or minus 2.") For present purposes this result may be taken to indicate that another set of measurements, made under similar conditions, would probably yield an average which would lie somewhere between 47 and 51 in.

In the above example it is understood that the units digit of the result is uncertain—that is, we cannot be sure about the value of the 9 in the 49 average. In any measurement or average we do not retain any figure beyond the first one that is uncertain. For instance, if the above value of 49 ± 2 in. is to be converted into feet (by dividing by 12), the result would be written, not

$$4.083 \pm 0.167 \text{ ft}$$

but 4.1 ± 0.2 ft. Use of the longer figures would be not only misleading but incorrect. In the same way, if 28 ± 2 ft were converted into inches, the result would be, not 336 ± 24 in., but 340 ± 20 in. In this case the zeros are not *significant* but are used to fill the vacant unit place. The best way to avoid ambiguity in writing significant figures is to express the number in the denary notation (page 24). Thus the number 58,000 should be written as 5.80×10^4 if it has three significant figures or as 5.8×10^4 if it has only two.

The following rules may be used for retention of significant figures in a computation:

1. In *addition* or *subtraction* do not carry the result beyond the first column that contains a doubtful figure. Thus, to obtain the sum of

2807.5		2807.5
0.0648	write the numbers as	0.1
83.695		83.7
525.0		525.0

The sum is correctly expressed as 3416.3.

2. In *multiplication* and *division* retain in the result only as many significant figures as there are in the quantity that has the *least* number of significant figures. Thus, if the calculation is 10.5 × 0.0041, direct longhand multiplication gives 0.04305 as the product. This is misleading, for neither of the original quantities is known to four significant figures, which is what the above result implies. The factor having the least number of significant figures is the second one (0.0041), and it has only two. Therefore only two significant figures should be retained in the result, which should then be written 0.043.[1]

3. Rule for *dropping figures* that are not significant ("rounding off"): If the first dropped figure is:

(a) *less than* **5,** the last figure retained should be left *unchanged.*
(b) *Greater than* **5, *increase by* 1** the last figure retained.
(c) *5 itself,* leave the preceding digit *unchanged if even,* but *increase it by* **1** *if odd.*

Thus 3.5401 becomes 3.5 if only two figures are retained; 8.737 rounds off to 8.74, to three figures; 4.85 becomes 4.8, but 4.95 is changed to 5.0.

SUMMARY

Physics is the prime example of an *exact science* because it deals to a large extent with *measured quantities.*

The *measurement* of any quantity must be expressed in terms of an arbitrary *unit,* and the unit must be the same kind of quantity as the thing to be measured. The process of measurement consists in comparing the quantity to be measured with the selected unit and expressing the result as a number.

In the *metric system* the various-sized units of a given kind are related by powers of ten (see Tables 2·1 and 2·2).

The *primary units* that we shall use for physical measurements are those of *length, mass,* and *time.*

Denary notation: A useful way of expressing very large or very small numbers in terms of powers of ten. Calculations can be carried out with the numbers in this form.

The *best value* of a measured quantity is the arithmetic *average* of a

---

[1] To state the result as 0.04305 implies that the value is known to within 1 part in 4300. Actually, the two-figure result shows this to be too optimistic by a factor of 100!

large number of independent measurements. The *average of the departures* of the separate measurements from the above value is a measure of the *reliability* of the result.

READING REFERENCES

1. Sawyer, W. W.: "Mathematician's Delight," Penguin, New York, 1946. An excellent and attractive introduction to or review of elementary mathematical operations. Read at least as far as p. 107. Chapter XIII gives a good introduction to trigonometry.
2. Loeb, L. B., and A. S. Adams: "The Development of Physical Thought," Wiley, New York, 1933. The significance of measurements and their units is discussed on pp. 74–83.
3. "Encyclopaedia Britannica," article on Measurement.

EXERCISES

1. Express your height in meters and your weight in kilograms.
2. How many cubic centimeters are there in a cubic meter? Thinking of a small cube of sugar as being 1 cm on an edge, visualize a cubical pile of such pieces a little over 1 yd on each edge. Is this a good way of obtaining an idea of what a million amounts to?
3. The dimensions of a certain size of photographic sheet film are quoted in England as $3 \frac{9}{16}$ by $4 \frac{3}{4}$ in. To which of the following Continental film sizes does this correspond: 6 by 9 cm; 24 by 36 mm; 9 by 12 cm?
4. Discuss the meaning of the question, "How many feet are there in 1 cm?" Can you give a numerical answer?
5. The speedometer of a European automobile is calibrated in kilometers per hour. Could such a car be driven at 75 km/hr and still be within the law in a state where the speed limit is 50 mi/hr?
6. What is the cost of 3000 m of wire if the price is quoted as 14 cents per 100 ft?
7. In a certain chemical process 750 lb of lime is used in a continuous run of 3 hr 45 min. Express this rate in kilograms per hour.
8. What is the value of the density of water in grams per cubic centimeter?
9. Knowing that 1 ft³ of water weighs 62.4 lb, that 1 U.S. gal contains 231 in.³, and that there are 8 pt to a gallon, show that a pint of water weighs about a pound.
10. If the weight density of gold is 1200 lb/ft³, find the volume in cubic inches occupied by a piece of this metal weighing 20 lb.
11. The radius of the nucleus of an oxygen atom, assumed spherical in shape, is 3.5×10^{-13} cm and its mass is $2.7 \ 10^{-23}$ gm. Calculate the "density" of the nuclear material, and compare it with that of water.

12. Ask 10 students to write down their independent estimates, to the nearest 0.5 in., of the width of a table. Tabulate the values, and calculate their average. Tabulate the residuals, and compute the average residual. Write the numerical result of this set of "measurements" in the form (average value) $\pm$ (average residual). Express the result also in centimeters.

13. Express, to the proper number of significant figures, the results of the following calculations:

(a) $3.47 \times 0.0039.$ (c) $(2.5)^3(10.08)/(14)(2.52).$

(b) $0.0704/12.85.$ (d) $(1683.1)(8.307 \times 10^{-6}).$

14. A student measures a certain quantity in a laboratory experiment and obtains the value 472.8. The most reliable value of this quantity, computed from theory, is known to be 473.6, expressed in the same units. What is the most reasonable way for the student to state the *percentage precision* of his result? Calculate the numerical value of this quantity in the present experiment.

Chapter 3

FORCE AND EQUILIBRIUM

In taking up the study of a new subject we are faced with the question of where to begin. In physics it is generally agreed that mechanics forms the best point of departure, and there are good reasons to support this contention. In the first place, as mentioned in the preceding chapter, mechanics attained a high degree of development early in the history of science, and people appealed to it for explanations of many diverse phenomena. In addition, ordinary mechanics deals with familiar and relatively simple devices that we can visualize and touch—weights and springs, levers and cams, cords and pulleys. Such objects and their behavior are matters of universal experience. From earliest childhood we begin to accumulate mechanical judgment, sometimes by painful experience. Learning to walk is essentially a matter of acquiring a certain special mechanical coordination, as is learning to swim, to skate, or to pilot an airplane. Whenever you lift a weight, open a door, or climb a flight of stairs, you perform what amounts to a mechanical operation.

3·1 The Nature of Force

In any of the operations just described you are conscious of using your muscles. You know that there exist certain devices called tools or machines which are capable either of reducing the muscular effort required for a given task or of replacing it altogether. We say that we, or the devices, exert *force*. For the present, a force may be taken to be anything capable of producing the same effect as direct muscular effort. In simple terms a force corresponds to our primitive notion of a push or a pull.

The simplest "impersonal" way of exerting a force is by means of a weight. Place a 10-lb weight on a table, and it exerts a steady, downward force on the table top. How *big* a force? It seems natural

31

to say that the magnitude of the push in this instance amounts to "10 lb of force" and in general to measure force in weight units. Thus we speak of a force of 10 lb, of 200 gm, of 16 tons, etc.—any convenient weight unit may be used.

Will such a 10-lb object still press down with as great a force when resting on the moon? Refinement of the present statements seems to be called for. This will be discussed in Chap. 5.

Because all weights act downward—that is, in the direction toward the earth's center—it should not be inferred that only downward forces can be brought to bear by the use of weights. By means

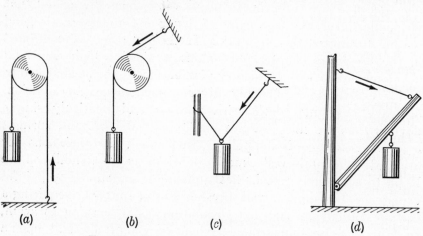

FIG. 3·1   Forces exerted by means of weights.

of very simple arrangements, weights may be used to exert forces in various directions in space. Thus by using a frictionless pulley and a weightless, perfectly flexible cord[1] a weight can be made to exert an upward pull equal in magnitude to the weight, as in Fig. 3·1a, or an oblique force of the same amount, as in Fig. 3·1b. The force brought to bear on the hook in either of the two remaining sketches of Fig. 3·1 is, however, different from the value of the weight, and such situations require further study.

[1] Such things do not exist, but in science we are continually compelled to approximate certain situations in order to make them manageable. We simplify such setups by *idealizing* them. Thus a frictionless pulley is approximated by one whose resistance to turning can be made extremely small compared with any of the applied forces in the setup. To the extent that this condition is realized, the statements made about the situation approach exactness.

3·2 Scalar and Vector Quantities

Many of the quantities discussed in physics and in everyday affairs can be completely specified by stating a single number. Your age, the volume of a lump of iron, and the temperature of the room are all examples of such so-called *scalar* quantities. A number, along with an appropriate unit, is stated; nothing more is required.

On the other hand, some of the things we talk about require us to state not only a number but a *direction in space* as well. Force is an example. It is not enough to know that a force of a certain magnitude acts on a body; if we want to know definitely what the effect will be, we must also specify the *direction* of the force. For example, the complete specification of a force acting on the sail of a boat might be "100 lb toward the northeast." An even simpler example is a type of quantity called a *displacement,* which is nothing more or less than a prescription of how to move something from one place to another by the shortest route. Thus the direct flight of an airplane from New York to Philadelphia could be described as "90 mi in a direction 37° west of south."

Any quantity, such as force or displacement, *that requires a statement of direction in space as well as of magnitude for its complete specification is called a vector quantity.* Very soon we shall meet other useful vector quantities such as velocity, acceleration, and momentum.

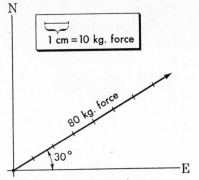

Fig. 3·2 Representation of a force vector.

Most persons are visual-minded and prefer to have things explained in the language of geometry (diagrams) rather than in terms of algebra (equations). Vectors lend themselves naturally to pictorial representation. We represent a vector in a diagram by drawing a straight-line segment whose length, on some convenient scale, is equal to the magnitude of the vector and whose direction is the same as the vector's. The segment is drawn outward from the point at which the vector is assumed to be applied, and an arrowhead is drawn at its extreme end. Figure 3·2 shows a vector representing a force of 80 kg acting in a direction 30° north of east.

3·3   Combination of Vectors

Can two or more forces act on a single body at the same time? In order to answer this question, we need only remember that one of the simplest ways to apply a force to a body is by pulling on a cord attached to the body. Obviously it is perfectly feasible to have several cords and to pull on each in a chosen direction and with a given amount of force.

There now arises a really fundamental question: "Given several forces acting on a body at the same time, is there a definite, unique, single force that would produce the same effect as the whole set? If so, how can we find its direction and magnitude?" It is plain that if such a force could be determined, a great simplification would be attained; for in almost all practical situations, even the simplest, not one but several forces act.

In order to see what to do about the case of several simultaneously applied forces, we first consider the case of displacements, which is simpler. Then we can use the result to find the answer to the force problem, for what is true of one kind of vector will be equally true of the other. This, in fact, is one of the advantages of the general idea of a vector: If we make use of only the vector characteristics of displacements in our argument (magnitude and direction), then the results will apply equally well to forces and indeed to vectors of any kind.

Suppose we think of two displacements applied in succession to a *particle*. A particle—an important idea in physics—is merely any object that is small enough for our purposes, small enough so that we do not have to worry about such things as its internal structure or any rotational motion it might have. In talking about atoms, an electron may often be considered a particle; in dealing with the solar system, the entire earth may for some purposes be taken to be a particle. On a diagram a particle is represented by a point.

Figure 3·3a shows a displacement of 10 in. to the right applied to a particle originally at point A, bringing it as a result to location B. Now a second displacement of 7 in. in the indicated direction leaves the particle in position C. Obviously the same end result could have been obtained simply by moving the particle directly in a straight line from A to C by means of the single displacement AC. In the language of vectors,

Displacement AB + displacement BC = displacement AC

It is important to notice that this equation does **not** say that the sum of the **magnitudes** (lengths) of the first two vectors is equal to that of the third. This sort of simple addition holds only for arithmetical numbers, such as the ones we use to specify scalars. Thus the total volume of oil carried by a tanker is merely the sum of the volumes in the several compartments.

A vector, on the other hand, prescribes an **operation.** The vector equation given above says only that the operation of moving the particle from A to B, followed by that of moving it from B to C, is equivalent, in its final result, to the single operation of moving it from A to C. As regards the length, AB plus BC is, of course, greater than AC. The vector AC is said to be the **resultant** of the vectors AB and BC, and the process of finding the resultant is called **combination** or **composition** of vectors.

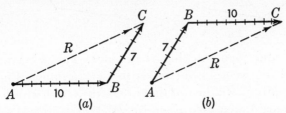

FIG. 3·3   (a) Resultant of two displacements. (b) Order of vector addition is immaterial.

An interesting point to note is that reversing the order of the two displacement operations yields exactly the same final resultant, as is obvious from Fig. 3·3b, where the original 7-in. vector was applied first, followed by the given 10-in. vector. A vector may be moved about as required and its point of application may be changed, provided only that its two fundamental attributes, direction and magnitude, are not altered. This suggests that perhaps we can even think of the two displacements in the above example as being applied **at the same time.** We can imagine this by having two persons move the particle simultaneously, one taking pains to move it only to the right a total distance of 10 in., while the other urges it continually in the direction of the oblique vector for a total distance of 7 in. The net effect would be to land the particle at C as before.

The preceding method for combining two vectors is readily generalized to include the case of any number of vectors. If, for instance, the three displacements a, b, and c are to be applied to a particle (Fig. 3·4), we may first lay off a, then from the end of it draw b. The resultant of these two vectors is r. We may now forget about a and b, having replaced their combined effect by r, and combine r in turn with the remaining vector c by drawing c from the end of r. Proceeding as before, the resultant of these two is now R, which is the actual resultant of all three original vectors a, b, and c.

It is evident that we need not have drawn the intermediate resultant r but could have proceeded directly by laying off a, b, and c

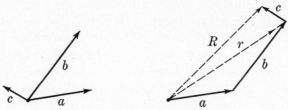

FIG. 3·4   Resultant of three vectors.

end to end and then drawing R at once. The scheme is not restricted to three vectors but holds for any number. Furthermore, the same resultant will be obtained regardless of the order in which the vectors are taken (see Exercise 2). We then have the general *polygon rule:*

To find the resultant of a number of vectors acting on a particle, lay the vectors off end to end, in any order. The single vector drawn from the initial point of the first vector to the end point of the last vector is the resultant, with regard to both direction and magnitude, of the whole set of vectors.

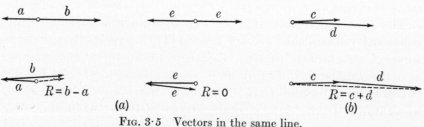

FIG. 3·5   Vectors in the same line.

3·4 Special Cases of Vector Combination

It often happens that a mechanical situation involves two vectors that lie along the same line. If the two are *oppositely* directed along the same straight line (Fig. 3·5a), it is clear that the magnitude of their resultant is merely the difference of the separate magnitudes and that its direction is that of the larger vector. If the two original vectors are in **the same direction** in a line, the resultant has a magnitude equal to their sum and the direction is obvious (Fig. 3·5*b*). These situations are special cases of the general rule in which the vector polygon (triangle) has merely "folded flat."

Another special case of frequent occurrence is that of two vectors that are **at right angles** to each other (Fig. 3·6). The magnitude of the resultant may then be computed by the familiar right-triangle rule of geometry (see page 477).

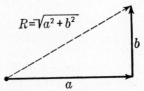

FIG. 3·6   Resultant of two perpendicular vectors.

In a general case where the vectors are oblique to each other (as in Fig. 3·4), it is still possible to find the magnitude and direction of the resultant, but longer trigonometric computations are required. For our purposes the best expedient for handling such a case is to make a *scale drawing* of the vector polygon and determine the resultant by measurement.

3·5 Vectors in Equilibrium

From the practical point of view, one of the commonest and most interesting mechanical situations we deal with is that in which the resultant of all the forces applied to a body is zero. This condition is termed *equilibrium*. In terms of the polygon construction it means that when all the vectors have been drawn end to end the last vector itself just succeeds in closing the polygon—no resultant can be or need be drawn.

The term equilibrium applies not only to forces but to sets of other vectors as well; however, our chief interest at this time is in forces. One may say that the main concern of a structural engineer is to design a bridge, crane, vehicle, or building framework so that it can maintain equilibrium under the action of the applied forces at all times. If the structure is not able to do this, there is no longer equilibrium; instead, motions set in that lead to collapse.

Let us next discuss in detail a few typical examples of equilibrium of forces in order to see how to use the general proposition stated on the previous page. It is important that you work through these examples carefully, for adequate understanding of the principles can be obtained only in this way.

3·6 Example of a Suspended Weight

A 50-kg weight hangs from a cord, which is firmly tied to a rope suspended between two hooks (Fig. 3·7a). Both cord and rope are of negligible weight and are perfectly flexible. What we want to know is the *tension force* in each of the two straight portions of the rope.

First let us make clear what we mean by the expression "the tension force in a rope," for this phrase will recur often in our discussions. The tension in a cord is the stress force existing in it—the force tending to pull it apart. If the cord is thought of as a string of particles, it is the force that any one particle exerts on its neighbor (on *either* side). If a spring scale were spliced into the cord at any point, it would read the value of the tension directly. The value of the tension is the same at all points of a segment of weightless cord acted upon only by forces at its ends. Thus in either Fig. 3·1a or Fig. 3·1b the tension is the same in the part of the cord

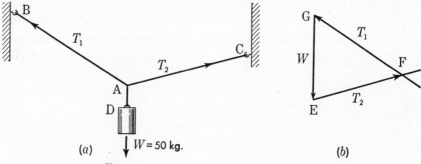

(a) W = 50 kg.   (b)

Fig. 3·7   Problem of a hanging weight.

to one side of the pulley as in that to the other side; for since the pulley is frictionless, it cannot exert any effective force *along* the cord. This is why it was correct to say that the pull on the hook in each case is equal in magnitude to the hanging weight.

Returning to our example, we begin by asking, "What is the particle whose equilibrium interests us, and what are all the forces acting on it?" In order to answer this question, note that the hanging weight is in a sense the cause of the existence of the problem and that the two quantities to be found are the tension T_1 in cord AB and the tension T_2 in AC which result. The knot at A, then, is really the point to which all three of these forces are applied, and so this is the particle whose equilibrium we wish to examine.

The next thing to do is to insert in the drawing of Fig. 3·7a vectors representing each force. All weights act downward by definition; therefore a vector representing the hanging weight is drawn straight down from the point A, as indicated in the figure. Then the tension vectors T_1

and T_2 are drawn outward from A along their respective segments of the cord. The only difficulty is this: We do not yet know **how long** to make each of these tension force vectors, for this is precisely what we set out to find. Nevertheless, we draw in some vectors provisionally as shown.

The way to find out the magnitudes of the two tension forces is to apply the polygon rule (page 36). Since the two tensions together with the weight W form a set of forces in equilibrium, these vectors must form a **closed polygon** when drawn end to end. This is done in Fig. 3·7b. First we draw the vector that is known completely, namely, W, using some convenient scale to represent this 50-kg force. Continuing the construction of the polygon, we next draw a line outward from the end of W, making it parallel to AC in the first sketch. True, it is not yet known where to terminate this vector T_2; but if this **were** known, we should then draw the third force vector from the end of T_2 parallel to AB and should have to land at the starting point G. The way to manage this is now clear. We simply construct the force triangle by working from both ends toward the middle. From E we draw a line of indefinite length out toward the right. Then from G we draw a line parallel to AB downward and to the right until it meets the previous line. This determines the point F, which is the end point of T_2 and the initial point of T_1, and the force diagram is complete. By measurement, the magnitudes of these two tensions can be found in terms of the scale used to draw W (see Exercise 5 at end of chapter).

3·7 A Further Example

A framed picture weighing 20 lb is hung by means of a picture cord passing over a nail, each half of the cord making an angle of 45 deg with the horizontal (Fig. 3·8a). How great is the tension force in each portion of the cord?

In this case the point whose equilibrium is of interest may be taken to be the nail. What forces act on it? The wall exerts an **upward** force **on the nail,** and the amount of this force is 20 lb, since the nail supports an object of this much weight. From the symmetry of the situation the tensions in the two parts of the cord are equal. These vectors are roughly drawn in the diagram of the actual setup. Next the construction of the force triangle is carried out exactly as in the preceding example except that here the two tensions are equal and the angle each makes with the horizontal is given as 45 deg. It is seen, then, from Fig. 3·8b that the force triangle has a right angle at F, and this makes it easy to compute T rather than to measure it on a scale drawing. By the familiar right-triangle rule,

$$T^2 + T^2 = (20)^2$$

or $2T^2 = 400$ and $T = \sqrt{200} = 14$ lb. Note that each of the two tension forces is greater than half the weight. This is reasonable, since in a sense the two parts of the cord not only are pulling down on the nail but are at the same time pulling against each other in the direction of opposite sides of the picture. Only if both cords were vertical would they act on the nail in the most effective fashion and have their minimum possible tension of 10 lb each.

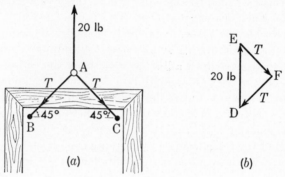

FIG. 3·8   Tension in a picture cord.

3·8 Component of a Force

As in the preceding example, it often happens that circumstances do not allow a force to be applied in its most effective direction. Take the case of a sled that is being pulled along by means of a rope (Fig. 3·9). If the tension force in the rope amounts to 15 lb, we can

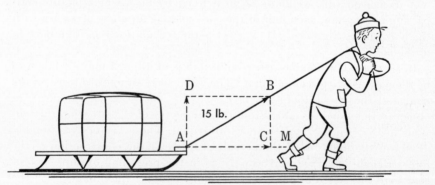

FIG. 3·9   Perpendicular components of a force.

represent it on the diagram by means of the vector AB drawn to some convenient scale. Now the rope is not pulling on the sled in the most effective direction to produce forward motion but comes upward at an angle. We are not so much interested in the force in the rope as in the force tending to move the sled forward. Nevertheless, we can find the effective value of the force in the rope as follows: First draw a line AM in the forward direction, through the point of attachment of the rope. Then from B, the end of the tension vector, **drop a perpendicular** onto AM. The segment AC thus cut off will then represent the effective value of AB in the forward direction. It is called the **component of the vector AB in the direction AM**. In this instance, we might refer to AC as the horizontal component of the tension in the rope, and its magnitude is, of course, represented by its length, on the same scale as the one used for AB.

What has become of "the rest" of the 15-lb tension? And if the rope is not acting in its most effective direction, what other result does it accomplish? These questions are answered by considering the **vertical** component of the tension, which is evaluated as before, by dropping a perpendicular from B onto the direction in question. This yields AD as the vertical component of the pull in the rope.

Thus, because of its inclination, the rope does two things: It pulls the sled along the ground with an effective force AC, and at the same time it tends to lift the front end of the sled with a force AD. We say that the tension force has been **resolved** into its horizontal and vertical components.

If you are familiar with trigonometry,[1] you can compute these two components, rather than measure them from a scale drawing. If θ is the angle that the original vector makes with the horizontal direction (Fig. 3·10), the values will be

Horizontal component $x = F \cos \theta$ (3·1a)
Vertical component $y = F \sin \theta$ (3·1b)

By resolving a vector into two components we have found a pair of vectors whose resultant is the given vector. Thus the resolution into components is the exact opposite of the process of compounding two vectors into a single resultant. Although in principle the directions in which the two components are taken need not be at right angles, they are usually taken this way in practice. In all the examples we shall deal with, only components at right angles will be called for, as in the example of the sled. This simplifies matters, for two vectors that are mutually perpendicular are completely

[1] Some essentials are given briefly in the Appendix, p. 477, and a condensed table of values of the sine and cosine appears on p. 483.

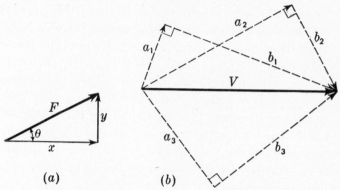

FIG. 3·10　Resolving a vector into components.

independent of each other. From the way the construction of a component was defined (page 41), one such force can have no component in the direction of the other.

3·9　Use of Components in Solving Equilibrium Problems

In many practical situations, resolution of the forces into components proves to be a simple and natural way of arriving at a solution. One case in point is that of a ramp, or *inclined plane.* Although it must have been used since prehistoric times for the raising of heavy loads (the screw and wedge are merely other forms of this same device), its fundamental principle was first worked out by the talented Netherlands scientist Simon Stevin near the end of the sixteenth century.[1]

Suppose, for example, that a cart is being pushed up a ramp (Fig. 3·11*a*) which rises 2 ft vertically for every 7 ft measured along the slope. If the cart weighs 140 lb, how large an uphill push is required to just hold it at rest on the slope? Any frictional forces are to be assumed negligible.

As in the previous examples our first question is, "What forces are exerted *on* the cart by its environment?" First there is the weight of 140 lb, which we represent by a downward vector of this magnitude, on some convenient scale. The weight of the cart is, in a sense, the force responsible for the cart's run downhill when no constraining push is acting. But the actual downhill force is obviously the component of the weight in the direction of the slope. By the construction described above, this is found to be the force F in the diagram. The answer to our question follows at once: The uphill push required to hold the cart at rest is a force

[1] For the highly original way in which he solved this problem, see **Ref. 2** (pp. 63–66), at the end of this chapter.

F' equal and opposite to F. Enough information is at hand for computing the magnitude of F (or of F'). The ramp may be thought of as forming a right triangle, the ratio of the short side to the hypotenuse being $2:7$. But the vector right triangle whose short side is F and hypotenuse W is similar to this one (since their sides are perpendicular). If two triangles are similar, their sides are in proportion, so that $F/W = \frac{2}{7}$, or, since W is 140 lb, $F = (2 \times 140)/7$, or 40 lb.

The other component of W, represented by vector P in the figure, is the thrust of the wagon against the roadway.[1] The magnitude of P is readily found, for P is the long side of the vector right triangle whose hypotenuse is 140 lb and whose short side we found to be 40 lb. Hence $P = \sqrt{140^2 - 40^2} = 134$ lb.

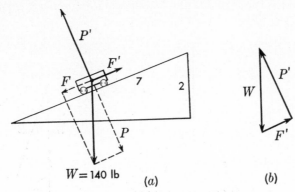

FIG. 3·11 Problem of a cart on a ramp.

We now have found all the forces acting on the cart and so have obtained the complete solution of the problem. Looked at from the point of view of the polygon scheme, the solution amounts to this: The forces acting **on the cart** from the surroundings are the weight W exerted on the cart because of the attraction of the earth, an uphill push F' exerted on the cart by some other outside agent, and a (perpendicular) thrust P' exerted on the cart by the roadway. These three are the only forces acting and must form a closed triangle if the cart is to be in equilibrium. It is evident that the triangle we should draw to find the magnitudes of F' and P' (Fig. 3·11b) is identical with either of the triangles already constructed in the first sketch of this figure when we were finding the components of W.

---

[1] The absence of appreciable friction in this problem automatically means that the force between cart and road must be **perpendicular** to the road; for if this were not so, it would have a component **along** the surface and this would amount to a frictional force. The force between cart and road is entirely a supporting thrust and has no drag component.

In the preceding example, the use of a little trigonometry leads directly to the result. The downhill component F is given by $W \sin \theta$, and the thrust against the plane P is $W \cos \theta$, where θ is the slope angle of the ramp. From the diagram, the sine of this angle is $2/7$; its cosine is then $\sqrt{1 - (2/7)^2} = 0.958$. Hence, putting in the numbers, $F = 140 \times 2/7 = 40$ lb, and $P = 140 \times 0.958 = 134$ lb, as before.

3·10 A Further Example Using Components—the Lawn Roller

As a second instance of the use of components, consider the case of a lawn roller (Fig. 3·12a). The roller weighs 100 kg and is pushed along on level ground by means of a handle making an angle of 30 deg with the horizontal. If a *horizontal* force of 40 kg is just sufficient to start the roller forward, what is the thrust in the handle when the roller is about to move and what is the force between the roller and the ground?

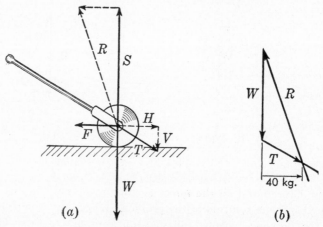

FIG. 3·12   Lawn-roller problem.

The forces acting on the roller are its weight W, the thrust T in the handle, the retarding force F, and the upward force S of the ground. In the figure these have all been drawn as applied at the center of the roller. Of the four forces all except T are either horizontal or vertical, and thus resolution into horizontal and vertical components suggests itself. The two components of T may be called H and V, respectively.

Taking first the horizontal components, these are H and F, and their vector sum must be zero for equilibrium. This makes $H = F$; and since F is known to be 40 kg, this is also the magnitude of H. In the same way, for the vertical components we must have the sum of the upward forces equal to the sum of the downward ones, or $S = W + V$. The value of V is readily found, for the triangle formed by H, V, and T is a 30°–60° right triangle, and this means that V is $1/\sqrt{3} = 0.577$ of H. Thus

$V = 0.577 \times 40 = 23.1$ kg. Also, $T = 2V = 46.2$ kg. Finally,

$$S = W + V = 123 \text{ kg}$$

and the solution is complete.

Actually, S and F may be considered to be simply two components of what might be called the **total reaction** R of the ground. If desired, its magnitude could be calculated, for it amounts to $\sqrt{F^2 + S^2}$. The number is left for you to compute.

If the problem were attacked by the polygon rule, the vector diagram would be as shown in Fig. 3·12b, leading, of course, to the same resultant R as found above.

3·11 General Procedure for Solving Examples

A general scheme for solving problems on the static equilibrium of a particle can now be summarized. This procedure has been found by experience to lead to a solution in a straightforward way and is recommended in solving the exercises at the end of the chapter.

1. Draw a simple sketch representing the situation described in the statement of the problem. This drawing need not be elaborate and may be done freehand. With a little practice you will be able to get lines reasonably straight and angles about the right size. Note down the numbers given in the problem directly on the drawing beside the objects to which they apply. The drawing then serves as a readily grasped visualization of what is stated verbally in the problem.

2. "Isolate" the body (particle) in whose equilibrium you are interested, and sketch onto the diagram vectors to represent *all* the forces exerted *on* the body *by* its environment. It is important to get these forces the right way round.[1]

3. Apply the principle of equilibrium, which says that the resultant of all the forces acting on the body must be zero. This is most conveniently done in many instances by using the polygon construction, and the polygon may be solved either by means of a carefully made scale drawing or, if the geometry is sufficiently simple, by calculation. In some cases, resolution of all forces into com-

[1] Thus in the example of the cart the particle in question was the cart—or, more specifically, the point known as its center of gravity (see below)—and one of the externally applied forces was the thrust of the ramp on the cart. It would have been wrong to take, instead, the push of the cart against the ramp; we were interested in the *cart* and wanted to write down all the forces acting *on it*.

ponents in two perpendicular directions before applying the equilibrium principle is more satisfactory. The solution may often be reached by using trigonometry.

3·12 Equilibrium under Gravity; Center of Gravity

While the principle of equilibrium applies, strictly speaking, only to a particle, we have used it in several examples where the object to which the forces were applied was an extended body. The fact that makes this possible is one that was already known to Archimedes in the third century B.C.:

Every material object possesses a certain point, called its *center of gravity,* where the entire weight may be considered concentrated.

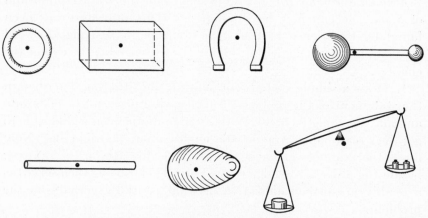

Fig. 3·13   Center of gravity of various objects.

This point is such that, if the body were suspended from it, it would remain in balance in any position. In Fig. 3·13, the dot shows the location of the center of gravity for a number of typical objects, each assumed to be composed of matter of uniform density.

The center of gravity of a body need not be within the object itself but is always located in a fixed position with respect to the body. Thus for the uniform ring shown in the first sketch, if a fine wire were stretched along any diameter and the whole suspended from a thread tied to the center of this wire, the ring would remain in whatever position it might be placed. To sum up, then, we may say that the use of the idea of center of gravity is a convenient way of replacing an extended object, for all gravity purposes, by a single particle.

If a body is supported at any point other than its center of gravity, it will tend to move until its center of gravity is as low as possible— that is, as near to the point vertically below the point of support as the setup allows. If an object is supported in such a way that any slight displacement *raises* its center of gravity, it is said to be in *stable* equilibrium; if this *lowers* the center of gravity, the body is in *unstable* equilibrium; if a displacement leaves the height of the center of gravity unchanged, the object is in *neutral* equilibrium.

A uniform circular cone standing on its base on a level plane is stable, for a slight tipping will raise the center of gravity (Fig. 3·14). Standing on its point, the cone is unstable. True, this body

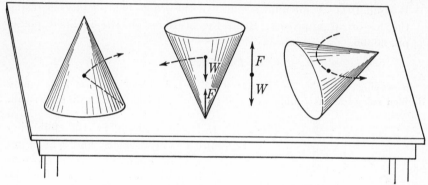

Fig. 3·14   The three types of equilibrium.

can be in equilibrium when so placed, provided that its axis is exactly vertical, for then the two acting forces—the weight and the upthrust of the plane—are in the same line, equal, and oppositely directed. But this equilibrium is not stable; for even the slightest displacement makes the cone rotate farther and farther from the vertical position, and it falls over. Finally, the same cone lying on its side will be in neutral equilibrium when placed on a horizontal plane. When given a slight displacement it tends neither to roll farther nor to return to its original position.

SUMMARY

Scalars and vectors: A scalar is merely a magnitude—a number. A vector has both magnitude and direction. Force is an example of a vector.

Resultant: The single vector that would produce the same effect as a given set of vectors. May be found graphically by the polygon rule (page 36) or by calculation.

Equilibrium: A situation in which the resultant of all the acting vectors is zero.

Component of a vector: The effective value of the vector in a chosen direction. Found graphically by projection (page 41) or by calculation.

Center of gravity: The point where the entire weight of a body may be considered to act. The center of gravity tends to get into as low a position as possible.

REFERENCE READINGS

1. Crew, Henry: "The Rise of Modern Physics," Williams & Wilkins, Baltimore, 1935. Read the accounts of the early work on composition of forces, the inclined plane, and center of gravity.

2. Taylor, Lloyd W.: "Physics, the Pioneer Science," Houghton Mifflin, Boston, 1941. A splendid account of the whole field of physics, using the historical approach. Read the sections on the inclined plane, pp. 63–66.

EXERCISES

In solving examples by measurement of scale drawings, use a decimally divided ruler such as a millimeter scale, and do not make the drawing too small.

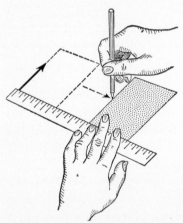

FIG. 3·15   Drawing parallel lines.

1. Decide which of the following quantities are scalars and which are vectors: the area of a cornfield; the tension in a towrope; your weight; the price of gasoline; the push used in opening a door.

2. Verify by means of a careful drawing the fact that the order in which vectors are combined is immaterial. Draw a set of four arbitrary vectors applied at a point. Then combine them by means of the polygon construction and draw the resultant. Combine a second time, taking them in a different order, and see whether the resultant obtained is approximately parallel to and of the same length as the one first obtained. Notice that a convenient trick for transferring a vector from one location on the page to another parallel one is to use a card sliding on a ruler, as shown.

3. Discuss the statement, "If a set of forces is known to be in equilibrium, any one of them must be equal and opposite to the resultant of all the others."

4. A patrol airplane flies 120 mi due east, 100 mi northeast, 160 mi

northwest, and finally 150 mi due south. How far is it then from its base, and in what direction must it fly (give approximate angle) to return? Solve by means of a scale drawing.

5. Find the approximate value of the tension in each cord in the example discussed on page 38 by actually measuring the vectors in Fig. 3·7*b*.

6. Can two forces of 600 and 1000 gm, respectively, acting at a point have a resultant of 1200 gm? What are the greatest and least values of the resultant of this pair of forces?

7. Solve the example of Sec. 3·7 by resolving all forces into horizontal and vertical components and applying the principle of equilibrium of forces.

8. A 10-kg iron ball hanging from a rope is pulled aside by a horizontal force of 6.0 kg. What angle does the rope make with the vertical when equilibrium is attained, and how large is the tension force in the rope? Solve graphically, using the polygon construction.

9. In Exercise 8, how large a horizontal force would be needed to pull the rope into an exactly horizontal position? Confirm your answer by sketching the vectors. In view of the result, make a conjecture as to the possibility of stretching a clothesline perfectly straight.

10. The tension in each band of a slingshot is 6.5 lb when the rubber is stretched to the extent shown in Fig. 3·16. Calculate the force acting on the stone at the moment when it is released.

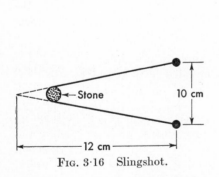

FIG. 3·16   Slingshot.

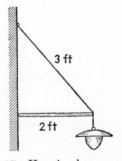

FIG. 3·17   Hanging-lamp problem.

11. A 1-ton steel girder 20 ft long is supported in a horizontal position by means of a chain 34 ft long whose ends are fastened to the girder at two points each 2 ft from an end and whose mid-point passes over the hook of an erecting crane. How large is the tension force in the chain?

12. A street lighting fixture weighing 30 lb is suspended as shown in Fig. 3·17. Find the tension in the chain and the thrust force in the horizontal strut, which is of negligible weight.

13. Two metal balls, each 4.0 in. in diameter and weighing 10 lb, are hung from a hook, each by means of a cord 3.0 in. long. Find the tension in either cord.

14. When does a lawn roller press harder against the ground—when pushed or pulled? Explain in terms of the forces acting.

15. A ramp rises 2 ft for every 15 ft measured along the slope. It is found that a force of 40 lb applied parallel to the incline will just pull a certain cart up. If friction is negligible, what is the weight of the cart?

16. A 200-lb cake of ice is allowed to slide down a board 10 ft long, which slopes down to the ground from a loading platform 3 ft high. If the frictional force between the ice and the board amounts to 6 lb, find the resultant force acting to move the piece of ice down the slope.

17. One end of an inclined pole rests on a block of wood floating in a pan of water; to the other end is tied a cord coming from a hook in the ceiling. What direction will the cord take?

18. Find the weight of the roller on the right (Fig. 3·18) if the system is to be in equilibrium. Friction may be neglected.

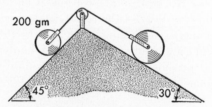

FIG. 3·18   Stevin's roller paradox.

19. Explain in mechanical terms why it is difficult to balance a pencil on its point. Is this feat actually impossible in principle?

20. A flat cylindrical box has a concealed lead weight fastened to a point at its inner edge (Fig. 3·19). Placed on an incline as shown, it will mysteriously roll *up* the slope when released. Explain in terms of the motion of the center of gravity G. Make such a box, and try the experiment.

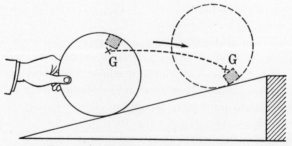

FIG. 3·19   Rolling-cylinder paradox.

Chapter 4

MOTION

4·1 Speed and Velocity

In the preceding chapter displacement was discussed as a typical vector quantity. It was seen that applying a given displacement to a particle means that the particle was moved a definite distance in a given direction. It may have taken one-hundredth of a second or a century to carry out this operation; there was no question of the *time* required. Yet in most practical problems involving motion the time element is of great importance. When you buy a railroad or air-line ticket, you expect the carrier not only to transport you a given distance in a given direction but also to do so in a given interval of time.

The vector quantity giving the *rate of motion* of a particle and *also its direction* of motion is called the *velocity* of the particle. The velocity of an extended object may be specified by stating the velocity of a specific particle or point in it, for instance, the center of gravity. Thus the velocity of an airplane may be given as "260 miles per hour toward the southwest."

In many cases the path of the motion is fixed and need not be further specified, and then the main concern is merely with the magnitude, or scalar part, of the velocity vector. This is called the *speed* of the motion.[1] Speed is another example of a derived quantity, representable as a combination of two of our fundamental units, distance and time, and the basic way to measure speed would be to use a tapeline and a clock. Thus if a car moves at a uniform rate over a path 100 mi long and takes 4 hr to do so, its speed is 100 mi divided by 4 hr, or 25 mi/hr (miles *per* hour). This means that if the car were to continue moving at its present

---

[1] Strictly speaking, we should try always to maintain this distinction between speed and velocity; you will find that it is not easy to remember to do so.

51

rate it would cover a distance of 25 mi in the next hr, 50 mi in the next 2 hr, etc.

This common-sense way of defining speed can be cast into the form of a simple algebraic relation. It is usual to let s represent the distance covered, t the elapsed time, and v the speed, assumed constant. Then what has been said above, using particular numbers, can be stated in general form as

$$v = \frac{s}{t} \qquad \text{or} \qquad s = vt \qquad \text{or} \qquad t = \frac{s}{v} \qquad (4 \cdot 1)$$

Note that s stands for **distance** (space), not speed.

We are at liberty to use any convenient units of time, distance, and speed that are **self-consistent.** Thus if you wish to measure distance in feet and time in seconds, the speed must be in feet per second; if you choose to measure time in hours and speed in kilometers per hour, you must measure all distances in kilometers or change them to this unit before using the relations (4·1). Every valid equation must be, as we say, **dimensionally consistent** (see page 65). Apart from this, there are no limits to our choice of speed units. Some common ones are miles per hour, feet per second, and knots.[1]

4·2 Motion with Variable Speed

Even if the car in the example just quoted had not moved at a constant rate during its 100-mi journey, 25 mi/hr would still represent a fact concerning the trip—namely, the **average speed.** Most actual journeys involve variable rather than constant speed.

We can represent the history of a train trip by means of a graph of **speed** against **time** (Fig. 4·1). The time is plotted along the horizontal axis and the speed along the vertical, a suitable scale being chosen for each. The curve was plotted from notes tabulated by an observer riding in the locomotive cab. At the instant when the engineer opened the throttle to start the train, the observer set a stop watch going. At frequent intervals during the journey he glanced at the watch and at the speedometer mounted in the cab and entered the two simultaneous readings of time and speed in his notebook.

---

[1] This is perhaps the only speed unit whose name is a single word rather than a combination of the names of distance and time units. It is one nautical mile (6080 ft) per hour.

The resulting curve shows that the train's speed increased gradually from its value of zero, at the start, to a fairly steady running speed of around 50 mi/hr. At about 30 min after leaving the station the engineer began to slow the train down in order to pass through a town at the more moderate speed of 30 mi/hr, after

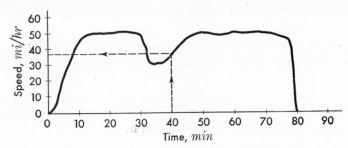

FIG. 4·1   Speed-time graph for a train trip.

which the former speed was resumed. Finally, at about 70 min the steam was cut off, and at 75 min the brakes were applied, bringing the train to rest at its destination at a time of 80 min.

4·3 Instantaneous Speed

The speed of the train during this run was far from constant; it varied between zero and its maximum value of 50 mi/hr. The curve enables us to determine the speed *at any instant.* Thus, at the time 40 min the speed (obtained by reading up to the curve and across to the scale at the left) was 36 mi/hr. What does this mean? It implies only that if the train had continued moving at the rate it was traveling at that moment it would have gone exactly 36 mi in the next hour. Actually, of course, the train did no such thing, for its speed changed drastically during the ensuing hour and, according to the graph, was really zero for part of this interval.

If no speedometer had been available, the log of the train journey would have had to be compiled from pairs of observations of time and distance, rather than time and speed. Then division of any distance interval by the corresponding time interval would give the *average speed* over the period in question, as we have seen. But what about the speed at some particular instant within this interval? We could, of course, take a *smaller* interval (but one that still contains the instant we are interested in), divide by the corresponding time difference, and again get an average speed.

Its numerical value might differ somewhat from the preceding. Once more, we could take a new and smaller interval and compute a new average speed. As we close down on the point in question, taking shorter and shorter intervals, the average values will tend to approach closer and closer to some ultimate *limit,* and it is precisely this limiting value which represents the instantaneous speed we are looking for.

The result of the preceding discussion can be put into exact form with the help of symbols. In mathematical work a small change in any quantity is represented by writing the Greek letter Δ (delta) directly before the symbol for the quantity. Thus Δx means "a small change in x." It is a *single* quantity and is *not* to be construed as meaning "Δ *times* x." The instantaneous speed now becomes the limit of the expression

$$v = \frac{\Delta s}{\Delta t} \tag{4.2}$$

as Δt is made very small. Even if Δt remains of finite size, the formula still gives the average speed over the interval. In fact, this expression then has the same meaning as Eq. (4.1). There, s really represented any *difference* in position (Δs) and t the corresponding *interval* of time (Δt).

4.4 Combination of Velocities

In the preceding chapter we became accustomed to the idea of two or more displacements or forces applied to a particle at the same time. Since velocity, like force or displacement, is also a vector, we might ask, "Is it possible for a particle to have two or more velocities at the same time?" What would this mean?

Consider the case of a barrel that a sailor is rolling across the deck of a barge moving down a river (Fig. 4.2). Assume that the sailor pushes the barrel with a speed of, say, 2 ft/sec in the direction shown by the vector. This vector represents the velocity of the barrel *with respect to the barge.* But the barge itself—and everything on it, including the barrel—has a forward speed of, say, 4 ft/sec. The velocity of the barrel *with respect to the earth* is the combination (resultant) of these two vectors; the barrel actually moves in a straight line in the direction AB with a speed of about 5 ft/sec. This would be its motion as perceived by a man on the bridge overhead (who is fixed in position with respect to the

earth), provided that he can refrain from thinking of the two partial motions of the barrel and concentrate only on their resultant.

This example not only tells us that a body can have two velocities at the same time but also brings out the fact that motion must
always be specified with respect to *something*—some *frame of reference,* as we call it. To talk about a motion without giving the

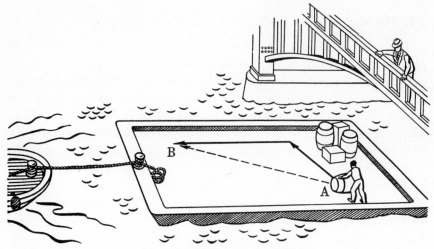

FIG. 4·2   Composition of velocities.

frame of reference is as meaningless as quoting the length of a table
without specifying the unit used. In the barge problem the barrel
had a certain velocity with regard to the barge, and the barge, in
turn, had a specified velocity with reference to the earth. The velocity of the barrel, referred directly to the earth, was the resultant
of the two partial velocities.

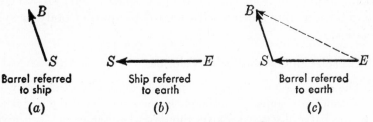

Barrel referred to ship	Ship referred to earth	Barrel referred to earth
(a)	(b)	(c)

FIG. 4·3   Scheme for naming resultant.

A good way to keep the relations straight when combining velocity
vectors that are referred to different frames can be illustrated in the
barge situation. Label the vector that represents the velocity of the
barrel with respect to the ship with B at the terminal point and S at

the initial point (Fig. 4·3a). Similarly, designate the velocity of the ship with respect to the earth by a vector labeled as in Fig. 4·3b. Then, to get the resultant, join the two vectors so that the two ends labeled S coincide. Draw the resultant by completing the triangle. The name of this resultant, in accordance with the scheme used for the other two vectors, is "the velocity of the barrel with respect to the earth," which is the vector required.

4·5   The Motions of the Earth

The common frame of reference for most motions occurring in practice is the surface of the earth, and it is usually unnecessary even to mention the reference frame in this case. But if we examine the matter, this is not the end of the story by any means. The fact is that the ground is itself in motion, owing to the earth's rotation. The eastward speed of the ground at middle latitudes, with respect to a frame of reference fixed at the center of the earth, amounts to some 700 mi/hr. The room in which you are sitting, and everything in it, partakes of this velocity, of which you are not at all conscious. Moreover, the earth itself races along its orbit around the sun at an average speed of about 67,000 mi/hr. The whole solar system, earth included, is found to be moving in the direction of the constellation Hercules at about 43,000 mi/hr. This is as far as we can go in tracing our motion, for no further reference frame exists. The resultant of all the velocity vectors mentioned, each taken in its proper direction in space, gives your velocity at any instant. Velocity with respect to what? Presumably with respect to the center of mass of the whole system of the stars. And here we are stopped. In fact, the theory of relativity specifically denies the possibility of determining motion with respect to space itself; all we can do is to determine our motion with regard to another body or system of bodies.

4·6   Examples on Combination of Velocities

1. The case of a motorboat crossing a stream is an instance of velocity composition quite similar in principle to the situation of the barrel rolling across the barge discussed above. Suppose that the engine can give the boat a forward speed of 8 ft/sec in still water and that the boat is headed straight across a river in which there is a current of 6 ft/sec. What path will the boat take, and at what point on the opposite bank will it land?

Here again we are dealing with a particle having two component velocities: The boat has a given velocity with respect to the water, and the entire water surface has, in turn, a certain velocity with respect to the earth. The resultant of these two velocities is what we want to find. Figure 4·4a is self-explanatory; as long as current and propeller speed remain constant, the boat crosses on the straight course indicated, at a speed of $\sqrt{6^2 + 8^2} = 10$ ft/sec. Note that the keel of the boat is always directed straight across the stream but that because of the current there is a sideward drift ("leeway") during the crossing. The downstream angle turns out to be about 37 deg.

2. Another interesting question immediately comes up: "How should this boat be headed in order to land directly opposite the starting point?" Your intuitive answer probably will be: "Head it upstream at the same angle at which it went downstream in the preceding example." This is not quite correct! In the problem just solved we were given both direction

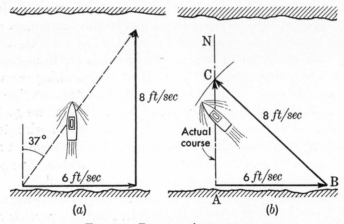

FIG. 4·4   Boat crossing a stream.

and magnitude of each of the two component velocities and were required merely to find their resultant. In the present case we know the direction and magnitude of the current (as before) and the magnitude of the boat's velocity with respect to the water but are required to find in what direction the boat must be headed in order that the *resultant shall have a given direction*—namely, straight across the stream. In the first problem we were told the values of two directions and of two magnitudes; here we are given three directions and one magnitude.

If we start to draw the vector triangle, the solution will suggest itself. First we draw the current vector (Fig. 4·4b), which we know in its entirety. From its end we are required to draw the 8 ft/sec vector in such direction that the closing side of the triangle is in the direction AN. This is easily done by setting a drawing compass for a radius representing 8 ft/sec, placing the point of the instrument at B, and scribing an arc that cuts the line AN. The crossing point C then tells us exactly where to draw the 8 ft/sec velocity vector, and the resultant AC represents the speed of the boat going straight across the stream. Now we are in a position to see that this vector triangle and the one in part a of the figure are different, and therefore the course angles also differ in the two cases.

As an exercise, make scale drawings for these two situations, and measure the angles and resultant speeds. Some additional exercises on velocity composition are given at the end of the chapter.

4·7 Acceleration

We have seen that, even though a moving particle may have a continually varying speed, we can always speak of its speed at any instant. In the example of the train trip (page 52) the vertical distance to the curve of Fig. 4·1 at any point represents the instantaneous speed at the corresponding time. In this motion, as well as in almost all others ordinarily observed—that of a bullet, a housefly, a pendulum, a violin string—the speed is far from constant. We shall want some quantitative method of describing the way in which speed changes. Figure 4·1 suggests how this may be done. It is clear that a portion of the curve which rises as we go to the right means increasing speed over this part; a flat, horizontal section implies constancy of speed; and a descending segment means decreasing speed. The steeper the slope of any section, the greater the rate of change (increase or decrease) of the speed.

This is precisely the idea that proves useful in discussing motion with variable speed. We define the **acceleration** of a particle at any instant as its **rate of change of velocity.** In symbols: If a represents the acceleration, Δv the change in velocity, and Δt the corresponding interval of time, then the average acceleration (in the limit where Δt is very small, the **instantaneous** acceleration) is given by

$$a = \frac{\Delta v}{\Delta t} \qquad (4·3)$$

In English units, for instance, we could say that a certain vehicle is changing its speed at the rate of 3 ft/sec **each second** or—more compactly stated—at the rate of 3 ft/sec/sec. This is usually written even more economically as 3 ft/sec². The "sec²" has no meaning intrinsically but indicates merely that acceleration has the dimensions of length divided by time **twice over**—one of the times being, so to speak, a part of velocity (see the preceding equation). Possible units for measuring acceleration are feet per second per second, centimeters per second per second, meters per second per second, etc.[1]

Velocity is a vector and time is a scalar, and therefore taking the quotient as in Eq. (4·3) has merely the effect of scaling down a vector; thus *acceleration is a vector.* In many applications the direction of motion is prescribed or understood, and in such instances it is usually a matter of indifference whether we define acceleration as rate of change of velocity or as rate of change of speed. Later (page 141) we shall have much to say about a particle moving around a circle with constant speed. In this case the velocity vector is of constant length but is continually altering its direction as the particle moves around the circle; hence the velocity *vector* is changing continually, and there is an acceleration.

Even in instances where the vector nature of acceleration is unimportant and only numerical values are wanted, we must still be careful to specify whether we are dealing with increase or decrease of speed. A rate of increase is called a *positive* acceleration; a decrease is a *negative* acceleration. The latter is sometimes referred to as a *deceleration.* In reality, no separate term is needed—a minus sign written before the numerical value is sufficient. Thus, if a car has a speed of 45 ft/sec at the instant when the brakes are applied and a speed of 15 ft/sec after the brakes have been acting for 3 sec, its average acceleration during the process will be $(15 - 45)/3 = -10$ ft/sec². The minus sign shows that the acceleration vector is opposite in direction to the velocity vector.

As a further example, suppose a car going eastward has its speed reduced from 35 ft/sec to 14 ft/sec in 3.0 sec. Then the average acceleration during this interval will be -7.0 ft/sec². The minus sign shows that the acceleration vector is directed westward (why?).

4·8 Motion with Constant Acceleration

To give an exact description of the motion of a body when there are accelerations is usually difficult and sometimes impossible. We need only think of such instances as the movements of the moon or the motion of a bullet entering a sandbank. Fortunately, however, the case of motion with *constant acceleration* is of great practical interest, and it is easy to describe quantitatively. We

---

[1] A "mixed" unit such as miles per hour per second is technically admissible but should be avoided. It is always good policy to have only one unit of a given kind in any problem.

find that this is the kind of motion possessed by a block sliding down an incline, by a stone falling freely in a vacuum, or in fact by any particle on which a constant force acts.

Let us consider a particle which moves always with constant acceleration a. For simplicity, assume that it starts from rest. This statement means only that the speed is zero when we start counting the time, but increases at a constant rate from that moment on. Thus, if the constant acceleration amounts to 10 cm/sec², the speed 1 sec after starting will be 10 cm/sec, the speed 2½ sec after starting will be 25 cm/sec, etc. In other words, the speed will change in proportion to the time. This is merely the idea inherent in the definition of acceleration and is expressed algebraically by

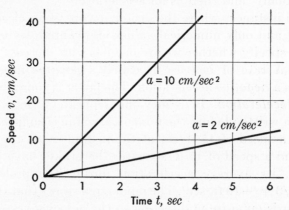

FIG. 4·5   Speed-time graphs for motion with constant acceleration.

Eq. (4·3), which reads $\Delta v = a\,\Delta t$ when solved for Δv. Here, since a is constant, the same thing will be true not only for a small time interval but for one of any size, and we may as well write

$$v = at \qquad (4\cdot4)$$

In the form of a graph, our result looks like Fig. 4·5, where speed is plotted as a function of time. Motion with constant acceleration, starting from rest, is represented by a straight line coming out of the origin O. Its slope depends on the numerical value of the acceleration.

4·9   Computing the Distance Covered

The question answered above—"What is the speed after a given time?"—is fairly straightforward. Less obvious is how to find the *distance* covered by the moving particle in a given time. In the case of motion at **constant speed** we found that equal distances were covered in equal times, and Eq. (4·1) told the whole story. Here, however, the particle is constantly increasing (or decreasing) its speed, and this affects the subsequent distances covered. Nevertheless, it is not difficult to see what happens.

Let us again resort to a picture. Assume the constant acceleration to be 4 ft/sec². The straight line *OM* in Fig. 4·6 then represents the motion on a speed-time graph. Suppose we are interested in knowing how far the particle will go in 12 sec. The graph shows [and so does Eq. (4·4)] that at this time the speed amounts to

$$(4 \text{ ft/sec}^2)(12 \text{ sec}) = 48 \text{ ft/sec}$$

Now this is the speed at the **end** of the 12-sec interval; the speed at the beginning was, of course, zero. Between these times the speed increased at a constant rate. Then it is reasonable to say that the distance covered would be the same as if the particle had moved all the while with a **constant** speed equal to the **average**[1] over the interval, or 24 ft/sec. On the graph this average speed is indicated by the horizontal dashed line. At any instant during the first half of the motion the true speed is below this line; at the corresponding point

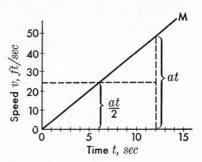

FIG. 4·6   Average speed over an interval.

during the last half it is an equal amount above. The result is that the average represents the motion exactly, as far as distances are concerned.[2]

Again we can express this result by means of algebra. Instead of talking about a particular time of 12 sec, we call the time interval *t*. The final speed, according to Eq. (4·4), is given by $v = at$, and hence the average speed is $at/2$. Then, if we imagine the accelerated particle replaced by one moving with this constant speed, the distance covered will be given by Eq. (4·1) as

[1] The average of two numbers is half their sum. In this example we have $(0 + 48)/2 = 24$.

[2] Galileo used this idea extensively (see Ref. 2); actually, it goes back to the fourteenth century.

$$s = \frac{at^2}{2} \qquad\qquad (4\cdot5)$$

The presence of t to the second power in this relation is interesting. It means that the distance covered increases as the **square** of the time. Hence, after 2 sec a constantly accelerated body will have

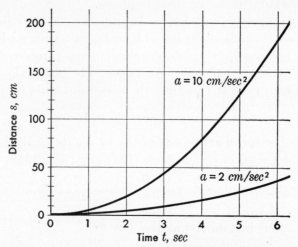

FIG. 4·7   Distance-time curves corresponding to Fig. 4·5.

gone *four* times as far as in the first second; at the end of 3 sec, **nine** times as far; etc. The distance-time graphs of Fig. 4.7 show this rapid increase.

4·10   General Relations for Motion with Constant Acceleration

Equations (4·4) and (4·5) enable us to answer all legitimate questions about motion with constant acceleration, starting from rest. For example, Eq. (4·5) would be used to find the distance covered in a given time or, conversely, the time required to cover a given distance. Similarly, Eq. (4·4) is a relation between final speed and time. In some cases the time is not explicitly given (or is not required to be found), and it is convenient to have a relation that does not involve this quantity directly. Such a relation is easily obtained by algebraically eliminating t between the two equations. Thus, if Eq. (4·4) is solved for t, we have $t = v/a$. Substituting this value in Eq. (4.5), we get $s = a(v/a)^2/2 = v^2/2a$, or $v^2 = 2as$.

For convenience, we can now collect Eqs. (4·4) and (4·5) and the last result, obtaining *three relations applying to motion with constant acceleration, starting from rest,*

$$v = at \qquad (4.6a)$$

$$s = \frac{at^2}{2} \qquad (4.6b)$$

$$v^2 = 2as \qquad (4.6c)$$

These expressions are still not as general as they might be, since they assume the body to be at rest until the acceleration is applied. Suppose, instead, that the body is originally moving with a speed v_0 (the initial speed) when a constant acceleration a begins to act. We can find the proper relations for this case by generalizing Eqs. (4·6).

First, we notice that the final speed after the acceleration has been acting for a time t will now be given by

$$v = v_0 + at \qquad (4.7)$$

This merely says that to the speed gained, at, we must add any initial speed v_0 that the particle already had.

Corresponding to Fig. 4·6, we now have the situation shown in Fig. 4·8. The average speed over the interval is $[v_0 + (v_0 + at)]/2 = v_0 + at/2$. Again thinking of the particle replaced by one moving at a constant speed of this amount, the distance covered will be, by Eq. (4·1), $s = (v_0 + at/2)t$, or

$$s = v_0t + \frac{at^2}{2} \qquad (4.8)$$

Finally, a relation corresponding to Eq. (4·6c) can be obtained by eliminating t between Eqs. (4·7) and (4·8). The result is

$$v^2 = v_0^2 + 2as \qquad (4.9)$$

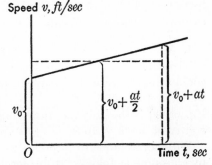

Fig. 4·8 Finding average speed when body is initially in motion.

Collecting Eqs. (4·7), (4·8), and (4·9), we have a set of **general relations describing motion with constant acceleration,**

$$v = v_0 + at \qquad (4.10a)$$

$$s = v_0t + \frac{at^2}{2} \qquad (4.10b)$$

$$v^2 = v_0^2 + 2as \qquad (4.10c)$$

These equations take the place of the set (4·6) when the particle is **initially in motion.**

Notice that each formula answers a specific set of questions. Thus either (4·6a) or its generalized counterpart (4·10a) can answer the question, "How fast will the body be going after a given time?" or its inverse, "How long will it take the body to attain a given speed?" (It is understood that the value of a or of any v_0 is given.) Similar statements can be made about the other formulas. In any event, these sets of formulas are capable of answering any legitimate question about motion with constant acceleration.

4·11　Examples on Motion with Constant Acceleration

At this point you may be tempted to ask, "Must I memorize these formulas?" The answer is a definite "No." Blind memorization of results is certainly not the way to gain an understanding of any subject, particularly physics. The important thing is to be able to follow the line of reasoning that originally produced the results. Regarding the above relations, you will find that you will soon recall them automatically through their repeated use in solving numerous examples. Besides, most examples may be worked by arguing the situation through, without any direct reference to the formulas. The latter method is to be preferred, and a number of examples of how this can be done will now be explained:

1. An elevator, starting from rest, is given a constant downward acceleration of 2 ft/sec² for 4 sec. How far does it go in this time? We could at once obtain the result from Eqs. (4·6), recognizing the fact that we know the values of a and t and wish to find s. Of the relations (4·6), Eq. (4·6b) is the only one involving a, t, and s; direct substitution gives $s = (2 \times 4^2)/2 = 16$ ft.

Without recourse to formulas we might have obtained the same result by reasoning as follows: If the acceleration of 2 ft/sec² lasts for 4 sec, the gain in speed will be 2×4, or 8, ft/sec. Since the elevator starts from rest, its average speed over the interval is then 4 ft/sec. If something were to move at a constant speed of 4 ft/sec for 4 sec, it would go a distance of 4×4, or 16, ft, which is the result obtained earlier.

2. As a second example, suppose a car increases its speed uniformly from 30 to 70 ft/sec in 8 sec. Find the distance gone in this time and the magnitude of the acceleration. First, we note that the average speed over this interval is $(30 + 70)/2$, or 50, ft/sec. Going at this speed for 8 sec, a body would travel $50 \times 8 = 400$ ft. The acceleration would be the change in speed per unit time, or $(70 - 30)/8 = 5$ ft/sec². Here we have obtained the result for the distance in a simple way, whereas use of the formulas would require us first to solve (4·10a) for a and substitute the

given numbers, obtaining $a = 5$ ft/sec^2 as before. Then, solving (4·10c) for s and putting in numerical values would give us $s = 400$ ft, as above. Formulas (4·6) would be of no use here, since they are valid only if the body is at rest either at the beginning or the end of the motion considered.

3. A train is running at 60 ft/sec when the brakes are applied, bringing it uniformly to rest at a station, 1200 ft ahead. Find the acceleration, the speed after 12 sec, and the distance gone in this time. To find the acceleration, we notice that the average speed of the train while being brought to rest amounts to 30 ft/sec. Then the total time will be $1200/30 = 40$ sec. As a result the acceleration will be the entire change (decrease) in speed divided by this time, or $-60/40 = -1.5$ ft/sec^2.

After 12 sec the speed will have decreased by $1.5 \times 12 = 18$ ft/sec, making the speed at that time $60 - 18 = 42$ ft/sec. The distance traveled in this interval will amount to the time multiplied by the average speed over the interval, or $12(60 + 42)/2 = 612$ ft.

4. A proton enters one section of a particle accelerator and gets a constant acceleration for 5.0×10^{-4} sec. If it leaves this section, which is 1.25 m long, with a speed of 4500 m/sec, find its speed on entering and the magnitude of its acceleration while inside. We note from the statement of the problem that the given quantities are v, t, and s, while v_0 and a are to be found. This will require the use of two of the relations (4·10). First, we can substitute the known quantities into the first of these formulas, obtaining $4500 = v_0 + 5.0 \times 10^{-4}a$, using the meter as the unit of distance. Next, solve (4·10b) for v_0, and put in numerical values, getting $v_0 = 2500 - 2.5 \times 10^{-4}a$. These two equations can be solved simultaneously, for instance, by multiplying the second through by 2 and adding the two equations, yielding $v_0 = 500$ m/sec. Substituting back into either equation, we then get $a = 8.0 \times 10^6$ m/sec^2.

A number of other examples on motion with constant acceleration are to be found at the end of the chapter.

4·12   Dimensions of a Result

In carrying out any calculation like those above you should always remember to attach the proper dimensions to a final result, for it is meaningless without this label. Thus the last figure obtained above was labeled *meters per second, squared*. How did we know what label to write down? For one thing, we knew that the quantity we were looking for was an acceleration; and since the meter was the unit of distance in all the data supplied, the answer would have to be in meters. However, there is a much surer way of getting the dimensions right, even in complicated instances, and that is to use the idea that *in any legitimate physical equation the dimensions of all the terms must be the same.* This means that we cannot have a member whose total dimension is a velocity equated to one whose dimension is that of acceleration—the dimensions must be homogeneous on both sides.

Now the dimensional labels attached to the various quantities may be treated just like algebraic quantities and may be combined, canceled, etc., just as if they were *factors* in the equation. This makes it possible to check on the dimensions all through a relation and to find out the label to be attached to the final result of a computation.

An example should make this clear. In Eq. (4·6c) suppose that we measure all quantities in English units—s in feet, v in feet per second, and a in feet per second per second. The 2 in the equation is a pure number and has no dimensions in terms of length, mass, or time. Assume that we wish to compute s, which will be given by $s = v^2/2a$. The dimensions of the right side of this relation will be

$$\frac{\dfrac{ft^2}{sec^2}}{\dfrac{ft}{sec^2}} = \frac{ft^2 \, sec^2}{sec^2 \, ft} = ft$$

The answer, then, will be expressed in feet. This is a length, the same as the s on the left side of the equation, which is thus correct as far as its dimensions are concerned. While dimensional consistency is a *necessary* condition for the correctness of an equation, it is not a *sufficient* one, for it is easy to write down physically meaningless combinations of quantities whose dimensions are correct. Nevertheless, we have here a valuable idea not only for finding the dimensions of a result but for catching errors in a mathematical deduction.

4·13   Motion of a Falling Body

As mentioned above, a particle falling freely a limited distance in a vacuum is found to have constant acceleration. This case represents one of the more important applications of the results obtained in the preceding sections. Moreover, it is found by experiment that, at any given place on the earth, *all falling bodies accelerate at the same rate* in a vacuum, regardless of any difference in their specific properties such as mass, density, or composition. This rate is called the *acceleration due to gravity,* and its symbol is g.

The numerical value of g is about 980 cm/sec^2 or 32.2 ft/sec^2 at sea level in middle latitudes and can be determined not only by direct observation of falling bodies but far more accurately by indirect methods (see, for instance, page 154).

The apparently simple fact underlying the motion of a falling object remained unrecognized for a long time. Aristotle asserted that "the downward movement . . . of any body endowed with weight is quicker in proportion to its size," and his authority kept this notion alive for centuries.[1] In the sixteenth century Galileo (and probably others before him) questioned the statement of Aristotle. Galileo is said to have allowed iron balls of very different weight to fall from the Leaning Tower at Pisa and to have noted that, within close limits, they struck the ground at the same time. Historically there is great doubt that this experiment was actually performed.

At first sight it seems natural to agree with Aristotle that a heavier object will fall faster—you need only drop a coin and a sheet of paper at the same instant in order to see that the coin reaches the floor much sooner than the paper. But repeat the test, first wadding the paper into a compact ball, and both will strike at essentially the same time. This suggests that it is merely the disturbing effect of the force of *resistance of the air* which makes the paper fall more slowly than the coin. If only compact and fairly heavy bodies are used, this effect is negligible and all bodies are observed to fall at the same rate provided that the distance is not too great. Despite the fact that Galileo had no way of eliminating the effects of the surrounding atmosphere (the air pump was not invented until about 1650), he was able to project his experiences and attain this simple ultimate result.[2]

4·14 Galileo's Inclined-plane Experiments

In a second series of experiments Galileo is said to have demonstrated the constancy of the acceleration of a falling body. Naturally, he did not have available modern instruments of precision such as chronographs, electrical timing devices, or high-speed cameras, and thus could not make accurate quantitative tests on actual falling bodies. But his ingenious mind saw that a ball rolling

---

[1] Recent historical research indicates that Aristotle's statements were intended by him to apply to the actual motion in air.

[2] Probably by clever surmise rather than by actual experiment.

down an incline would have the same *type of motion* as one falling freely through space, and the motion of the rolling ball could be made slow enough so that it might be timed by ordinary means (Ref. 4). Figure 4.9 shows that, if the acceleration along the incline is found to be constant, then the acceleration imposed by gravity must also be constant; for the former is merely a component of the latter, and as long as the slope is constant the two accelerations bear a constant ratio to each other.[1]

Having recognized the motion of a freely falling body to be one with constant acceleration, we may now use the formulas and

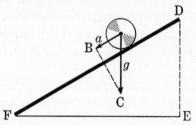

FIG. 4·9   Acceleration on an incline.

methods developed above for computing velocities, distances, etc., merely by putting g in place of a. Thus Eqs. (4.10) become, for free fall,

$$v = v_0 + gt \qquad (4·11a)$$

$$s = v_0 t + \frac{gt^2}{2} \qquad (4·11b)$$

$$v^2 = v_0^2 + 2gs \qquad (4·11c)$$

You must remember to use the appropriate numerical value for g in a given problem—980 cm/sec² if working in metric (cgs) units and 32 ft/sec² if the data are in English units.[2]

A simple test of the relation (4·11b) may be made as follows: To one end of a 10-ft length of cord tie a small weight, such as a wooden or metal ball. Fasten similar weights at the 1-, 4-, and 9-ft points. Standing on a table or ladder, hold the far end of the string, letting the entire string hang freely, with the first weight just an inch or two off the floor. Now release the cord, and observe that the sounds of the four impacts with the floor

[1] The value of the ratio in any particular case is easily found, since, in the similar triangles ABC and DEF, $a/g = DE/DF$. Compare p. 43, where the same thing was done for force components.

[2] Although 32.2 ft/sec² is closer to the standard value of g, we may use simply 32 in numerical problems in this work.

occur at perfectly regular time intervals. This shows that in 1, 2, 3, . . . units of time a body falls from rest distances proportional to 1^2, 2^2, 3^2, . . . as described by Eq. (4.11b) when v_0 is set equal to zero.

4·15 Motion of a Particle Thrown Upward

A stone thrown straight upward is subject to the acceleration of gravity all the time that it is in the air, which means that it *loses its upward speed at the rate g.* This implies that it must, at some instant, finally lose all its original upward speed and come momentarily to rest at the highest point it attains, then immediately start downward, gaining downward speed all the while at the rate g until it again reaches the ground. It can be shown that, neglecting air resistance, the speed on hitting the ground is equal to the speed with which the stone was initially thrown upward. The velocity of the body changes all the time it is in flight, but its acceleration is constant throughout, amounting always to g in the downward direction. It is often difficult for students to realize that a body may momentarily have *zero velocity* and at the same time a *definite acceleration,* as is true for the vertically thrown stone when it is at the topmost point in its flight (Fig. 4·10).

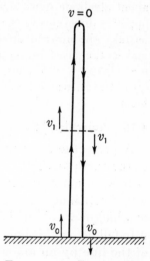

FIG. 4·10 Projectile thrown vertically upward.

The stone thrown upward takes as long to fall back from the highest point as it did to reach it—in fact, the downward part of the flight is exactly the same as the upward part, except that everything takes place in reverse order. Thus, in spite of the fact that the process as a whole is not an instance of free fall starting from rest, it is none the less possible to use the simplified forms of Eqs. (4·11) by working with either half of the flight by itself. If we had not been watching the stone until the instant it arrived at the top, we should say that the remaining motion was that of a stone dropped from this point with zero initial speed.

As an illustration, suppose that a stone is thrown straight upward with an initial speed of 14.7 m/sec. How high will it go, and how fast will it be going 1 sec after projection?

To answer the first question, we need compute only the height from which the stone must *fall* in order to attain the speed quoted. This is given at once by Eq. (4·11c) as $s = v^2/2g$. Changing 14.7 m/sec to 1470 cm/sec, this is $(1470)^2/(2 \times 980)$, which, to three significant figures, turns out to be 1100 cm. With regard to the second question, we find first that the total time of ascent, which is the same as the time of descent, is, by Eq. (4·11a), $t = v/g = 1470/980 = 1.50$ sec. Then, 1 sec after projection, the stone will be 0.50 sec from the top. At this time it will have the same speed as it will have 0.50 sec *after* reaching the top. But this is given by Eq. (4·11a) as $v = 980 \times 0.50 = 490$ cm/sec. This result may be seen more directly by noting that the upward speed after 1 sec is 980 less than 1470, or 490 cm/sec.

If the formulas are to be used to get a solution, we must be careful about algebraic signs, since the motion may at times be in either of two opposite directions in the vertical line. To solve the present example, let us take the upward direction to be the positive one. Notice that this makes the acceleration *negative*. Use, first, Eq. (4·11c) with $v = 0$: $0 = (1470)^2 - 2 \times 980s$, or again $s = 1100$ cm. Then substitute values into (4·11a), which becomes $v = 1470 - 980 \times 1$, or $v = 490$ cm/sec as before.

4·16   Projectiles; Effect of Air Resistance

A projectile is any particle thrown into space near the surface of the earth and left to itself or, rather, to the influence of gravity. If it were not for gravity or the resistance of the air, the particle would continue moving with its initial speed along the straight line in which it was launched.[1] The earth's attraction, however, causes it to fall below this line, and its position after any time will fall short of the line by an amount equal to the distance a particle released from rest would fall in this interval. The result is that the projectile describes a curve called a *parabola* (Fig. 4·11).

A useful way of regarding the motion of a projectile is to consider the initial velocity resolved into its vertical and horizontal components, as in the diagram. Gravity affects only the first of these, decreasing it at the rate g. The horizontal component, being perpendicular to the direction of the only acting force (gravity), is unaffected, and hence this component remains constant throughout the flight. The general motion of a projectile, then, may be looked upon as a combination of the motion of a particle shot vertically upward with an initial speed v_V and at the same time moved horizontal with a constant speed v_H.

[1] This will be justified in the next chapter (p. 77).

The parabolic path of a projectile is symmetric around a vertical line drawn through the highest point, which also marks the mid-point of the *range*. The particle comes into the ground at the end of its flight at the same angle as it was initially projected (*angle of elevation, θ*). This was not always believed. In the sixteenth century a common view was that the path of a missile consisted of three parts: a "violent mode" during

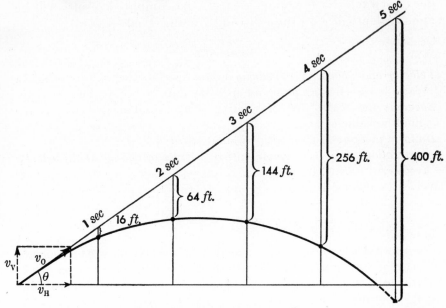

FIG. 4·11   Path of a projectile.

which the line of projection was followed exactly, a "mixed mode" when gravity began to make the particle deviate from this line, and a final "natural mode" in which gravity assumed complete control and the object plunged directly to earth! Curiously, this general notion persists with some people even today.

Our discussion of falling bodies and projectiles has assumed, all along, that the resistance force offered by the air is negligible. Since the air is present in almost all practical problems, why do we not compute what happens under actual circumstances? The answer is that we do not know how to do this in a general case. The resistance offered to the motion of a body through the air depends on many factors in a complicated way—on the speed, size, shape, and surface texture of the body and on the density and other properties of the air. It is possible to compute the resistance only in special instances, and even then we must appeal to experiment for part of the solution. Thus our procedure has been to discuss the ideal case where there is assumed to be no air resistance and where the results can be expressed with particular simplicity. As long as the speeds involved are not excessive, the simple formulas give quite satisfactory results. For instance, if the distance of fall of a heavy, compact body does not exceed a few hundred feet, the computed results will be almost identical with those found by actual trial.

SUMMARY

Velocity and speed: The *velocity vector* specifies the rate at which a particle traverses its path and gives the direction of motion.

Speed is the *scalar* part of velocity. The instantaneous speed is the limiting value of $\Delta s/\Delta t$.

Uniform motion: Motion with constant speed; $s = vt$.

Acceleration: The vector representing the *rate of change of* the *velocity* vector with time. Its magnitude is given, at any instant, by $\Delta v/\Delta t$.

Velocities and accelerations, like any other vectors, may be compounded or resolved into components.

Motion with *constant acceleration* is described by Eqs. (4·10).

Free fall: Neglecting air resistance, the motion is one with a constant downward acceleration—the same in value for all bodies. At a standard place on the surface of the earth, the value of the *acceleration due to gravity* is $g = 980$ cm/sec² $= 32$ ft/sec². The motion is described algebraically by Eqs. (4·11).

Projectile: Any particle moving freely under gravity. If thrown upward at an angle with the horizontal, at or near the surface of the earth, a projectile follows a *parabola.*

READING REFERENCES

1. Taylor, Lloyd W.: "Physics, the Pioneer Science," Houghton Mifflin, Boston, 1941. Read, at this time, Chap. 3.
2. Holton, Gerald: "Introduction to Concepts and Theories in Physical Science," Addison-Wesley, Cambridge, Mass., 1952. Like the preceding reference, this book gives a thorough insight into the development of physical ideas. In connection with the material of the present chapter, read Chaps. 2 and 3.
3. Harsányi, Zsolt: "The Star Gazer," translated by Paul Tabor, Putnam, New York, 1939. If you have not yet read this story of Galileo's life, examine at least the section beginning on p. 65, where an imagined account of the Leaning Tower experiment is given.

4. Moulton, F. R., and J. J. Schifferes: "The Autobiography of Science," Doubleday, New York, 1945. Galileo's own conception of experiments on acceleration is found on pp. 85–86.

EXERCISES

In the examples on falling bodies and projectiles, use $g = 32$ ft/sec^2 = 980 cm/sec^2, and disregard the effects of air resistance.

1. If the total distance covered by the train in the example discussed in Sec. 4·2 was 60 mi, what was the average speed for the run?

2. A car maintains a speed of 20 mi/hr for 3 hr and then rapidly changes to a speed of 40 mi/hr, which it maintains for the next 3 hr. How far does it go altogether? What is its average speed over the 6-hr interval?

3. A motorist is compelled to hold his speed down to 20 mi/hr while passing through a populated zone 10 mi long. How far must he then go at 40 mi/hr in order to make his average speed for the whole trip 30 mi/hr?

4. A low-pressure storm center is drifting at a speed of 15 mi/hr in a direction 30° north of east. How fast is it moving eastward? How fast northward? Solve by computation.

5. A submarine, preparing to surface, is moving at the rate of 10 knots on a straight course sloping upward at an angle of 15 deg with the horizontal. At what rate is the needle on the depth gage, which is marked in fathoms, falling? (This problem is a forceful argument for the adoption of the metric system!)

6. Raindrops striking the windows of a car moving at constant speed make streaks whose angle with the vertical is 60 deg. If the rain is falling vertically with a constant speed of 20 ft/sec, how fast is the car moving?

7. A freighter steams due north at 16 km/hr, and a steady wind blows from the southeast with a speed of 28 km/hr. Find by a scale diagram the direction taken by smoke from the funnel, as seen by a man on the ship.

8. The guns of a bomber have a muzzle speed of 2700 ft/sec. If the airplane is flying through still air at a speed of 450 ft/sec, find the *velocity* with respect to the *ground* of the bullets from (a) the nose gun, (b) the tail gun, (c) the waist gun, assuming that these fire directly forward, backward, and sideward, respectively.

9. If in Exercise 8 the tail gun had a muzzle speed numerically less than the forward speed of the airplane, would the projectile emerge from the gun at all? What would be seen by a stationary observer located off to one side?

10. Can a homing pigeon whose maximum flying speed is 13 mi/hr fly directly back to a city lying 20 mi due south of its point of release if there

is a 12 mi/hr wind blowing from the west? If there is a 14 mi/hr wind? Make rough sketches for each case, and decide how long each trip will take, explaining your answers fully.

11. Fill out the numbers in the following table. What regularity do you notice among the figures in the last column? Explain in terms of Eq. (4·7).

Motion of a Body Falling From Rest

Time t, sec	Speed v attained, ft/sec	Distance fallen s, ft	s/16
1			
2			
3			
4			
5			

12. A stone dropped over a cliff is observed to hit the ground below, 4 sec later. What is the height of the cliff, in meters?

13. A train starts from rest and reaches a speed of 54 ft/sec after traveling 1000 ft. Compute the time needed and the acceleration.

14. With what speed would a body have to be shot upward to go as high as the Empire State Building (1250 ft)?

15. A freight train going at a constant speed of 30 ft/sec passes a station at the instant when a passenger train starts out in the same direction. If the passenger train moves with a constant acceleration of 2 ft/sec², how far beyond the station will it overtake the freight train? How do the speeds of the two trains compare at this time? Explain.

16. A train running at 60 ft/sec is brought to rest by its brakes in 8 sec.

(a) Compute its acceleration.
(b) How far did it travel while coming to rest?
(c) How far did it go during the first 4 sec?

17. A car starts from rest and reaches a speed of 80 ft/sec after 10 sec.

(a) How far has it gone?
(b) What speed did it have after 5 sec?
(c) How far did it go in the last 5 sec?

18. Solve Example 3, page 65, by using the general formulas.

19. Solve Example 4, page 65, without the use of the general formulas.

20. A stone thrown straight downward with a speed of 20 ft/sec from the top of a tower hits the ground 2 sec later. How high is the tower?

21. While a train is running at a steady speed of 30 ft/sec, the engineer opens the throttle farther and the speed increases to 50 ft/sec in the next

16 sec. How far does the train go in this time, and what is its acceleration?

22. How long a time is required for a stone dropped from the top of the Empire State Building (height 1250 ft) to travel the distance between two points 850 ft and 226 ft from the ground?

23. Describe the motion of a shell fired from a mortar, (a) as seen by an observer in a helicopter hovering a considerable distance directly above the line of fire; (b) as seen by an observer standing a considerable distance directly behind the mortar.

24. Construct a diagram similar to Fig. 4·11 for a ball thrown at an angle of elevation of 30 deg with an initial speed of 80 ft/sec. Find an approximate value for the range on level ground by scaling off the diagram.

25. A hunter aims his gun directly at a monkey hanging from the limb of a distant tree. At the instant the monkey sees the flash, he lets go of the limb, falling freely. Will he be hit by the bullet? Justify your answer.

Chapter 5

FORCE AND MOTION

5·1 Dynamics and Newton's Laws of Motion

Chapter 4 was concerned with the branch of mechanics called *kinematics,* which deals with motion in the abstract. Certain special kinds of particle motion such as uniform motion and motion with constant acceleration were described, but no question was asked concerning the applied *forces* or their relation to the resulting type of motion. This question belongs to another branch of mechanics called *dynamics.* This will now be discussed.

The rational basis of dynamics—and indeed of all of mechanics— was given a precise formulation for the first time by Newton in 1687 through the medium of his *laws of motion.* These laws, which rank among the greatest generalizations in all of science, are of universal applicability and hold in any mechanical situation whatsoever.[1] Their correctness has been verified by countless experiments, including astronomical observations of extraordinary precision. We shall take up a discussion of each of these laws in turn, attempting to use some simple facts of ordinary experience as a point of departure.

5·2 Inertia and the First Law

Suppose that you are a passenger in an automobile which has stopped at a crossing and that the driver then makes an abrupt "jack-rabbit" start. You find that you fall back in your seat as the car jerks into motion. How does this come about? Certainly, there was no obvious force pushing *back* on your body—the only acting force you can think of is the suddenly applied *forward* pull of the motor. Also, a person standing in the road would observe that both you and the car moved forward, your motion being slower than

---

[1] With the possible exception of certain extreme conditions, for which the description provided by the theory of relativity is significantly more accurate.

that of the car during the first moments. Having recovered from this bad start, imagine the car to be running along at constant speed when the brakes are suddenly applied. This time you feel yourself pitching forward as the car comes to rest.

Both the effects described—and a host of others of a similar nature—can be accounted for by recognizing the fact that, *if a material body is at rest, it tends to remain at rest; if in motion, it tends to continue moving.*

Abundant further illustrations can be drawn from everyday experience: A prolonged, strong pull is needed to start a heavy hand truck into motion; once in motion, a large retarding force is required to bring it to a stop. A magician is able, with a deft jerk, to remove a tablecloth from a set dinner table without disturbing any of the china or silverware. The slight force of friction acting between the cloth and the tableware does not last long enough to set the latter into motion. By means of a dinner knife, one coil after another may be "sliced out" from the bottom of a stack of coins without appreciably moving those above. (Try it.)

Newton introduced the term *inertia* to describe the universal property of all material bodies that apparently causes them to persist in their state of rest or of motion. Thus the word may be construed as suggesting a certain sluggishness on the part of all matter. The first law of motion, sometimes called the *law of inertia,* may be freely stated as follows:

Every body remains in a state of rest or of uniform motion in a straight line (constant vector velocity) unless acted upon by a resultant external force.

Others, among them Galileo, certainly must have come to this same conclusion. Speaking of the flight of a projectile, Galileo said that the horizontal motion remains uniform except as influenced by air resistance. The idea was evidently "in the air" around the middle of the seventeenth century.

5·3 Interpretation of the First Law

Most people comprehend quite readily that a stationary, inanimate body will, in the absence of actions from the outside, remain at rest and will not of its own accord begin to move about; but they find it harder to believe that a moving body will, under the same circumstances, persist in its motion forever. This view is understandable, for every actual motion that we initiate eventually dies out. A stone rolled along the pavement comes to rest after going only a short distance. But replace the stone by a billiard ball and the pavement by a flat, level steel track; then the ball, if propelled with the same initial speed as before, goes a very much greater distance before coming to rest. If we could conduct the whole experiment in a chamber from which the air had been exhausted, we should expect the ball to go still farther. The successive refinements introduced all operate toward reducing the external (that is, frictional) forces; and, with the guidance of the superb intuition of a Galileo or a Newton, we, too, can see that in the limiting case of *zero* external force the body would be expected to persist in its motion indefinitely. This view is in direct conflict with Aristotle's pronouncement that the continued application of force is needed to maintain motion.

The original difficulty has been only in freeing our thinking from the earthbound experience that a frictionless mechanism does not exist. But the nearer a situation approaches the condition of zero external force, the more nearly are the predictions of the first law seen to be fulfilled. In the motion of a star we have perhaps one of the closest observable approximations to the ideal case, for the negligible amount of matter in "empty" space cannot exert appreciable retardation. Truly enough, observations extending over many decades show the motion to be uniform.

The phrase "in a straight line," which occurs in the statement of the first law, has not yet been discussed. The moving body will persist in *direction* as well as preserve its *speed*—in other words, it will maintain a constant vector velocity. Further, it is understandable from the discussion of reference frames (page 55) that a path may be straight in one system yet curved in another. By "straight line" here is meant a path that is straight either in a system fixed with respect to the stars or in one moving uniformly with respect to such a system.

A car going along a straight, level road at constant speed is in equilibrium. The downward pull of gravity is balanced by the upthrust of the road; the forward pull of the engine counterbalances the retarding forces of friction and air resistance. The resultant force is zero. If this car comes to a curve, the pavement must supply, usually through friction, an additional force to deflect the car from its straight path, compelling it to round the curve. This force we shall discuss later as centripetal force (page 142). If the road is slippery and therefore unable to exert a sufficient inward force, the car's inertia causes it to continue on its "natural" straight-line path, in accord with the first law, and it skids off the road.

5·4   Effect of a Constant Force

The first law, general as it is, really has limited applicability, since it treats only of bodies subject to *no* resultant external force. In the great majority of practical cases, outside forces *do* act, and we should like to know what happens under such circumstances.

Newton provided an answer in the form of his **second law of motion.** Let us approach the formulation of this generalization by considering an experiment with a car that moves on a pair of rails. Provision is made for applying a constant forward pull of desired magnitude. This may be done conveniently by means of a string passing over a pulley and tied to a descending weight (Fig. 5·1),

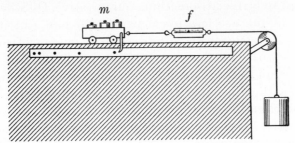

Fig. 5·1   Experiment on the second law.

but the details of how it is done need not concern us—the main thing is to be able to apply a steady pull of desired magnitude. Provision is made also for varying the total mass of the car by adding or removing small masses provided for that purpose.

Finally, there is a timing mechanism of some kind for recording the position of the car at specified instances. In a practical version of the apparatus this is usually done by allowing regularly timed electric sparks to jump from the car to a metal plate placed alongside, thus marking the car's position at each of these times by the perforations produced on a paper tape. By measuring the distances between perforations on the tape the motion of the car can be analyzed completely.

With a given mass on the car we apply a given force and record the resultant motion. When the tape record is analyzed, we find that the motion of the car took place with **constant acceleration.**

If the experiment is repeated with a different mass and a different acting force, the numerical value of the resulting acceleration may turn out to be different, but in each trial it remains constant through the car's journey. Thus we come to the conclusion that *a body acted upon by a constant force moves with constant acceleration.* This already says a great deal. For one thing, it dispels the Aristotelian notion that "it takes a steady push to keep something moving." A steady resultant forward push, we have just found, would cause the object to go faster and faster at a constant rate. The first law says that it takes *no force whatsoever* to keep a body moving with constant velocity.

5·5 Experimental Basis of the Second Law

Having shown that a constant force results in a constant acceleration, we shall now look into the question a little further and attempt to arrive at something quantitative. On what does the magnitude of the acceleration depend, and how can it be computed? This question can be answered by making two series of experiments with the above apparatus. In the first of these, we hold the *mass* of the car *constant* and apply, in succession, *different forces.* Each time, a paper trace is made and measured and the resulting acceleration determined. When the values of the applied force are written down in one column and the values of the acceleration in an adjoining column, a simple relation between these two quantities becomes apparent: With the mass held constant, *the acceleration is found to be directly proportional to the applied force.*

In the second series of trials the applied *force* is kept *constant,* but the *mass* of the car is *changed* from one test to another. Again a simple relation is found: Doubling the mass of the car results in an acceleration just one-half as great as before, tripling the mass reduces the acceleration to one-third its former value, etc. Thus, with the force held constant, *the acceleration is found to be inversely proportional to the mass.*

We now have sufficient information to draw a general conclusion. Using the symbol f for force, m for mass, and a for acceleration, the two experimental results can be expressed as follows:

1. Keeping m constant, $a \propto f$

2. Keeping f constant, $a \propto \dfrac{1}{m}$

where the standard symbol $\propto$ means "is proportional to" (see page

472). If we combine the two results, we have

$$a \propto \frac{f}{m} \qquad \text{or} \qquad f = kma$$

where k is a *constant of proportionality* whose numerical value will depend on the units used to measure f, m, and a.

5·6 Absolute Units of Force

It is convenient to have $k = 1$, so that the equation becomes simply

$$f = ma \qquad (5·1)$$

If we choose to continue measuring m and a in the units used up to now, this means that we must select a *new unit* for the measurement of force. According to Eq. (5·1), this so-called *absolute unit of force* will be such that it can give one unit of mass one unit of acceleration, for then every quantity in our equation will have the value 1. In metric cgs units the new force unit, called *one dyne,* is *the force required to give a one-gram mass an acceleration of one centimeter per second per second.* In English fps (foot-pound-second) units the absolute force unit is *one poundal* and is *the force needed to give a one-pound mass an acceleration of one foot per second per second.*[1]

These new absolute units bear a simple, definite relation to the ordinary force units we have used up to now. To discover the connection, consider a freely falling body. Using cgs units, its acceleration, as we already know, will be 980 cm/sec². If the body in question has a mass of m gm, the force acting on it during its fall will, by Eq. (5·1), amount to $980m$ dynes. But at a standard location an m-gm mass will be attracted by the earth with a force of m gm. Thus we have

$$m \text{ gm force} = 980m \text{ dynes force}$$

and hence

$$1 \text{ gm force} = 980 \text{ dynes force} \qquad (5·2)$$

A dyne is therefore 1/980 gm force. Similarly, we find that

$$1 \text{ lb force} = 32.2 \text{ poundals force}$$

so that 1 poundal is 1/32.2 lb force.

---

[1] The actual dimensions of the absolute unit of force are those of mass times acceleration, or ML/T^2. Thus "dyne" is an abbreviation for gram-centimeters per second per second and "poundal" for foot-pounds per second per second.

The fact that we are able to cancel m from both sides of Eq. (5·2) is significant—it explains why all bodies fall at the same rate. We need only grant that m has a twofold aspect—that this single quantity represents on the one hand the inertia of the body and on the other hand the measure of the earth's attraction for the body (at a standard place). Then for a falling object we can write in general $mg = ma$, and the cancellation of m leaves simply $a = g$. To put this another way: A heavier body has a greater gravitational force mg acting on it during its fall, but at the same time it exhibits an inertial effect ma that is greater by the same factor m. The result is that the whole process is *independent of m*. We shall return below (page 88) to a more detailed discussion of gravitation.

5·7 Newton's Formulation of the Second Law

Although Eq. (5·1) is a concise and adequate algebraic expression of the gist of the second law, it does not quite correspond to the original verbal statement published by Newton, which may be put as follows:

The rate of change of momentum of a body is proportional to the applied force, and the change takes place in the direction in which the force acts.

In order to interpret this statement and reconcile it with $f = ma$, we must first define what is meant by *momentum*. This is a typical example of a term that is used vaguely in everyday affairs (the speeding car "had a lot of momentum") but that is given a precise and unique definition in physics. *Momentum* is simply a name for *the product of the mass and the velocity of a body*. In symbols, using M to represent momentum,

$$M = mv \qquad\qquad (5·3)$$

Momentum is a vector quantity and thus is subject to all the propositions governing vectors.[1] If you ask *why* Newton took the trouble to define this quantity as he did, the answer is that this particular combination of m and v is found to be a useful one.

But to return to the above statement of the second law: It speaks of the *rate of change* (in time) of momentum. In view of Eq. (5·3) a change in the value of the momentum of a body would

---

[1] Strictly speaking, the quantity under discussion should be called *linear* momentum in order to distinguish it from a quantity called "rotational" (or "angular") momentum to be mentioned later.

be represented by $\Delta M = \Delta(mv)$. But, if the mass remains constant,[1]
$\Delta(mv)$ becomes simply $m \, \Delta v$. If we now divide both sides of

$$\Delta M = m \, \Delta v$$

by an interval of time Δt, we have

$$\frac{\Delta M}{\Delta t} = m \, \frac{\Delta v}{\Delta t} \tag{5·3a}$$

In the limiting case of Δt extremely small, $\Delta M / \Delta t$ becomes the instantaneous *rate of change* of momentum, and $\Delta v / \Delta t$ becomes merely our definition of the *instantaneous acceleration* (page 58). Thus, in the limit, the last equation, taken together with Newton's statement $\Delta M / \Delta t \propto f$, gives us the familiar result $f \propto ma$, which is the form in which we originally stated the second law. You will hear more of the quantity M below.

The second part of the statement of the law, describing the agreement in direction of the applied force (the cause) and the change in momentum (the effect), is in accord with experience and needs no further comment.

5·8 Numerical Examples

In all calculations where Newton's second law is used in the form $f = ma$, the best procedure is to remember that *the force should be expressed in absolute units*. If it is originally given in any other units, you should convert it to absolute units before substitution in this relation. A number of illustrative examples will now be given. Be certain that you understand the solutions before attempting the exercises at the end of the chapter.

1. A 1000-kg car traveling along a straight, level road increases its speed uniformly from 5 to 25 m/sec in exactly 20 sec. Neglecting friction, what tractive force was exerted by the motor during the pickup? We notice, to begin with, that a mass (the car) is given an acceleration (which we can compute), and we are asked to find the required force. It is well to change the given quantities to cgs units for substitution into $f = ma$. First of all, the acceleration will be given by $(2500 - 500)/20 = 100$ cm/sec². The mass is 1000 kg, or $1000 \times 1000 = 10^6$ gm. Substitution in $f = ma$ gives us $f = 10^6 \times 100 = 10^8$ dynes. Once finished with the equation, we may, if desired, express this result as $10^8/980 = 1.02 \times 10^5$ gm force or, even better, as 102 kg force.

---

[1] This is by far the commonest case in practice, but the second law is applicable even in situations where the mass of the body varies during the motion.

2. Neglecting friction, what is the acceleration of a 5-lb car (Fig. 5·1) when the counterweight has a mass of 3 lb? Applying the second law to the **complete system** consisting of car and counterweight, we see that the acting force (absolute units) is $3 \times 32 = 96$ poundals and that the total mass moved is 8 lb. At first sight, you may think that the mass moved is merely that of the car, but in reality the acting force must oppose not only the inertia of the car but that of the counterweight as well. Notice that the counterweight acquires the same acceleration as the car, since they are connected by a cord of constant length. The acceleration is given by $a = f/m$ or $a = {}^{96}\!/\!_8 = 12$ ft/sec^2.

It is interesting to inquire the value of the tension force existing in the cord while the system is in motion. The offhand answer, "Three pounds," is not correct! The right answer is found by applying the second law to only one or the other part of the system—say, the car. The tension in the string (call it T) constitutes the entire force acting on the car. Its value is given by ma, where m is now the mass of the car only. Hence

$$T = 5 \times 12 = 60 \text{ poundals} = 1.88 \text{ lb force}$$

This is considerably less than 3 lb, the value of the counterweight. "The rest" of the latter is used to oppose the inertia of the counterweight itself.

3. An elevator weighing 640 lb is descending with an acceleration of 4 ft/sec^2. What is the tension force F (in pounds) in the supporting cable? We see (make your own sketch) that the two forces acting on the elevator are (1) its weight, 640×32 poundals downward, and (2) a force of $F \times 32$ poundals upward. The difference of these is the cause of the observed downward acceleration. Substitution in $f = ma$ gives $640 \times 32 - F \times 32 = 640 \times 4$; transposing, $F \times 32 = 640 (32 - 4)$, or $F = 560$ lb tension. The fact that this turns out much less than the static weight of the car is reasonable, since the cable in a sense is permitting the car partly to "give in" to the earth's attraction by virtue of the downward acceleration. If the problem had stated that the car had an **upward** acceleration of 4 ft/sec^2, the tension would similarly turn out to be 80 lb **greater** than the car's static weight. The detailed computation in terms of $f = ma$ is left for you to work out.

Finally, what is the tension in the cable when the elevator is ascending at a **constant speed** of 6 ft/sec? Since a constant speed has already been reached, there is no acceleration and consequently no inertial forces are involved. The car is in equilibrium when at rest or when moving either upward or downward with constant speed; the cable tension in all three instances is **the same** in magnitude as the static weight.

4. The following example will show how the momentum-change form of the second law can be used conveniently in some situations: A bullet weighing 40 gm acquires a muzzle speed of 490 m/sec during the 0.004 sec

it takes to go the length of the gun barrel. What average force, in kilo-grams, did the propelling charge exert on the bullet during this time? Here it is simpler to write down the momentum change of the bullet rather than to compute its acceleration. The value of ΔM is $40 \times 49{,}000$, in gram-centimeters per second. The time interval is 0.004 sec. Hence, by $f = \Delta M/\Delta t$, the force will be $(40 \times 49{,}000)/0.004 = 4.90 \times 10^8$ dynes, or, dividing by 980 and by 1000, this becomes 500 kg force.

There are two good ways to guard against mistakes in converting units. The first is to use the dimensional labels as factors, as explained on page 66. Thus if we are required to change the above result of 4.90×10^8 dynes to gm force, we may recall that the number 980 has something to do with the change but may not know whether to multiply or divide by this factor. However, here the number 980 really represents "980 dynes/gm force," and thus if we wish to get the result in gm force, we can do so only by dividing: $\dfrac{4.90 \times 10^8 \ \cancel{\text{dynes}}}{980 \ \dfrac{\cancel{\text{dynes}}}{\text{gm force}}} = 5 \times 10^5$ gm force. Another way to keep things straight in a simple case like the above is to reason somewhat as follows: "Grams are larger than dynes (by a factor 980); therefore, if I want to express a given magnitude in a *larger* unit, there will be *fewer* of them in the result. Thus I must *divide* by 980."

5·9 The Third Law

For our purposes, we may state Newton's third law of motion almost exactly in his own words:

To every action there is an equal and opposite reaction.

Here again we encounter new terms, "action" and "reaction," which must be defined before the statement can be properly interpreted. We shall take each of these terms to mean a *force* and appeal to some facts of ordinary experience in order to bring out the implications of the law.

In a static case the truth of the law is at once evident, as we saw from the discussion in Chap. 3. To take a simple instance, if a 10-lb weight rests on a level table, it presses down on the table top with a force of 10 lb. It is equally true that the table pushes up on the weight with a force of the same magnitude. Again, if you pull with a force of 100 lb on a rope tied to a post, the post pulls on your hand with an equal force. You are able to produce a tension of 100 lb in the rope only because the post can *resist* with a force this great.

A dynamic example would be the firing of a gun. The projectile goes forward; the gun, as a result, goes backward ("kicks"). The explosion of the propelling charge exerts both a forward force on the

bullet—the *action* in this case—and an equal rearward force—
the *reaction*—on the gun. The explosion does not, strictly speaking,
blow the bullet out of the gun—it really blasts the bullet and the
gun *apart*. The third law declares that in any case where a force is
exerted by one body on another the second body of necessity exerts
an equal and opposite force on the first. It is important to notice
that the two forces, action and reaction, are exerted *not* on *the
same* body but on each of *two different* bodies.

In the example of the car and counterweight (page 79) the action
force might be taken to be the tension T in the cord attached to the
car. The dynamic (or inertial) reaction is the quantity ma. If the
string should break, both forces would immediately become zero.
If a ball is struck by a bat, the action force of bat against ball
drives the ball forward; the equal and opposite reaction force of
ball against bat slows down or even reverses the original forward
movement of the bat.

5·10 Conservation of Momentum

The third law may be given a useful alternative form by bringing
in the previously defined quantity that we called "momentum"
(page 82). Consider any pair of bodies acting on each other—the
gun and bullet, the bat and ball, or even two objects not in contact,
such as a magnet and a nearby piece of iron. By making use of the
momentum-change form of the second law, the equality of action
and reaction may be written

$$m_1 \frac{\Delta v_1}{\Delta t_1} = m_2 \frac{\Delta v_2}{\Delta t_2}$$

where the subscripts 1 and 2 refer to each of the two bodies. Now,
for any pair of interacting bodies, Δt_1 and Δt_2 must be equal—for
example, the ball is in contact with the bat just exactly as long as
the bat is in contact with the ball. Therefore the last relation
becomes simply

$$m_1 \Delta v = m_2 \Delta v_2 \tag{5·4a}$$

or

$$\underset{\text{forward}}{\Delta M_1} = \underset{\text{backward}}{\Delta M_2} \tag{5·4b}$$

Thus another statement of the third law would be as follows: In the
absence of forces from the outside, any change in the momentum of
part of a system of particles results in an equal and opposite change

in the momentum of some other part; *the total momentum, considered vectorially, remains constant.* This law is readily verified by experiment.

5·11 Applications of the Third Law

Applying Eq. (5·4b) to the gun and bullet, where both start from rest, we have

$$mv = mv$$
$$\text{bullet} \quad \text{gun}$$

If the bullet's mass is 40 gm and that of the gun is 20 kg and if the muzzle speed is 30,000 cm/sec, the gun if unrestrained will start back with a speed given by $40 \times 30,000 = 20,000v$, or $v = 60$ cm/sec. In using this equation we must express both masses in the same unit and both velocities in the same unit. If gun and bullet were subject to no other forces after parting company, each would continue to move with uniform speed in opposite directions forever (first law). This would be the case if, for example, a gun were fired at a point far out in space, where frictional and gravitational forces could be neglected.

If the gun were firmly fixed in the ground rather than free to recoil, the reaction would be transmitted to the whole earth instead of to the gun alone. However, because of the enormous mass of the earth compared with that of the bullet, the recoil velocity would be immeasurably small. In principle, the earth must be in a continual state of submicroscopic trembling due to countless actions occurring at all times such as the raising of weights, starting and stopping of vehicles, the breaking of waves, etc.

The conservation of momentum applies to any system of particles, even if there are explosions, collisions, or indeed any type of mechanical interaction between the members of the set. Thus, if a high-explosive shell should detonate while moving through the air, the individual fragments will have various momentum vectors immediately thereafter but their vector resultant will be exactly the same as the momentum of the shell just before it burst. It turns out that, while the pieces may fly off in many different directions with different speeds, their center of gravity just after the explosion will continue to move as if the explosion had not occurred.

The propulsion of a rocket by the ejection of a jet of rapidly moving gas constitutes an important modern application of the third law. Combustion of fuel within the rocket generates large volumes of gaseous products that stream out at the tail with high speed. Corresponding to this rearward momentum of the gases, an equal forward momentum is thus given to the body of the rocket. If, in addition to the fuel, the rocket carries along its own supply of oxygen for combustion, there is no reason why it should not be able to fly beyond the earth's atmosphere. In fact, its performance would actually be much better in the absence of air resistance. Contrary to an often-heard opinion, a rocket does not need the surrounding air "to push back against." It reacts on its own exhaust gases, and what happens to these gases is of no concern to the rocket once they have left.

5·12 Relationship between the Three Laws

You may have noticed by this time that the propositions which Newton stated in the form of his three laws are really not independent. The fact is that both the first and the third laws are logically connected with the second, which occupies a dominant position in physics. Nevertheless, it is useful to have the separate statements for purposes of application to special problems.

The first law is merely a special case of the second, as can be seen by considering what happens when $f = ma$ is applied to a situation where the acting force is zero. Since we are talking about a body of definite mass, $f = ma$ tells us that a must be zero if f is zero; and zero acceleration means that the body must continue at rest or in uniform motion in a straight line, which is exactly what the first law says. The second law, if taken together with the conservation of momentum (which can be deduced from experiment), leads to the third law simply by reversing the line of reasoning given in Sec. 5·10.

Questions dealing with the three laws of motion and with other ways of formulating the principles of mechanics have been the subject of much discussion since Newton's time. A notable contributor to our understanding of the subject was Ernst Mach, the nineteenth-century Austrian physicist and philosopher of science whose work was one of the main sources of stimulation of Einstein's earlier thinking on relativity.

5·13 Gravitation

Perhaps no achievement of Newton's is so widely known to the general public as is the law of gravitation—a fact at least partly attributable to the delightful story of the falling apple. Seriously appraised, this discovery is certainly comparable in importance with any generalization in the whole realm of science. The history of its development, sketched in bare outline in Chap. 1, is a fascinating story. If you have not yet done so, you will find it profitable to seek out the details by reading some of the references listed on page 13 or Refs. 1 and 2 at the end of the present chapter.

The first of the astronomical laws discovered by Kepler states that all the planets move in ellipses in whose common focus the sun is situated. His second law says that a planet moves along its orbit in such a way that the line joining sun and planet sweeps over equal areas in equal intervals of time (Fig. 5.2). According to his third law the square of the time of revolution of each planet around

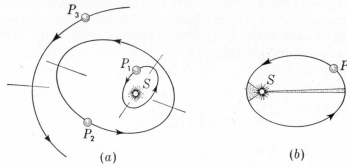

FIG. 5·2 The solar system according to Kepler's laws.

the sun is proportional to the cube of its average distance from the sun. Kepler's laws are valid also for the motion of a satellite (moon) about a planet.

It remained for Newton, however, to synthesize Kepler's purely empirical laws into a single *dynamical* proposition and thus to bring gravitational problems within the scope of mechanics. He further succeeded in showing that the motion of the moon in its orbit around the earth could be explained in this manner and concluded that the forces exerted by the sun on the planets, by the planets on their satellites, and by the earth on bodies at its surface are essentially of the same nature and represent particular examples of a universal *gravitation* which must exist between any two bodies in the universe. The *law of universal gravitation* may be stated this way:

Every particle in the universe attracts every other particle with a force that is directly proportional to the masses of the particles

and inversely proportional to the square of their distance apart.
In symbols,

$$f = \frac{Gm_1m_2}{d^2} \tag{5·5}$$

where f is the force of attraction, m_1 and m_2 are the two masses, d is their distance apart, and G is a universal constant (the same in all such computations) whose numerical value depends on the units chosen for the other quantities in the equation. It is called the **constant of gravitation** and is not to be confused with g, the value of the acceleration due to gravity at the earth's surface.

5·14 The Value of G; Dual Aspects of Mass

While the force of attraction between astronomical bodies may be enormous, that between objects of ordinary mass is extremely small. It was not until Cavendish, at the end of the eighteenth century, succeeded in measuring the force of attraction between metal spheres in the laboratory that a reasonably good value of G was obtained. The present best value, not very different from his, amounts to

$$G = 6.670 \times 10^{-8}$$

when f is in dynes, m_1 and m_2 in grams, and d in centimeters. This is numerically so small that two small 1-lb masses placed 1 ft apart attract each other with a force of only about half a billionth of an ounce; but if one of the bodies is the earth and the other is a pound mass at its surface, the force between them at a standard place is, of course, 1 lb—the weight of the pound mass.[1]

The law of gravitation throws further light on the distinction between mass and weight, which was touched upon earlier. If we say that a certain object weighs 1 lb at the earth's surface, we mean that this is the amount of the earth's gravitational attraction for it at that location. If the same object were taken to the distance of the moon, its weight (that is, the force of attraction) would become less than 0.0003 lb. If it were taken to the center of the earth, its weight would become zero, since then the attractions of all the particles making up the earth would be equally distributed in all directions and their resultant would be zero.

---

[1] The general phenomenon described by Eq. (5·5) is called *gravitation;* if one of the bodies is a planet or other astronomical body and the other an object at or near its surface, we speak of *gravity.*

There is no reason to believe, however, that *the force required to give the body a specified acceleration* would be different in any location in which it might be placed. Thus, despite the fact that its weight (a fortuitous quantity changing from place to place) may vary, the *inertia* of the body (as fixed solely by the *mass* of matter in it) remains constant. And while it is true that weighing at a selected location is a convenient means of measuring the mass of an object, the matter might be determined equally well by comparing the inertia of the body with that of the standard pound. Thus we recognize that *mass has two aspects—inertia and gravitation.*

5·15 The Tides; Astronomical Applications

The gravitational attraction of the moon, and to a lesser extent of the sun, for the waters of the earth manifests itself in the tides. The tidal effect depends on the difference of the attractive forces at the near and far sides of the earth. This is the reason why the moon's effect turns out to be much greater than that of the sun.

Exact calculation of the tidal forces at various places on the earth's surface is a complicated mathematical matter; but a qualitative explanation, particularly of the curious fact that there is a high tide not only on the side nearest the moon but also on the opposite side, is not difficult. The ocean waters are pulled toward the moon on the near side and, in a sense, whirled outward on the far side. According to Eq. (5·5) the moon's attraction for a unit mass of ocean water on the near side of the earth is greater than that for a unit mass of the solid earth (taken on the average at its center), and this in turn is greater than the attraction for a unit mass of water on the far side, since the distances increase in this order. Consequently, under the existing forces, the three entities take up new positions that amount to their being "stretched out" as shown in exaggerated form in Fig. 5·3. Relative to the solid earth, there are therefore high tides at two opposite points on the earth simultaneously. Because of friction, these points are not directly in line with the moon but lag a considerable distance behind.

The greatest triumphs of Newton's law of gravitation are undoubtedly in astronomy, where its predictions, computed years in advance, are verified by observation to the extent that has come to be known as "astronomical accuracy." Observed movements of double stars show that the law is valid even for distances millions of times as great as that of the earth from the sun. In fact, astronomers have such confidence in the law that slight discrepancies between observed and computed positions of one body sometimes cause them to search for and find previously unobserved bodies. This happened in connection with the discovery of the planets

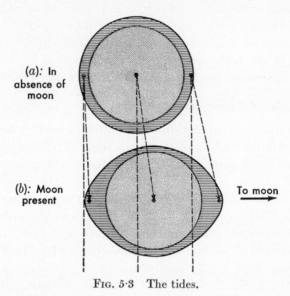

(a): In
absence of
moon

(b): Moon
present

To moon

FIG. 5·3   The tides.

Neptune and Pluto. Even the refinements introduced by the theory of relativity have been found to modify the predictions of the Newtonian law only by something of the order of 1 part in 10 million.

5·16 Significance and Implications of Gravitation

The scope of Newton's work on gravitation is admirably assessed by L. W. Taylor (Ref. 1, below):

Newton's discovery of the law of universal gravitation opened up a whole new world of scientific adventure. For two hundred years following the publication of the *Principia* the principal pursuits in physics and astronomy consisted in developing in detail the implications of that monumental work. The beautiful way in which many astronomical and terrestrial problems, theretofore insoluble, yielded to the new mode of approach was a constant delight to the entire scientific world.

Newton lived to see his ideas gain wide acceptance, but only after much controversy and intense disputes with his contemporaries. It must be remembered that neither Newton nor anyone after him gave any mechanism for gravitational force. In Newton's time, the notion that bodies completely isolated from each other should nevertheless be able to interact was puzzling and distasteful. Perhaps only because this same idea of "action at a distance" arose later in connection with electrical and magnetic forces did it gain acceptance, acquiring a plausibility born of familiarity.

Both Newton's law and the much later formulation belonging to the theory of relativity[1] sidestep any inherent explanation of the nature of gravitation. They tell merely how to compute its magnitude in terms of known circumstances. Of course the question of the *ultimate* nature of any phenomenon is not within the scope of science at all.

SUMMARY

Newton's laws of motion:

1. Every body remains in a state of rest or of uniform motion in a straight line unless acted upon by external forces.

2. A body acted upon by a constant force acquires a constant acceleration, in the direction of the force, such that $f = ma$. (For the statement in terms of momentum, see Sec. 5·7.)

3. To every action (force) there is an equal and opposite reaction.

Momentum: The momentum of a body of mass m moving with velocity v is mv. In the absence of external forces, the vector momentum of a system remains constant.

Law of gravitation: $f = Gm_1m_2/d^2$, where f is the force of attraction, G is the gravitational constant, m_1 and m_2 are the two masses, and d is their distance apart.

READING REFERENCES

1. Taylor, Lloyd W.: "Physics, the Pioneer Science," Houghton Mifflin, Boston, 1940. A masterly treatment of the development of Newton's laws is found in Chaps. 10 and 11.
2. Whitehead, A. N.: "Science and the Modern World," Mentor Book M28, New American Library, New York, 1948. Inexpensive paperback edition of a highly significant book by one of America's foremost philosophers. Read especially Chap. III on the laws of motion.
3. Freeman, Ira M.: "Invitation to Experiment," Dutton, New York, 1940. A presentation of physics based on simple experiments that can be performed with common objects. Read Chap. 6 on dynamics.
4. Moulton, F. R., and J. J. Schifferes: "The Autobiography of Science,"

---

[1] Which seeks to put the blame for gravitation on a "warping" of space that takes place in the vicinity of massive bodies.

Doubleday, New York, 1945. A generous selection from Newton's "Principia" will be found on pp. 171–194.

5. Lodge, O.: "Pioneers of Science," Macmillan, New York, 1910. A well-written book. Read the biography of Newton.

6. Andrade, E. N.: "Isaac Newton," Parrish, London, 1950. This excellent short biography depicts Newton's personality as well as his scientific work.

EXERCISES

1. A fly crawls at constant speed straight out from the center of a uniformly rotating phonograph turntable. Does Newton's first law apply to the fly? Give a reason for your answer.

2. A package falls off a shelf in a train moving along a straight, level track.

    (a) If the speed of the train is constant, what is the path of the package as seen by an observer on the train? By an observer standing alongside the track?

    (b) If the train is accelerating, will the object hit the floor directly beneath the point at which it left the shelf?

3. In the experiments described on page 80 a third series might have been performed in which a was held constant while the relation between f and m was determined. If these tests had been performed, what relation between f and m would have resulted? Is it necessary to carry out this series of tests in order to arrive at the result $a \propto f/m$?

4. Forces of 10 lb toward the north, 8 lb toward the southwest, and 12 lb toward the east act on a body of mass 4 lb that is free to move. Specify its resulting acceleration vector.

5. A horse hitched to a wagon starts it in motion. Is it true that during this process the rearward force exerted by the wagon on the horse is exactly equal to the forward pull of the horse on the wagon? If so, how does the horse manage to set the wagon in motion? It is assumed that the horse has adequate traction with the ground. You will find it of interest to look at page 183 of Ref. 1 in this connection.

6. One end of a piece of rope is tied to a 1-lb mass; the other end is free. If you are handed the free end of the rope and asked to produce a tension of more than 1 lb in the rope, how can you do this? Give a reason for your answer.

7. In place of the car and counterweight (page 79) a system consisting of two unequal weights attached to a cord passing over a suspended pulley is often used (Fig 5·4). If the two masses are 880 and 1080 gm, find the magnitude of their resulting acceleration by applying the second law to the system consisting of both masses. Find the tension in the cord by applying this law to the heavier of the two masses only. Do the same for the lighter mass. Compare the two values of the tension thus obtained.

8. A certain jet fighter airplane has a mass of 14,000 lb when combat-loaded. When flying at a speed of 400 mi/hr the engine is throttled up to exert a forward thrust of 6000 lb force in excess of the resistance force of the air. What will then be the acceleration of the airplane, assuming it to be flying level?

9. A proton, mass 1.67×10^{-24} gm, is acted upon by a force of 2.40×10^{-9} dyne while traversing one section of a particle accelerator ("atom smasher"). What is the magnitude of its acceleration, and by what factor does this exceed g?

10. In the worked example 3, page 84, how did we know which way around to take the difference in expressing the resultant force—that is, why did we not write it as $F \times 32 - 640 \times 32$?

FIG. 5·4 Another apparatus for testing the second law.

11. A 150-lb bellboy carrying a 40-lb suitcase rides in an elevator that has an upward acceleration of 1.5 ft/sec². Find the pull on his arm and the force with which his feet press on the floor of the car.

12. What fraction of the weight of a passenger on a roller coaster is supported by the car at the instant when the car has an acceleration whose downward component amounts to 8 ft/sec²?

13. What is the total pull in the drawbar of the end coach of a train (mass of coach 32 tons) if the train has an acceleration of 1 ft/sec² as it goes up a grade rising 1 ft for every 10 ft along the track? Neglect friction.

14. A 60-gm bullet is going 4×10^4 cm/sec when it encounters a plank 4 cm thick. The bullet emerges from the other side with a speed of 1×10^4 cm/sec. Assuming that the plank offered a constant resistance force to the bullet during penetration, compute the magnitude of this force, in kilograms.

15. According to a perennial problem found in many physics books, a man finds himself marooned at the center of a perfectly frictionless ice-skating rink. How can he get off? What is the net effect if he thrusts his arm forward? What could he do if he found a pebble lying next to him on the ice?

16. Which has more momentum, a 100-gm bullet moving with a speed of 800 m/sec or a 500-kg boat with a speed of 15 cm/sec? What would happen if the bullet embedded itself in the boat's mast when the two were moving directly toward each other at the above speeds?

17. Two teams, each of which can exert a maximum pull of 1000 lb, engage in a tug of war. If, at a certain instant, team A is pulling with a

force of 800 lb, how hard is team B pulling if the rope is stationary? What is then the tension in the rope? Would it be possible for a stronger team C to exert a pull of 1200 lb in a contest with team B? If so, under what conditions?

18. A 20-gm ball moving to the right at a speed of 60 cm/sec collides centrally with a 50-gm ball at rest. After the impact the two objects rebound, and the heavier ball is observed to be moving to the right with a speed of 20 cm/sec. Find the velocity (direction and magnitude) of the lighter one after impact.

19. In connection with the footnote on page 83, try to think of at least two examples of motion in which the mass of the moving body changes as the motion proceeds.

20. A machine gun fires bullets at a target with constant frequency. Compare qualitatively the average thrust on the target when (a) the face of the target is a steel plate from which the bullets rebound and (b) the target is a heavy block of wood in which the bullets embed themselves.

21. In a table of physical data, such as the "Handbook of Physics and Chemistry," look up the values of g at several places in the United States. By about how much (in per cent) do the extreme listed values differ?

22. An ideally smooth and plane table is set up at a given location on the suface of the earth with its top in an absolutely level position. A smooth, perfectly round steel ball is placed at rest on the table near one edge. Describe any subsequent motion the ball will have.

23. A storekeeper in a mountain village uses a spring balance that was adjusted at sea level with standard weights. To whose advantage is this— his or the customer's?

24. Compute the mass of the earth (that is, how much more matter there is in the entire earth than in a 1-gm mass) by considering the force of gravitational attraction between the earth and a 1-gm mass located near its surface. The effective distance apart of the two objects is the radius of the earth, 6.3×10^8 cm. By definition the attraction amounts to 1 gm force. The only quantity whose value is not known is the mass of the earth, which may then be computed from Eq. (5·5). Verify the fact that this mass amounts to about 6×10^{27} gm. Approximately how many tons is this?

25. If the gravitational attraction between the earth and the moon were suddenly to cease, how big a steel cable would be needed to keep the moon in its present orbit? The mass of the earth is 6.0×10^{27} gm, that of the moon is 7.3×10^{25} gm, and the distance between their centers is 3.8×10^{10} cm. Take the breaking strength of steel to be 25 ton/in.^{2} Compute the diameter of the required cable, in English units.

Chapter 6

MECHANICAL ENERGY

In the preceding chapter, the seemingly arbitrary concept of momentum was introduced. This was found to simplify the description of certain mechanical principles—a good enough reason for burdening the subject with an additional technical term. In the following pages you will see how yet another concept—that of *energy*—arose almost through necessity, developing into one of the most significant ideas in all of science.

It takes but little experience to realize that there are other things in our physical surroundings besides matter in its various forms. A bullet in flight is, in some way, different from the same bullet at rest; a hot flatiron, although it looks exactly as it did when cold, has new attributes; an electric cable assumes important new properties as soon as the switch is closed. In every case where matter undergoes changes, some form of energy is involved. In this chapter we examine the nature of the energy connected with purely mechanical processes.

6·1 Kinetic Energy

Imagine a massive particle located far out in space, so that it is subject to no external forces whatever. Now let a force of constant amount and direction be applied. As we have seen, the only effect of this force would be to change the state of rest or motion of the particle. In particular, suppose that the particle was originally at rest and that the force was allowed to act over a given interval, after which it ceased. The particle is now in motion and by virtue of this motion has the ability to produce certain effects that it could not produce when it was at rest. For instance, by impact it can deform and shatter another body and in turn impart motion to the fragments; or it may strike a nail sticking in a board and drive it in; or it may encounter a spring and compress it. A moving body is said to possess energy of motion, or **kinetic energy.**

97

We should like to have some quantitative way of expressing the kinetic energy of a moving body. This is readily arrived at by computing what happens in the case already referred to, where a constant force f is applied to a free particle of mass m initially at rest (Fig. 6·1). According to Newton's second law the constant force will produce a constant acceleration a of the particle, given by $f = ma$.

Speed 0   Speed v

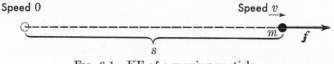

FIG. 6·1   KE of a moving particle.

Let us multiply both sides of this equation by s, the distance that the particle moves forward during the time that the force is applied. Then

$$fs = mas$$

Using one of the relations applying to motion with constant acceleration [Eq. (4.6c), page 63], we can replace as by $v^2/2$ and get

$$fs = \tfrac{1}{2}mv^2 \tag{6·1}$$

The quantity fs on the left is defined as the mechanical **work** done on the particle by the applied force, while the quantity $\tfrac{1}{2}mv^2$ represents what we set out to find—the kinetic energy (abbreviated **KE**) acquired by the moving body. This means that under the assumed circumstances (a free particle, f being the only acting force) the **total work done** by this force **is equal to the kinetic energy acquired.** The KE of a particle of mass m moving with a speed v is given by $\tfrac{1}{2}mv^2$. This statement is true even if the force varies the motion, or if the particle is already in motion when the force is first applied (in this case $\tfrac{1}{2}mv^2$ is the **gain** in KE). The acquired KE depends in any instance only on the mass of the particle and its final speed.

6·2   Work

At first sight it would seem that in attempting to find an expression for the newly defined quantity KE we have succeeded only in bringing in the equally unfamiliar concept of work. The latter, however, is essentially a simple and natural idea and one of very broad applicability. In general, **work is said to be performed whenever a force succeeds in moving the body to which it is applied.** Notice here again the use of a common word in a special and restricted sense. In the scientific meaning of the word, no force, however large, does work unless it *moves* the particle acted upon. As in the example of the previous section, the measure of the work done is the magnitude of the force multiplied by the distance moved. Thus we write

$$W = fs \qquad (6\cdot2)$$

Work may be expressed as any force unit multiplied by any distance unit, such as foot-pounds, gram-centimeters, or kilogram-meters. In the metric cgs system the *absolute unit* of work is a dyne-centimeter, which has a special name—one *erg*. This is a very small unit, and hence for practical purposes 10 million (10^7) ergs is called one *joule*.[1] The absolute English unit of work, corresponding to the erg, is one *foot-poundal*.

The left-hand side of Eq. (6·1) must be expressed in absolute units since we used the second law in the form $f = ma$ to obtain this equation. This means that the right-hand side—the KE—is also given in absolute units by the expression $\frac{1}{2}mv^2$. Thus the KE is given in ergs when m is in grams and v is in centimeters per second. Both work and energy are scalar quantities. They may be measured in the same units.

If the direction of the applied force differs from the direction in which the motion takes place, then the work done is the distance moved multiplied by the component of force *in the direction of motion*. For instance, if a sled is being pulled along a level road as in Fig. 3·9 (page 40), the work done in moving forward 10 ft would be, not 10 ft times 15 lb, but 10 ft times the forward component AC of the pull in the rope.[2] The work done by the vertical component would be zero, since no motion takes place in the vertical direction as long as the front end of the sled does not actually lift up.

6·3 Potential Energy

Work done on a body may not always appear in the form of kinetic energy. For instance, slowly to hoist a freely suspended weight of amount w through a distance h requires an amount of work equal

[1] Named for J. P. Joule (pronounced "jo̅o̅l"), English amateur scientist of the nineteenth century.

[2] In trigonometric form, this component is given by 15 cos θ lb, where θ is the angle that the rope makes with the horizontal. The work done in a 10-ft forward motion would then be $W = 150 \cos \theta$ ft-lb.

to *wh*. At the end of the process the weight is again stationary and thus possesses no kinetic energy. And yet it does have a latent energy of some kind, for in descending again to its former level it can be made to raise another weight; or it can stretch a spring in the process; or if allowed to fall freely, it can demolish something by impact. By virtue of having been raised to a higher level, the body clearly acquires the ability to do work.

When at its higher level the object is said to have energy of position, or gravitational *potential energy* with respect to its former location. Gravitational potential energy must always be specified with regard to some chosen reference level. This may be the floor of the room, sea level, or even the center of the earth—the lowest point from which a weight can be considered raised or to which it can descend.

The potential energy of a raised weight is measured simply by how much work had to be done in order to hoist it up to its present position. Work is force times distance, and the force required is equal to the weight of the body. But if absolute units of energy are wanted, the force must be expressed in such units and hence the force must be taken to be mg, where m is the mass of the object. The expression for the potential energy (abbreviated PE) of a mass m raised through a distance h is then, in absolute units,

$$PE = mgh \qquad (6\cdot3)$$

For example, if m is in grams, g in centimeters per second squared, and h in centimeters, the PE will be in ergs.

Besides the energy of position of a raised weight there are other forms of potential energy. When a watch is wound, work is done in moving the particles of the spring slightly farther apart against the elastic forces that act between them. The wound-up spring thus has a type of energy of position, or PE. Steam under pressure in a boiler has PE for a similar reason. A stick of dynamite has, in a sense, chemical potential energy; so has a lump of coal. Atomic energy, almost a catchword of our time, will be given attention later in this book.

6·4 Energy Transformations

In many mechanical processes, transformations of energy are found to occur. As an example, let us look at the situation pictured in Fig. 6·2. A body of mass m has been slowly hoisted from the ground to a height h. In the process an amount of work mgh was done on it, and this is the measure of the PE of the object in its elevated position. The body is now allowed to fall. Assuming no resisting forces, the resultant force acting on it during the fall is mg. Under the action of this constant force the body acquires KE, just as in the general example of Fig. 6·1. Meanwhile, theh eight above the ground—and hence the PE—is contin- ually getting smaller. Thus we say that, as the body falls, its initial PE is gradually *transformed* into KE.

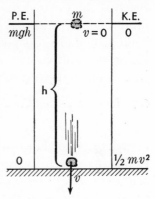

FIG. 6·2 Conversion of PE into KE.

By the time the body is about to strike the ground, it has lost all its PE (measured with reference to the ground), and it then has an amount of KE just equal to the PE it has lost: We know from Eq. (4.6c) (page 63) that a body falling a distance h from rest will acquire a speed given by $v^2 = 2gh$. Merely multiplying both sides of this relation by $\frac{1}{2}m$ gives $\frac{1}{2}mv^2 = mgh$. The left-hand side of this equation is the *KE acquired,* while by Eq. (6·3) the right-hand side represents the *PE lost.* The two quantities are equal.

If, on returning to ground level, the mass hits a spring, it will do work in compressing the spring; when the position of greatest com- pression is reached, all the KE of the mass will have been reduced to zero and the compressed spring will now possess elastic PE. The work done in compressing the spring to this point can be measured in a separate experiment. When this is carried out, it is found that, no matter what the mass and speed of the striking body or whether it compresses a stiff spring a short distance or a weaker spring a greater distance, *the work of compression is just equal to the KE of the striking body.* This KE in turn has been found equal to the initial PE of the body in its raised position. There has been, then, a transformation of the PE of the raised weight to KE of the mov- ing mass to elastic PE of the spring. Nor is this the end of the proc- ess. The compressed spring, if not restrained, will again flex itself, thus once more imparting KE to the body, which will be projected upward and, in an ideal case, return to the point from which it was originally allowed to drop. This sequence of events will repeat itself indefinitely.

Another example of energy conversion is provided by a simple pendulum—a particle hanging by a thread and free to swing in a vertical plane. If the particle is drawn aside, work is done on it and this work is then present in the form of PE, for the displacement has raised the particle. Now, if released, it swings back toward its initial position, acquiring KE at the expense of its PE until, having reached the bottom, its energy is all in kinetic form. But the pendulum does not stop at this point; the inertia of the particle carries it on past its lowest point, and it now goes "uphill" along its arc, losing KE and gaining PE until it reaches a height on the far side just equal to its height before release. The process then repeats.

6·5 Dissipation and Conservation of Mechanical Energy

If we examine any mechanism that we can actually construct, we invariably find that the energy originally put into the system seems to disappear after a time. A ball that is started rolling on a horizontal surface eventually comes to rest. The weight falling onto a spring, described in the preceding paragraph, will not quite attain its original height after each rebound. The swings of a real pendulum become smaller and smaller and finally stop altogether.

What becomes of the energy originally present in each of these systems? It is impossible to construct a working mechanism involving no friction, and it is friction and other resistive forces that, as we say, *dissipate* the energy initially supplied. This means that the system performs work against resistive forces and that this work is converted, not into PE or into KE of parts of the mechanism, but into other forms, notably into *heat energy.* Thus it is found that, whenever work is done against dissipative forces, heat appears. The block projected onto a horizontal floor comes to rest, but it is observed to be slightly warmer than before. In a similar way, heat is found to appear in the spring onto which a weight is dropped and —although more difficult to detect—in the surrounding air which was churned up by the moving mass. You will find out later (Chap. 8) that heat energy can be measured and that when this and all other forms of energy possessed by a system are taken into account a statement of great importance and generality can be made about the total energy of the system.

For the present, however, we are interested mainly in mechanical energy, and any energy converted into heat is simply thought of as no longer useful to us. A system in which no dissipative forces are found is called a *conservative* system. For such an arrangement *the sum of the PE and KE of the system remains constant;* energy may be converted from one of these forms to the other, but its total amount remains invariable. This principle is called the **conservation of mechanical energy** and is a consequence of the way in which we defined PE and KE in the first place. It is, in fact, the sole justification for making the definitions of these quantities in the form that we did.

The great virtue of the energy principle just stated is that it *allows us to work out mechanical problems without troubling with incidental details* of the setup. In place of working out the forces in detail, we use the energy principle and go directly to the result desired. This procedure will become clear if you work through the solutions of the following examples:

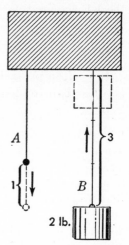

1. A box containing a concealed mechanism has two cords coming from holes in the bottom (Fig. 6·3). The internal construction is hidden from us. All we know is that it is some sort of combination of levers, pulleys, etc., but does not involve such things as springs, which must be compressed or stretched. It is found that, when cord A is pulled down 1 ft, 3 ft of cord B is pulled up into the box. Assuming negligible friction in the mechanism, how hard must cord A be pulled in order to lift slowly a 2-lb weight attached to cord B? Since all motions are performed slowly, no KE is involved and the energy principle states that the work done by the acting pull must be just equal to the work done on the raised weight. If we call the acting force f, in pounds, then the work done by it in pulling cord A out a distance of 1 ft must equal the work done on the 2-lb weight, which goes up 3 ft, or $f \times 1 = 2 \times 3$, and thus $f = 6$ lb. We have found the required force despite the fact that we know nothing of the design of the mechanism inside the box.

FIG. 6·3 Concealed mechanism ("black box").

In many applications the use of the energy concept makes it unnecessary to employ the second law, for the energy principle represents in a way a once-and-for-all application of this law. The energy method is particularly direct in situations involving the **distance** moved. Consider the following problem:

2. The motors of a 6000-lb electric trolley bus exert an effective forward force of 600 lb. Starting from rest, how far must the bus travel on a level road before its speed amounts to 40 ft/sec? Neglect friction. If we choose

to solve the problem by the method of Chap. 5, we should begin by using the second law to compute the acceleration that the given force can impart to the 6000-lb mass and then use one of the relations for motion with constant acceleration in order to find the distance required to attain the 40 ft/sec speed. The calculation would go thus:

$$a = \frac{f}{m} = \frac{(600)(32)}{6000} = 3.2 \text{ ft/sec}^2$$

Then $s = v^2/2a = (40)^2/(2)(3.2) = 250$ ft. The energy principle, on the other hand, yields the required distance by means of a single computation: Equating the work done by the acting force (absolute units!) to the KE acquired, $fs = \frac{1}{2} mv^2$ or

$$(600)(32)s = \frac{1}{2}(6000)(40)^2 \qquad \text{or} \qquad s = 250 \text{ ft}$$

as before.

It is often possible to use the energy method even when friction is present, provided only that the amount of the frictional force is known.

3. A boy coasting on a sled comes to a hill, which rises 1 m for each 5 m along the slope. The combined mass of boy and sled is 20 kg, and the constant frictional force opposing the motion amounts to 1 kg. If the sled has a speed of 10 m/sec just before encountering the hill, how far up the slope will it go before coming to rest? Here we can say that part of the initial KE of the sled is converted into PE as it ascends, while the rest is dissipated in the form of work done against friction, this work being, of course, irrecoverable. If we call the distance of ascent along the slope s, the energy statement becomes

Initial KE = final PE + work done against friction

or, using absolute cgs units throughout so that each term in the equation is an energy in ergs,

$$\frac{1}{2}(2 \times 10^4)(10^3)^2 = (2 \times 10^4)(980)\left(\frac{s}{5}\right) + (10^3)(980)s$$

Here $s/5$ represents the vertical height attained, the slope being 1 in 5. The factor 980 appearing in each term on the right converts the force in grams to force in dynes, since absolute units are called for throughout the energy equation. On solving the equation, we get $s = 2 \times 10^3$ cm = 20 m.

To solve the problem without using the energy idea, we should first have to compute the downhill component of the weight of the sled and add to it the force of friction in order to get the total force opposing the sled's motion. Then by using the second law, the (negative) acceleration imparted to the given mass could be found. Finally the relation $v^2 = 2as$ would have to be used to find the distance traveled. The relative simplicity and directness of the energy equation are evident in this example.

6·6   The Energy Principle and Machines; Perpetual Motion

By discussing a concealed mechanism above, we saw that the energy principle can furnish much information without requiring us to know the detailed construction of a device. At the same time, if the structure of a mechanism is known, the energy principle can be used to tell us even more about its operation.

The ancients were concerned with explaining the operation of so-called *simple machines*—the lever, pulleys, an inclined plane, etc. The principle of the lever was already understood by Archimedes, 20 centuries before the origin of the energy concept. Basically a lever is any pivoted rigid body to which forces may be applied.

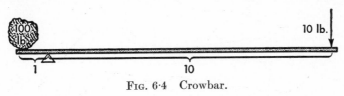

10 lb.

1   10

Fig. 6·4   Crowbar.

By proper choice of the arrangement a small force applied at one point may enable the lever to exert a large force at another point, as in the use of the common crowbar to lift a heavy weight. By experience it is found that when the friction is small the applied and the exerted forces turn out to be *inversely* proportional to their perpendicular distances from the pivot point. Thus it is easily possible to lift with the crowbar a load of 100 lb by applying a force of only 10 lb, provided that the perpendicular distance from the pivot to the load force is one-tenth the distance of the applied force (Fig. 6·4). At first sight something appears to have been obtained for nothing: a force of 100 lb has been exerted by using a force of only 10 lb. This at once makes us suspect that something is wrong and we appeal to the energy principle not only to resolve the difficulty but to explain the experimental fact concerning the behavior of the lever.

Suppose the lever is any rigid body, with applied and load forces as shown in Fig. 6·5. Neglecting friction, the energy principle enables us to say that when the lever is turned slightly by the applied force the work done *by* this force is exactly equal to the work done *on* the load—neither more nor less. The distance moved by the point of application of each force is shown on the diagram, and hence the work equality may be stated as $f_1 s_1 = f_2 s_2$, or $f_1/f_2 = s_2/s_1$. But because the lever is rigid we have $s_2/s_1 = h_2/h_1$; and upon combining this with the last relation the result is $f_1/f_2 = h_2/h_1$, which is the lever principle.

The work statement $f_1/f_2 = s_2/s_1$ shows that we really do not get anything without payment when using a lever, for while a larger *force* is obtained, the *distance* we are compelled to move its point of application is larger than the distance the load is moved in exactly the same ratio. The *work* obtained from the machine is no greater than that put into it. If friction is appreciable it is less, for part of the work put into the device is dissipated in the form of heat.

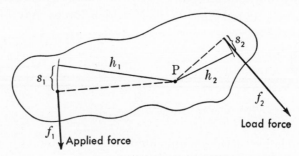

FIG. 6·5 The lever principle.

In much the same way, the behavior of other machines may be analyzed in a straightforward way by using the work principle (see Ref. 3).

The work principle explains at once the futility of trying to devise a *perpetual-motion machine*—a device that, without continued input of work, would furnish unlimited energy or even keep itself running indefinitely. No actual machine can be built that does not involve friction or other dissipative forces to some degree, however small. Hence any energy delivered to the device will eventually drain away in the form of heat and the machine must stop unless more energy is supplied from outside sources.

6·7 Comparison of KE and Momentum

Which is the proper measure of the quantity of motion of a body, its kinetic energy or its momentum? A brisk controversy over this question existed during the latter part of the seventeenth century, and leading scientific men took sides in the argument. It was finally recognized that both KE and momentum are useful quantities for specifying quantity of motion and that each has its special function and purpose. If you look again at Eq. (6·1), you see that the KE stored up in a mass M by the application of a force f that succeeds in moving it a distance s is measured by the product fs. Consequently the KE is a measure of *how far* the body could move under the action of a constant opposing force f before coming to rest.

On the other hand, the momentum form of the statement of the second law was $\Delta M/\Delta t = f$, or $f\,\Delta t = \Delta M$, and for a finite change this amounts to $ft = M$. This says that the momentum is a measure of *how long* the body would persist in motion under the action of a constant opposing force f. Summing up, we may say that the KE is more directly useful in problems involving the *distance* moved under a constant force, while the linear momentum is the determining quantity if the question is one of the *length of time* that the motion persists.

Another distinction between mechanical energy and momentum is revealed by the conservation principles. Conservation of momentum holds for *any* isolated system, regardless of the nature or violence of the interactions between its parts, but conservation of mechanical energy will not be maintained if what we called dissipative forces are present. However, there is a larger principle relating to the conservation of *all* types of energy, including that which is dissipated ultimately into heat. This will be discussed later after you have seen how heat came to be recognized as a form of energy.

6·8 Power

In talking of work thus far, no mention has been made of the *time* required to perform a given amount of work. The energy principle itself deals only with the *total amount* of work or energy in a system. There may be great differences in the time taken to put a given quantity of energy into a device and the time during which this energy is again released. In winding a watch, for example, the work of storing elastic potential energy in the spring may be done in about 10 sec, while this same amount of energy is returned to the surroundings over a period of perhaps 30 hr as the watch runs down.

In many applications there is a need for specifying the time rate of doing work, and this is the definition of the mechanical term, *power*. In symbols, if ΔW represents a quantity of work done (or the change in energy of a system) and Δt is the time during which this change takes place, then the power P is given by

$$P = \frac{\Delta W}{\Delta t} \tag{6·4}$$

Power may be measured in any units that express work divided by time, such as foot-pounds per second, gram-meters per hour, or ergs per second. One of the metric units of power has been given a special name: A rate of working of one joule (10^7 ergs) per second is called one *watt*.[1] A larger unit, useful in rating practical machines, is the *kilowatt*, equal to 1000 watts. Engineers in English-speaking countries use the *horsepower* (hp) as a practical unit. It is a rate of working equal to 550 ft-lb/sec. One horsepower is equivalent to 0.746 kilowatt.

SUMMARY

Work: Mechanical work is the scalar quantity obtained by multiplying a force by the distance its point of application moves. The force in question is the component in the direction of motion.

Energy: The capacity of a body for doing work. It is a scalar and is measured in work units.

KE: Energy of motion. *PE:* Energy of position or configuration.

Work or energy units: The absolute cgs unit is one erg (dyne-centimeter). Other units are foot-poundals, gram-centimeters, foot-pounds, kilogram-meters, etc.

Kinetic energy of a mass m moving with a speed v is $\mathrm{KE} = \frac{1}{2}mv^2$ absolute units.

Potential energy (gravitational) of a body of mass m that has been raised a vertical distance h is $\mathrm{PE} = mgh$, in absolute units.

Energy principle (conservation of mechanical energy): In the absence of dissipative forces, the sum of the PE and KE of an isolated system remains constant. This means that any change in either PE or KE results in an equal and opposite change in the other.

Use of energy principle in problem solving: See pages 103–105.

Power: The time rate of doing work. $P = \Delta W/\Delta t$. One watt is a rate of working of 1 joule (10^7 ergs)/sec. One horsepower = 550 ft-lb/sec.

---

[1] After James Watt, eighteenth-century mechanician and inventor, whose improvement of the steam engine revolutionized industry.

READING REFERENCES

1. Swann, W. F. G.: "Physics," Wiley, New York, 1941. Chapter V gives a brief but penetrating discussion of the utility and common sense of the energy concept.
2. White, L. A.: Energy and the Development of Civilization, in "The Scientists Speak," pp. 302–305, Gaer, New York, 1947. The book is a collection of the excellent radio talks on science presented on the New York Philharmonic broadcasts.
3. Taylor, Lloyd W.: "Physics, the Pioneer Science," Houghton Mifflin, Boston, 1941. In addition to presenting the historical background of the energy principle, some interesting and practical applications are given. See Chaps. 22 and 23.
4. Ruhemann, Martin: "Power," Sigma Books, London, 1946. A delightfully easy-to-read little book. Read the first four chapters at this time.

FILMS

"Energy and Its Transformations," Encyclopaedia Britannica Films. 16 mm, sound, 1 reel.

"Simple Machines," Encyclopaedia Britannica Films. 16 mm, sound, 1 reel.

EXERCISES

1. Convince yourself of the smallness of the erg as a unit of work by expressing in ergs the work done in lifting a 1-lb weight a vertical distance of 1 ft. Give the result also in joules. Which unit is of a more convenient size for expressing energies of ordinary magnitude?

2. In the first exercise worked out in Sec. 3·9, page 42, how much work is done in pushing the cart 28 ft up the ramp? In the diagram, which force is the one that does the work?

3. In Exercise 18, page 96, momentum was conserved, as it must be in any interaction such as a collision. Was energy conserved, also? If not what percentage of the original KE was lost? What became of this "lost" energy?

4. A sled starts from rest and coasts down a frictionless hill. Using the energy principle, find how fast it is going when it passes a point that is 36 ft lower than the starting point, measured vertically. Does the answer depend on either the mass of the sled or the shape of the hill?

5. With each blow of a hammer a carpenter drives a nail 1 cm into a board. If the hammer head weighs 1 kg and has a speed of 8 m/sec just before striking, what is the average force acting on the nail during each blow?

6. If a ball is projected smartly onto the end of a row of identical highly elastic balls in contact with each other, the end one springs for-

ward with the same speed as the ball that approached and all the others remain at rest. Projecting two balls simultaneously at the row causes two to leave, etc. Assuming negligible loss of energy at collision, can you explain the observations? Try the experiment, using marbles resting in a track formed by placing two books side by side.

7. Solve Exercise 14, page 95, by using the energy principle.

8. How much work must be done by a cyclotron in imparting a speed of 1.0×10^{10} cm/sec (about one-third the speed of light) to a deuteron of mass 3.3×10^{-24} gm?

9. A boy throws a 1-lb ball vertically upward, moving his hand straight up a distance of 3.0 ft in doing so. The ball is observed to be moving upward at 4.0 ft/sec when it passes a point 11 ft above the lowest position of the boy's hand. What average upward force was exerted in throwing the ball?

10. A V-2 test rocket weighing 14 tons rose vertically and attained a height of 65 mi above the ground. Compute its PE at the top point, relative to the starting level. If the average thrust of the jet amounted to 30 tons force and the charge burned until the rocket reached an altitude of 33 mi, find the work done against air resistance on the upward flight. Express all energies in ton-miles.

11. A spider of mass 2×10^{-5} lb climbs straight up his web at a speed of 0.2 ft/sec. What power is he exerting?

12. In athletics, surprisingly great amounts of power are often exerted for short periods of time. Assume that a 120-lb high jumper must raise his center of gravity 4.5 ft in order to clear a bar set 6 ft from the ground. How much work does he do in "taking off"? If the take-off lasts $\frac{1}{3}$ sec, what power is he expending? Give the result in horsepower.

13. Each second, 3 m³ of water passes over a waterfall 8 m high. If the water is used to drive a turbine, how much useful power in kilowatts is obtainable, assuming that 20 per cent is dissipated in the machine?

14. What power is being expended by a locomotive whose constant pull imparts a speed of 60 ft/sec to a 400-ton train after moving it a distance of 1600 ft from rest if a constant resistive force of 8 tons acts all the while?

Chapter 7

MOLECULES IN MOTION

One of the important conclusions reached in Chap. 6 was that any mechanical energy given to a practical machine eventually disappears through the action of friction, impact, and other agencies. It was mentioned that this dissipated energy ultimately reappears as heat. The inquiry was pushed no further than this. Now, however, we shall want to look more thoroughly into the nature of heat and to examine the evidence for believing that *heat is a form of energy*—a view hardly more than a century old. We shall also follow the development of some ideas concerning the structure of matter and see that when mechanical energy is converted into heat it is simply changed into the energy of random motion of the atoms and molecules of which all matter is composed.

7·1 Physical States of Matter

If you examine the many different kinds of matter found in your surroundings, you discover that there are three broad physical states into which all samples may be sorted. Some specimens are *solids,* such as a lump of stone or a block of steel; others are *liquids,* as water or oil; still others are *gases,* such as air or steam. A solid is characterized by the fact that it preserves both its shape and its volume except when very considerable forces are brought to bear on it. A liquid has no rigidity of form and will flow even under the influence of its own weight, but like a solid it has a definite volume and resists strongly any attempt to change that volume. Gases have neither rigidity of shape nor a definite volume; a quantity of a gas—any amount—will fill completely any vessel to which it is admitted.

There are cases in which it is difficult to decide whether the state of a substance is liquid or solid. A stick of sealing wax will shatter when dropped on the floor but will flow like a liquid if a small force is applied over a long period of time. However, the criterion for a

111

true solid is usually assumed to be the existence of a characteristic *crystalline structure* (see Fig. 7·1). Substances that are apparently solid, such as waxes, glass, metal alloys, but that do not crystallize are *amorphous* solids.

A substance such as water is familiar to us in all three states of aggregation—as ice (its crystalline, solid form), as liquid water, and as a gas (steam or water wapor). The main circumstance that determines in which state we find the substance is its *temperature*.[1] Supplying heat to a block of ice causes it to change to liquid water at a perfectly definite temperature called the *melting point*. The

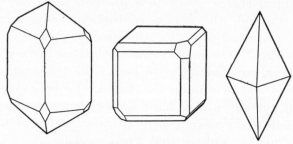

FIG. 7·1   Some natural crystals.

sharpness of this transition is characteristic of crystalline solids, while amorphous solids gradually soften and then liquefy as they are heated.

A liquid standing in an open vessel gradually decreases in amount and finally disappears, and it can be shown that the liquid has been converted into its *vapor,* or gaseous, form in the process. The rate of this so-called *evaporation* is found to increase if the liquid is warmed, if its exposed surface is increased, if the vapor that comes off is swept away by fanning, etc. At the same time the liquid is found to be cooled by the process of evaporation.

If the temperature of the liquid is raised sufficiently, not only does evaporation take place at the free surface but bubbles of vapor form all through the body of the liquid and it is said to *boil.* For each kind of liquid, this takes place at a definite temperature that depends only on the pressure acting on the free surface.

[1] To give a formal definition of temperature is difficult and, at this point, unprofitable. The temperature of a body may be thought of as that property which determines the sensation of warmth or coldness received from it. The physical content and significance of the temperature concept will be brought out by the subsequent discussion.

7·2 Atoms and Molecules

From very early times, philosophers speculated about the constitution of matter and looked for a rational explanation of such phenomena as boiling, melting, evaporation, and crystallization. Because they found it difficult to imagine that the process of mechanically dividing and subdividing a piece of matter could continue without limit, they made the hypothesis that all matter is composed of ultimate, indivisible particles, which they called *atoms;* and they further assumed that these atoms are in a continual state of motion. The introduction of this idea is generally ascribed to the Greek philosopher Democritus, about 400 B.C.

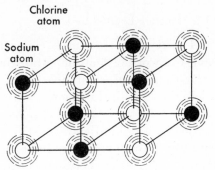

Chlorine atom

Sodium atom

FIG. 7·2 Small portion of a crystal of common salt.

While the early thinkers did not appeal to experiment as a basis for their hypotheses, the atomic concept proved to be an exceedingly fortunate "hunch" and enabled the ancients to give at least a qualitative explanation of most of the phenomena described in Sec. 7·1. As a theory, of course, their atomic idea proved sterile. As far as we know, it failed to suggest new experiments; or if further tests did occur to the thinkers of that time, they probably disdained to carry them out.

The picture of matter afforded by the atomic hypothesis is a vivid one. It is interesting to turn briefly to some of the observations mentioned above and to see how they can be accounted for on this basis. The characteristic crystal form of a solid suggests that its ultimate particles are themselves arranged in a definite pattern in space, being held in such an array by powerful forces between them, but able to oscillate about their positions of equilibrium. Thus the picture of a crystal is that of myriads of tiny atoms arranged on some kind of invisible framework in space and vibrating all the while (Fig. 7·2). If heat is supplied to such a system, the energy of motion of the atoms is increased and at a given temperature they attain enough energy of vibration to break away from the forces holding them in place. The solid is then said to *melt.*

We now have the liquid state of the substance in which the particles are free to move about, sliding over each other and otherwise showing the observed behavior of liquids. Because of their frequent collisions, not all the particles in the liquid have the same speed of motion. If a faster moving individual finds itself near the surface and moving upward, it may escape and become a particle of the vapor. This process, going on all over the surface, is evaporation, as mentioned above. If the temperature is raised sufficiently, or if the outside pressure is reduced, a point is reached at which bubbles of separated particles form all through the body of the liquid and it boils. The escaping particles become independent entities, moving about in the space above the boiling liquid.

7·3 Pressure Exerted by a Gas

Twenty-three centuries elapsed between the time of Democritus and the work of Dalton,[1] who studied the proportions by weight in which chemical substances interact and was led to the conclusion that the chemical elements must consist of atoms which combine in different ways to form molecules of various compounds.[2] Here at last was quantitative experimental evidence for the existence of atoms. But even more imposing was the calculation for the first time of a relation between certain molecular quantities through a theoretical consideration of the pressure exerted by a gas on the sides of its container. This was accomplished by Daniel Bernoulli[3] toward the middle of the eighteenth century, and the computation was refined a little more than a century later by Joule.

Bernoulli ascribed the pressure of a gas to the countless impacts of its tiny, swiftly moving molecules on the sides of the container, the rapid succession of blows being equivalent to a steady push. By simply computing the rate of change of momentum of all the

---

[1] John Dalton, English chemist, whose work near the beginning of the nineteenth century contributed much to making chemistry ultimately a separate branch of science.

[2] Strictly speaking we should always make this distinction, but in practice we find ourselves using the terms "atom" and "molecule" without discrimination, particularly in nonchemical discussions. Perhaps "particle" is the best general term for any independent unit of matter.

[3] One of the most gifted members of a Dutch-Swiss family from which came more than a dozen eminent scholars and scientists. Among his accomplishments is the aerodynamic principle bearing his name and on which the fundamental law of airplane flight is based.

molecules striking a given surface and equating the result to the average force on that surface, the following expression is obtained for the gas **pressure**, or force exerted per unit area of surface, in terms of various attributes of the molecules themselves:

$$p = \tfrac{1}{3}nmv^2 \tag{7·1}$$

Here p is the pressure, n the number of particles in each unit volume, m the mass of each particle (assumed to be the same for all particles of a given kind of gas), and v the average speed, computed in a specified way, of all the particles (the individual speeds are not all the same at any instant, since collisions are continually changing the values). The pressure on the container is to be measured in absolute units (dynes per square centimeter), n is the number of particles per cubic centimeter, m is in grams, and v in centimeters per second.

A mathematical derivation of Eq. (7·1) is given in the Appendix, page 478; it is not difficult to follow. Mere inspection of (7·1) shows that the dependence of p on the other quantities is reasonable: We would expect the pressure to increase with n, the "crowdedness" of the particles, as well as with m, the mass of each. Also, increasing v, the speed of their motion, increases both the frequency of collision with the vessel and the momentum involved in each collision, so that the pressure depends on v twice over, or on v^2. However, it is only the rigorous mathematical deduction that can supply the numerical factor $\tfrac{1}{3}$ or tell us that the averaging of the v's must be done in a certain way.

The Joule-Bernoulli relation, Eq. (7·1), was the first step in what developed into one of the most important and comprehensive physical doctrines, the **kinetic theory of matter.** In what follows, you will get some idea of how this theory not only gave us a detailed explanation of the behavior of matter in terms of its molecular constitution but also furnished a mechanical interpretation of the nature of heat.

7·4 Speed of Molecular Motion

The development of the kinetic theory has been so extensive and complete that we must confine ourselves to brief mention of representative items here. First let us notice that Eq. (7·1) leads at once to a numerical value for the average particle speed. The product nm on the right-hand side of this equation is the number of particles in each unit volume times the mass of each particle. It thus represents merely the total mass in unit volume, or the **density** D (page 23) of the gas. The equation may thus be written

$$p = \tfrac{1}{3}Dv^2 \qquad \text{or} \qquad v = \sqrt{\frac{3p}{D}} \qquad (7\cdot2)$$

The density is readily measured by weighing a vessel of known volume that is filled with the gas in question. The pressure p is also measurable, being determined by the reading of a suitable gage, and hence substitution of a pair of experimental values in Eq. (7·2) will give us a value of v.

Let us make this calculation for ordinary air at standard pressure and room temperature. The numerical data are $p = 1.01 \times 10^6$ dynes/cm² and $D = 0.00121$ gm/cm³. Substituting into (7·2) gives us

$$v = \sqrt{3(1.01 \times 10^6)/0.00121}$$
$$= 5.0 \times 10^4 \text{ cm/sec,}$$

or nearly $\tfrac{1}{3}$ mi/sec!

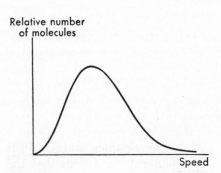

Relative number of molecules

Speed

FIG. 7·3 Distribution of molecular speeds.

Difficult to believe as this conclusion is, there are experimental ways of measuring molecular speeds directly, and these agree with the calculation. As a matter of fact, the direct measurements are in harmony with a refinement of the theory associated mainly with the name of Maxwell (see footnote, page 332).

In the first place, as already pointed out for liquids, not all the particles of a gas are moving at the same speed at any moment. The Joule-Bernoulli equation makes use of the idea of "average speed," but unless we know what fraction of the particles are moving in various speed ranges both below and above the average, we cannot make detailed calculations about the behavior of the gas. Maxwell, about a century ago, computed what would happen if the motions of the molecules were assumed to be completely random. He found that, under such circumstances, the molecular speeds would settle down to a distribution represented by a curve like that shown in Fig. 7·3. Most of the particle speeds cluster around the "hump" of the curve, but all values from indefinitely small ones to indefinitely large ones are represented by some particles.

The curve of Fig. 7·3 is really a probability curve. It states the chance of finding a molecule in any selected speed range. Thus the most probable speed is that corresponding to the crest of the curve. The chance of finding a molecule that is moving at half this speed is, as seen from the diagram, only about half as much; at twice this speed, less than one-fifth as much. Maxwell's great and novel contribution was in showing that, although the tremendous numbers of particles in a gas could not be followed individually, very definite statements could be made about the aggregate. As Chalmers has put it (Ref. 4):

To the Victorians, with their fervent belief in natural law, Maxwell's conclusions were little short of staggering. He opened their eyes to the possibility that regularity in physical phenomena did not necessarily imply the existence of "natural law," but might be a mathematical consequence of the operation of pure chance.

We shall find that the acceptance of the notion of probability had a profound influence on the further development of physical theory during the last century.

7·5 The Brownian Motion

Common evidence for the rapid motion of gas particles is the speed with which gases diffuse through each other. If a bottle of ammonia is uncorked in a room, it is soon detected by its odor many feet away. The rapidly moving molecules actually travel several miles in a few seconds, but they strike billions of other molecules in this time, and each encounter results in a sudden change in direction, so that the actual path of any individual is a jagged succession of short displacements, as in Fig. 7·4.

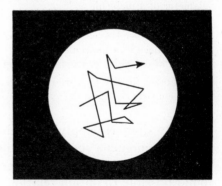

Fig. 7·4   Brownian motion.

A phenomenon first observed by a nineteenth-century botanist, Robert Brown, provides us with the nearest thing to direct visual evidence for molecular motion. If water containing very small solid particles in suspension is viewed under a microscope, the particles are seen to be in continual, haphazard motion, the path of any one resembling the sketch of Fig. 7·4. The explanation of this so-called *Brownian motion* is that the small bits of suspended matter are being continually buffeted by molecules of the liquid. Since there is practically no chance that the effects of these random impacts will exactly cancel out at any instant, the particle experiences a succession of recoils in various directions. This phenomenon is observed also for solid particles suspended in air. The application of theory to extensive quantitative observations on the Brownian motion makes possible the computation of the number of molecules in a given quantity of matter, and the fact that the result agrees numerically with that obtained by entirely different methods is excellent confirmation of the soundness of the whole kinetic-theory picture.

7·6   Extension of the Kinetic Theory

The Joule-Bernoulli equation was the result of applying mechanical concepts to the discussion of gas pressure. It was able to yield an explanation of gas pressure, as well as a value for molecular speed. Still other consequences of this equation will be taken up

Table 7·1   Molecular Magnitudes for Air* at Standard Temperature and Pressure

Number of particles per cubic centimeter (the same for all gases)	2.7×10^{19}
Diameter of a molecule	3.7×10^{-8} cm
Mass of a molecule	4.8×10^{-23} gm
Average distance traveled by each molecule between collisions	1.0×10^{-5} cm
Average speed of a molecule	4.9×10^{4} cm/sec
Number of collisions per second for each molecule	4.9×10^{9}

* Averages for the mixture of nitrogen and oxygen molecules of which the air largely consists.

later. By similarly applying mechanical principles to the consideration of phenomena such as the diffusion of one gas through another or the transfer of heat or of motion through a gas, it has been found possible to obtain relations which yield the size, mass, number, and other properties of the individual molecules in terms of measurable large-scale properties of the gas. It is not feasible to give the details of these developments here, but some typical numerical results are shown in Table 7·1. When we realize that most of these figures represent the concordant results of quite diverse experimental methods, we begin to lose any remaining doubt about the validity of the molecular concept.

The picture of the nature of a gas which the theory presents is that of a swarm of swiftly moving molecules, continually colliding with each other and with the sides of their container. The molecules themselves are small compared with their average distance apart, and they "occupy" their container only in the sense that their rapid motion prevents the entry of other objects—in the same way that an army occupies a territory, as Maxwell himself put it. A gas is mostly empty space with a tiny amount of finely divided matter dispersed in it.

Despite their frequent encounters the particles of a gas are observed never to settle out. The collisions, then, must be assumed to be perfectly elastic, involving no loss of energy.[1] In fact, the collision between two molecules must be thought of not as the actual bumping together of hard spheres but as a close approach of two intense centers of force which repel each other powerfully when the distance between them becomes small (Fig. 7·5). This type of "collision" involves no net change in energy.

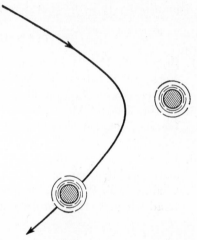

What has just been said must apply not only to collisions between gas molecules but to those between the particles of liquids and of solids as well. The kinetic theory for these two states is not so well developed as that for gases, for the phenomena are more complex. At low pressures the molecules of a gas are essentially without influence on each other except

FIG. 7·5 Nature of the collision between two molecules.

at the instant of impact, but in compressed gases and especially in liquids and solids the particles are close to each other at all times, and forces between them make the situation extremely complicated. In this respect, then, a gas at low pressure is the simplest form of matter.

[1] There can be no net loss of energy simply because there is no other variety to which the energy of the moving molecules can be changed—it is already in the form of heat energy (molecular motion).

SUMMARY

Physical states of matter—solid, liquid, gas. Temperature is one factor determining the state of a sample of matter.

Kinetic theory of matter assumes that all materials consist of individual particles (molecules) which are in continual motion.

Pressure exerted by a gas is the result of molecular impacts.

Joule-Bernoulli relation for magnitude of the pressure: $p = \frac{1}{3}nmv^2$. This and further development of the theory yield information about the molecules themselves—their number, average speed, size, mass, frequency of collision, etc.

Maxwell distribution law describes how speeds are apportioned among molecules of a gas in equilibrium. This distribution is of a *statistical* nature, depicting the condition of a large aggregate of particles.

Brownian motion: Observational evidence for molecular motion. Agrees quantitatively with other determinations of molecular magnitudes.

READING REFERENCES

1. Bragg, W. H.: "Concerning the Nature of Things," Harper, New York, 1925. Interesting for its lucid description of the structure of matter. An outstanding nontechnical presentation.
2. Perrin, Jean: "Atoms," translated by D. L. Hammick, Constable, London, 1923. A clear description of the ideas of the kinetic theory, including the author's important experimental contributions.
3. Born, Max: "The Restless Universe," Blackie, Glasgow, 1935. Read, at this point, Chap. I of this highly original book.
4. Chalmers, T. W.: "Historic Researches," Scribner, New York, 1952. Read Chap. VIII on Molecular Physics.

FILM

"Molecular Theory of Matter," Encyclopaedia Britannica Films. 16 mm, sound, 1 reel.

EXERCISES

1. In terms of the kinetic theory give a qualitative explanation of the fact that water boils at a lower temperature on top of a mountain than at sea level.

2. If the evaporation of a liquid involves a greater rate of escape of the faster molecules, how does this affect the average speed of those left behind? Explain, on this basis, the cooling effect produced by evaporation.

3. In his article on Probability in the ninth edition of the Encyclopaedia Britannica, Prof. Callendar describes the state of the molecules of a gas as "a homogeneous chaos, with that uniformity in the midst of

diversity which is characteristic of probability." Discuss the implications of this well-phrased statement.

4. The entries in Table 7·1, page 118, are interrelated in various ways. For instance, using the first item in the table and the fact that the density of air at standard temperature and pressure is about 0.0013 gm/cm³, verify the value given for the mass of an "air molecule."

5. Compute the average number of collisions per second of a molecule in the air from the values of the two preceding entries in Table 7·1.

6. Suppose a molecule in the air were to "lose" even as little as one-billionth (10^{-9}) of its KE at each collision with its neighbors. Using the value given in Table 7·1 for the number of collisions per second, compute about how long it would take before all the KE of the molecules would be gone.

7. A vacuum tube of 20 cm³ volume, initially containing a negligible amount of gas, has a small leak, so that air leaks in at the rate of a billion molecules each second. Assuming that, as the pressure changes, m and v in Eq. (7·1) remain the same, find how long it will be before the tube is full of air. In reality, will the leaking continue at the original rate? What effect will this have on the time elapsing before the tube is full?

8. A newly perfected vacuum technique permits the attaining of pressures as low as 10^{-15} of standard atmospheric pressure. Referring to Table 7·1, decide how many air molecules remain, per cubic centimeter, in such a vacuum.

9. An idea of how numerous molecules are may be obtained from the famous problem of Socrates' cup of poison. Suppose the volume of the fatal potion was 200 cm³ and that each molecule of the liquid occupies a volume of 4×10^{-23} cm³. If these molecules have since been dispersed uniformly throughout the waters of the earth, how many of them will you find in the next glass of water you drink? The total volume of water on the globe is about 10^{24} cm³, and a drinking glass holds about 250 cm³.

10. Compute the diameter of a water molecule in this way: Liquid water is found to be 1250 times as dense as water vapor at standard temperature and pressure. How many molecules are there, then, in 1 cm³ of liquid water (see first item in Table 7·1)? Assuming each molecule to be a sphere that occupies a volume equal to the cube circumscribing it, compute the length of the edge of this cube, which will then be the diameter of the molecule. This rough method gives only the correct order of magnitude, since the molecules of the liquid cannot realistically be assumed to be arranged in rows just touching each other.

Chapter 8

HEAT AND ENERGY TRANSFORMATIONS

In this chapter we continue the examination of the connection between heat and molecular motion and succeed in getting an interpretation of temperature in kinetic-theory terms. This leads to a consideration of energy transformations, particularly those involving heat and mechanical energy. The results form the basis of a general point of view called *thermodynamics*.

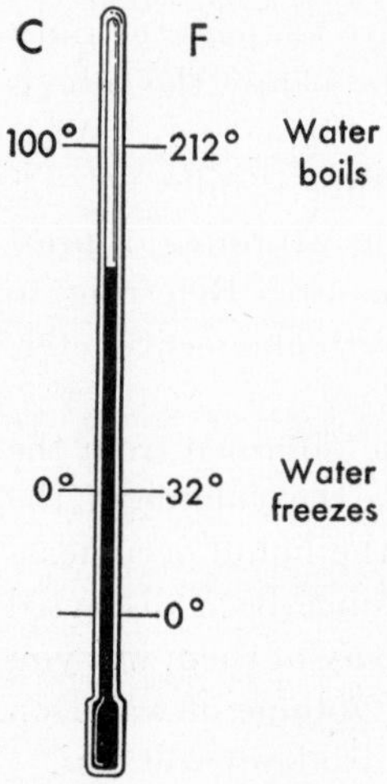

8·1 Temperature and Thermometers

FIG. 8·1 A liquid-in-glass thermometer.

The concept of temperature was briefly described in a semi-intuitive way in the preceding chapter as the factor associated with our perceptions of relative hotness or coldness. The usual method of measuring this property of a sample of matter is to put the body in question in contact with the bulb of a liquid-in-glass thermometer (Fig. 8·1). The operation of this instrument depends on the fact that the volume occupied by the liquid—usually mercury —increases as its temperature is raised. This expansion proves to be one of several properties of matter that can be used conveniently to measure temperature.

Before an actual temperature reading can be made, however, the instrument must be calibrated—that is, a scale must be affixed to it. In the *centigrade* system,[1] which is universally used for scientific work, the scale is determined by using the freezing point and boiling point of water. The thermometer bulb is put into melting ice and the place on the stem where the thread of mercury comes to rest is

[1] A recent international congress recommended changing to the term *Celsius* scale, named for its original proponent, but the designation "centigrade" seems too well established to be given up.

arbitrarily marked 0°C. Next the bulb is placed in the steam rising from the boiling water, and the position of the end of the mercury thread is marked 100°C. The intervening space along the stem is divided into 100 equal parts, each being 1 centigrade degree. The scale may be extended in both directions beyond the fixed points. The instrument is now ready for use in measuring temperatures within its range of operation.

For the *Fahrenheit* scale, in everyday use in English-speaking countries, the fixed points were chosen in a different way.[1] On this scale the freezing and boiling points of water turn out to be, respectively, 32 and 212°F. The relation between a temperature reading t_C on the centigrade scale and the corresponding reading t_F on the Fahrenheit scale is given by $t_F = \tfrac{9}{5} t_C + 32$.

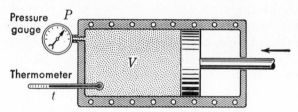

FIG. 8·2   Experiment on the gas laws.

While the mercury thermometer proves to be the commonest and perhaps most convenient instrument for measuring temperatures within the ordinary range, the best thermometer from the point of view of understanding what goes on in principle is one that uses a gas as the working substance. Such a *gas thermometer* proves to be a more fundamental form of instrument. Under proper circumstances, its indications are very nearly independent of the particular gas used.

Let us see what happens when we change the condition of a sample of gas confined in a vessel. In an ideal experiment we could imagine a quantity of any gas—air, for example—contained in a cylinder which is closed at one end with a gastight but freely movable piston (Fig. 8·2) to which external force can be applied. Surrounding the apparatus is a chamber equipped with heating coils and refrigerating pipes so that the temperature of the gas can be varied at will. There are obviously three quantities determining the condition of the gas at any time; the *pressure* confining it, the *volume* it occupies, and the *temperature* at which it is kept.

[1] Details are given in Ref. 2.

If we are interested in finding out what relation, if any, exists between these quantities, we do not try to vary all conditions at the same time. Instead, we conduct partial experiments. In each of these, one of the three factors can be held constant while the relation between the remaining two is investigated. This, you may recall, is exactly the method of attack that was used (page 80) in finding the experimental connection between the quantities involved in Newton's second law.

8·2 Boyle's Law

In the first investigation suppose the temperature of the gas to be held constant while the relation between pressure and volume is studied. Using the apparatus of Fig. 8·2, we measure the volume occupied by the gas when a given pressure acts, recording the values of both volume and pressure. Next the pressure is changed by a definite amount. The corresponding volume is measured, not at once, but after waiting for the gas to come back to its original temperature, since it is a fact of experience that compressing a gas warms it, while allowing a gas to expand cools it. After the original temperature is again reached, the values of volume and pressure are noted, the applied pressure is again changed, and the procedure continued in this way until a sufficient number of pairs of values are available for consideration.

Inspection of the data shows that *if the temperature of a confined gas is held constant, the volume is inversely proportional to the pressure.* This statement is called *Boyle's law*.[1]

In symbols the law may be stated as follows:

If t is held constant,

$$V \propto \frac{1}{p} \qquad \text{or} \qquad pV = k_1 \tag{8·1}$$

where p represents the pressure and V the volume and k_1 is a quantity that stays constant during the whole experiment. Its numerical value depends on the kind and mass of gas used and on the temperature at which the experiment is carried out.[2] The inverse

---

[1] After Robert Boyle, who discovered the relation by essentially the above procedure about the middle of the seventeenth century. He was noted for important early work in chemistry as well as in physics.

[2] Still another way to express the law would be $V_1/V_2 = p_2/p_1$. If this is not evident to you, look again at p. 475.

proportionality between p and V means, for instance, that doubling the applied pressure will make the volume decrease to half its former value. This is at once understandable on the basis of the kinetic theory; for if the volume is halved, the molecules will hit the sides of the vessel on the average twice as often and thus will exert twice as much pressure as before.

8·3 Gas at Constant Volume; Absolute Zero

The next thing to do in examining the behavior of a confined gas is to hold a new quantity constant—say, the *volume*—and experimentally determine the connection between the pressure and the temperature. In terms of the ideal apparatus of Fig. 8·2 the procedure is to lock the piston in a fixed position and then record pairs of values of temperature and pressure. As might be expected, the pressure is found to increase as the temperature is raised, which simply says that gases (like nearly all other substances) tend to expand when heated.

The best way to study the results is to make a graph of pressure as a function of temperature. When this is done, the points are

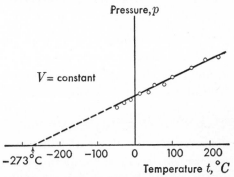

FIG. 8·3   Pressure-temperature curve of a gas at constant volume.

found to fall quite well along a straight line, as shown in Fig. 8·3. In practice, the range over which the data points can be obtained will be limited by circumstances. For example, the gas will liquefy when sufficiently cooled, and this imposes a lower limit on the working temperatures.

Assume now that the straight line representing the experimental results is extended to the left until it cuts the temperature axis. The crossing point is found to come at $-273.2°$ on the centigrade scale. Moreover, in every such experiment, no matter which gas is used, the extension of the data line is found to meet the temperature axis at this **same point** (see Fig. 8·4).

This temperature of $-273.2°C$ is called the **absolute zero.** Unlike the centigrade zero, which depends on the behavior of a particular substance (water), the absolute zero represents a fundamental point common to all substances. Experimentally, temperatures within a few thousandths of a degree of the absolute zero have been attained.

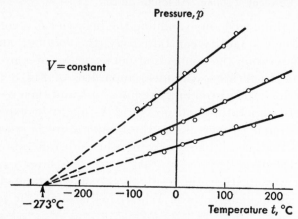

FIG. 8·4   Pressure-temperature curves at constant volume.

It is remarkable that the entirely different line of reasoning of the science of thermodynamics leads, by a more compelling and more general argument, to this same absolute zero of temperature. How this comes about will be indicated below.

8·4   Absolute Scale; General Gas Law

The fundamental significance of the absolute zero suggests that, for theoretical purposes at least, all temperatures should be measured upward from this point. If this is done, we have what is called the **absolute scale** of temperature whose starting point is the absolute zero and whose degree is taken to be the same size as the centigrade degree. On this basis the melting point of ice is 273° abs, the boiling point of water is 373° abs, etc. (see Table 8·1).

With T as the symbol for temperature measured on the absolute scale, the result of the pressure experiment may now be stated in either of the following forms:

If V is held constant,

$$p = k_2 T \qquad \text{or} \qquad \frac{p_1}{p_2} = \frac{T_1}{T_2} \tag{8.2}$$

where k_2 remains constant throughout the experiment. Its value is determined by the kind and amount of gas used and by the volume at which it is kept.

The third and final experiment that might be carried out on a gas involves holding the pressure constant while the relation between

Table 8·1   Temperatures of Various Objects

Center of a hot star	40,000,000° abs
Center of the sun	25,000,000
Surface of a hot star	50,000
Sun's surface	6,000
Carbon-arc lamp	4,000
Melting iron	1,800
Boiling water	373
Melting ice	273
Dry ice (solid carbon dioxide)	200
Liquid air, boiling	88
Liquid helium, boiling rapidly	0.7

volume and temperature is determined. The surprising result is that, for any sample of gas, the data points on a volume-temperature graph (Fig. 8·5) again fall on a straight line which, extended backward, cuts the temperature axis at the very same point

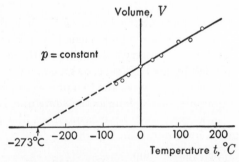

FIG. 8·5   Volume-temperature curve of a gas at constant pressure.

$(-273.2°C)$ as in the previous experiment. The results of the experiment may be put in symbols:

If p is held constant,

$$V = k_3 T \quad \text{or} \quad \frac{V_1}{V_2} = \frac{T_1}{T_2} \qquad (8·3)$$

Experiments of the kind described above were first carried out by the French physicists Charles and Gay-Lussac around the beginning of the nineteenth century, and the resulting generalizations are connected with their names. If we wish to summarize all that we have found out about the behavior of gases, we can combine Eqs. (8·1), (8·2), and (8·3) in a single statement, which may be written in either of the following forms:

$$pV = KT \qquad \text{or} \qquad \frac{p_1 V_1}{p_2 V_2} = \frac{T_1}{T_2} \qquad (8 \cdot 4)$$

Here K is a constant whose numerical value depends only on the kind and mass of gas used. This relation tells us what happens when any or all of the variables p, V, T are allowed to change and may be called the *general gas law*. In using it for computation the important thing to remember is that *all temperatures must be expressed on the absolute scale.* It is only by this device of measuring T upward from the place where the experimental line cuts the temperature axis that we can write the equation in the simple forms shown in Eq. (8·4). For instance, if a gas is at 15°C, the value to use in a calculation is not 15 but 15 + 273, or 288° abs.

Example: A chemist collects 500 cm³ of chlorine gas on a day when the laboratory temperature is 27°C and the barometer stands at 74 cm. What volume will this gas occupy under *standard conditions,* that is, 0°C and 76 cm pressure?

The designation of air pressure in terms of the height at which the column of mercury stands in a barometer is usual in problems of this type. Thus, while "centimeters of mercury" is not explicitly of the dimensions of pressure (force divided by area), it serves as a convenient way of specifying this quantity. In using Eq. (8·4), the two pressures may be expressed in *any* kind of pressure unit, just as long as the *same* unit is used for both. The temperatures, however, must be measured on the absolute scale. Substituting the given information in Eq. (8·4),

$$\frac{(74)(500)}{(76)(V_2)} = \frac{300}{273} \qquad V_2 = 443 \text{ cm}^3$$

8·5   Heat Energy and Molecular Motion

The fact that the kinetic energy of the molecules of a gas depends on the absolute temperature was referred to above. The kinetic theory makes it possible to get an exact relation between these two quantities for a gas at not too high pressures. This is of great significance to our whole understanding of the nature of heat.

Let us multiply both sides of Eq. (7·1), page 115, by V, the volume of the gas. The result is $pV = \frac{1}{3}(nV)(mv^2)$. But nV is the volume multiplied by the number of particles in unit volume, and hence the product represents merely the total number of particles N in the whole sample of gas. Also, mv^2 is proportional to the average KE of each molecule; therefore the entire right-hand side of the above relation is proportional to the total KE of all N molecules of

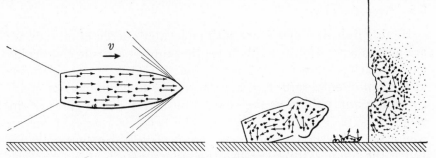

FIG. 8·6   Bullet striking a target.

the gas. Now, if we compare this result with the gas equation $pV = KT$, we come to the remarkable conclusion that *the KE of the molecules of a gas is proportional to the absolute temperature.* This gives us, then, a direct mechanical picture of what the elusive concept of temperature really means. It also confirms the idea, anticipated above, that *heat is a form of energy—the energy of motion of the molecules.*

The only difference between heat energy and the KE of finite objects is that heat is *random, disorganized motion* on the part of the individual molecules while the KE of the movement of the body as a whole represents an *orderly motion* of all its particles. Through friction, impact, or

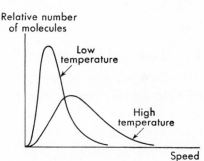

FIG. 8·7   Effect of temperature on molecular speeds.

other dissipative processes, organized particle motion may be converted into additional random motion of the molecules of a body. Thus Fig. 8·6 attempts to represent what happens on a molecular scale when a bullet strikes a target. The visible, large-scale motion of the object as a whole is converted into molecular motion—heat. For simplicity the random part of the motion of the molecules before impact is not shown in the sketch.

Supplying heat to a gas leaves its molecules with a new Maxwell distribution, as illustrated by the two curves in Fig. 8·7. At the higher temperature, the peak of the curve is lower and broader, and the position of the peak has shifted to the right, corresponding to a higher average molecular speed.

8·6   Avogadro's Law

Having linked temperature with molecular energy of motion, we are now in a position to explain another important rule concerning gases, which is known as *Avogadro's law*. It states that, *for all gases at the same temperature and pressure, the total number of molecules in a unit volume is the same.* Consider any two gases at the same pressure. Then Eq. (7·1), page 115, becomes $n_1 m_1 v_1^2 = n_2 m_2 v_2^2$, where the subscripts 1 and 2 refer, respectively, to the two gases. But if the temperatures are also the same for both gases, we must have $m_1 v_1^2 = m_2 v_2^2$, from which it follows that $n_1 = n_2$. This justifies the above statement, which was originally arrived at from chemical considerations, Avogadro's law is the basis for designating the first item in Table 7.1 as having the same value for all gases. The number of molecules in one chemical volume (22,400 cm³) of a gas, measured at standard temperature and pressure, is called *Avogadro's number* and is equal to 6.025×10^{23}. It is one of the important fundamental physical constants.

8·7   Quantity of Heat; Units

Long before science had arrived at an interpretation of heat as a form of energy, it was thought of as an invisible, weightless fluid that could be made to pass from one body to another. This idea has a certain naturalness, and today we still speak of heat as *flowing* from a warm object to a cold one. It is a fact of experience that heat always passes from a warm to a cold body of its own accord, never in the reverse direction; this suggests that the *difference in temperature* of the two is the agency causing the heat flow, in much the same way that a difference in level causes water to flow from one tank to another which is at a lower level.

There is much experience pointing to the fact that temperature is only one aspect of the phenomenon of heat. A cupful of boiling water and a bucketful of boiling water are both at the same temperature; yet they produce decidedly different heating effects when poured into a bathtub containing a given quantity of water originally at room temperature. You might expect, however, that if a series of experiments were made in which *equal* masses of matter at the same initial temperature were put into a given amount of water at room temperature, the temperature rise would be the same in every case. This is not so; the temperature rise in any instance is found to depend on the kind of material of which the hot body is composed.

By carrying on such "mixture" experiments in which heat is allowed to pass from one object to another under controlled conditions, it is found that what we can call the *quantity of heat* passing into or out of a body is proportional to both the mass of the body and the temperature change which it undergoes, and depends in addition on the nature of the substance. Thus if ΔQ represents the change in the quantity of heat, m the mass, and Δt the temperature change of the object, we may write

$$\Delta Q = sm\,\Delta t \qquad (8 \cdot 5)$$

where s is a constant of proportionality, called the *specific heat,* whose value depends on the kind of material used. It is assumed that no changes of state occur in the process.

Up to this point we have not specified a unit for the measurement of Q, although we know from the kinetic theory that Q is of the nature of energy. Nevertheless, it is common to use a unit based entirely on thermal measurements, and this is defined by choosing water as a standard substance. The metric unit of heat quantity, *one calorie,* is defined as *the amount of heat entering or leaving one gram of water when its temperature changes by one centigrade degree.*[1] This definition fixes the value of s at unity for water; most other substances have much smaller values. The numerical value of s for a given material is the same in both the English and metric systems.

8·8   Mechanical Equivalent of Heat

If any device in which there is considerable dissipation of mechanical energy is examined closely, the heat into which the "wasted" energy has been converted will usually be apparent.

---

[1] A larger unit, the *kilogram-calorie,* is 1000 times as big and is used for many practical purposes, such as specifying food values. The English unit of heat quantity is the *British thermal unit* (Btu), defined as the quantity of heat required to raise the temperature of one pound of water one Fahrenheit degree.

The bearings of a machine become warm; a pump for compressing air is hotter than can be accounted for through friction alone; a nail is sensibly warmed after a few blows by a hammer. Always there is something to show for the dissipated work. The mechanical energy that is "lost" to the system reappears in the form of heat energy, as we have seen.

The rational basis for this idea was first provided through observations and experiments by Rumford[1] at the close of the eighteenth century. While observing the boring of a gun barrel, he was impressed by the large and apparently unlimited amount of heat evolved by the cutting of the metal and noted that the heat developed seemed to increase with the work done by the horse which provided the motive power for the lathe. He actually carried out rough measurements of the heat produced and so arrived at the first numerical estimate of what has come to be called the *mechanical equivalent of heat*—the "price" paid for heat in terms of work, or the relation between calories and ergs.

It required the careful and ingenious experiments of Joule toward the middle of the century to clarify the situation. By comparing the heat and mechanical work obtainable from an electric current, he arrived at a value of the equivalent that was not far from Rumford's rough figure. Moreover, he checked this value by other experiments on the conversion of work into heat, using a variety of processes such as solid friction, the resistance of liquids flowing in pipes, the stirring of liquids, and the compression of air. Regardless of the method used, the "rate of exchange" of work for heat was always found to be, within reasonable limits, the same. The value is

$$4.18 \times 10^7 \text{ ergs (4.18 joules)} = 1 \text{ cal} \atop 778 \text{ ft-lb} = 1 \text{ Btu} \left.\right\} \qquad (8\cdot6)$$

The amount of heat equivalent to a moderate quantity of mechanical energy is surprisingly small. Conversely, large and obvious portions of mechanical energy may seem to vanish in certain processes; yet delicate observations are often needed to show that any heat is generated at all. Two examples will serve to bring this out:

[1] Count Rumford (Benjamin Thompson), one of the most picturesque characters in the history of science. He was a statesman, scientist, adventurer, and engineer and was the founder of the famed Royal Institution of London, which fostered some of the most important scientific research of the nineteenth century.

Example 1: Assuming that all the initial potential energy of the water at the top of a fall is converted into heat when the water strikes the rocks below, how much higher in temperature is the water at the base of Niagara Falls (height 160 ft)? To find a solution, we note that a mass m lb of water, falling 160 ft, would lose $160m$ ft-lb of gravitational PE. This would eventually be converted into heat by the impact, and since 778 ft-lb is equivalent to 1 Btu, the quantity of heat developed would be $160m/778$ Btu. Any quantity of heat ΔQ is, by Eq. (8·5), expressible as $sm\ \Delta t$; so here we have $160m/778 = 1 \times m \times \Delta t$. Notice that m, the mass of water considered, drops out, leaving the result $\Delta t = 0.21$ Fahrenheit degree.

Example 2: How fast must a 3200-lb automobile be going in order that its KE be equivalent to the energy required to heat a gallon of water from room temperature to the boiling point? The KE of the car, in foot-poundals, is given by $\frac{1}{2} \times 3200 \times v^2$, where v is the speed in feet per second. The heat quantity is $1 \times 8 \times 142$ Btu, since a gallon of water has a mass of about 8 lb and the temperature change is from 70 to 212°F. Changing to foot-poundals by multiplying by 778×32, this can be equated to the expression for the KE. On solving, $v = 133$ ft/sec, or just over 90 mi/hr!

The impressive disparity between equivalent amounts of mechanical and heat energy can be ascribed to the fact that ordinary mechanical speeds are very low compared with the speeds of molecular motion at ordinary temperatures.

8·9 Conservation of Energy

At about the time of Joule's work on the mechanical equivalent of heat, J. R. Mayer, a German physician working in Java, arrived at a generalization that has since become known as the *conservation of energy*. Mayer observed that blood drawn from the veins of patients in the tropics was redder than in the temperate zone. This suggested to him that there must be a lower rate of body heat loss in equatorial regions. From here he went on to surmise:

Let the quantity of mechanical work performed by an animal in a given time be collected and converted by friction or some other means into heat; add to this the heat generated immediately in the animal body at the same time, we have then the exact quantity of heat corresponding to the chemical processes that have taken place.

Pushing on to the final generalization, Mayer and others concluded in effect that *it is impossible to create or destroy energy—*

what disappears in one form must reappear in another. Unlike the limited conservation principle for mechanical energy discussed in Chap. 6, this statement refers to the constancy of the *total* amount of *all kinds* of energy in a system, including heat, chemical, electrical, and other forms. In anticipation of the conservation principle, we have already seen (page 106) the impossibility of constructing a perpetual-motion machine. However, the importance of the principle goes far beyond this. It is the most significant and far-reaching generalization in all of science.[1] No valid exception has ever been encountered.

Experiments like those of Joule involve the transformation of work into heat, but we know that the reverse process is also possible. A *heat engine,* such as the steam engine or the internal-combustion engine, is merely a device for obtaining mechanical energy from heat energy. It is easy to see that in such a process the relation between heat and work must be the same numerically as the value quoted above; that is, each calorie of heat converted must yield 4.18 joules of work—the same ratio as in the opposite process, when work is changed to heat. If the two numbers were not identical, it would be possible to build an engine that alternately converted energy in one direction and then the other in such manner that the difference would be left over after each cycle of events and we should be able to create unlimited amounts of energy from nothing.

8·10　Thermodynamics and the Thermodynamic Temperature Scale

Thermodynamics is a general procedure for dealing with the relations of heat and mechanical energy. It is founded on two laws (postulates). The *first law of thermodynamics* is merely a restricted statement of conservation of energy in which the principle is applied to exchanges between heat and work. It restates, in effect, the constancy of the numerical relation between heat and work as expressed by, say, 778 ft-lb = 1 Btu.

The *second law of thermodynamics* originated from considerations of what happens in a heat engine. Any such device takes in heat (for example, from a boiler or from the combustion of gases in the cylinders), transforms part of this heat into work (by propelling a vehicle, turning an electric generator, etc.), and discharges the

---

[1] Except for Einstein's principle of mass-energy conservation (p. 409), which explains, among other things, the source of "atomic energy."

remainder of the heat to a body at lower temperature (such as a steam condenser, or the outside air). The important fact is that, in any engine that can be devised, only part of the heat taken in can be converted into mechanical work. A steam engine, for example, can at best change only about 30 per cent of the heat of its fuel into mechanical work. The rest is lost to the surroundings. No heat engine can be 100 per cent efficient.

The second law expresses the inherent impossibility of building any device that would convert heat completely into work. This law obviously goes beyond anything contained in the first law. According to the latter, the quantity of heat produced by vigorously stirring a liquid is just equivalent to the work done by the stirrer. The second law, however, tells us that the reverse process does not occur of itself: We would not expect the water in a pail suddenly to start rotating, while at the same time its temperature dropped.

Consideration of a great variety of natural processes convinces us that a certain bias, or one-way tendency, exists in nature: Work can be completely frittered away in the form of heat, but heat is not completely convertible into work. Mechanical energy tends to degrade to the less available energy form called heat. In the example of Fig. 8·6, page 129, mechanical energy was represented as orderly molecular motion, whereas heat was shown to be disorderly, or random, molecular motion. The second law of thermodynamics, taken in connection with the kinetic theory, generalizes this to say that there is a continual tendency in the universe toward a state of increasing molecular disorder.

In discussing the measurement of temperature, earlier in this chapter, it was pointed out that, while the gas thermometer is far superior to a liquid-in-glass instrument, the readings of the former are still to some extent dependent on the particular gas used. Early in the development of the science of thermodynamics it was shown that an *absolute thermodynamic scale* of temperature could be defined in terms of the operation of an ideal heat engine, quite independent of the properties of any particular substance. The zero of this temperature scale turns out to be the same as the absolute zero previously defined by means of an ideal gas thermometer, and the two scales are identical throughout.

In only slightly more than a century, thermodynamics has developed into a powerful and extremely practical branch of science. Its applications, especially in chemistry and engineering, have yielded many valuable results. There is an interesting parallel between the two ways of handling mechanical problems (Newton's laws; the energy principle) and the two ways of dealing with heat problems (kinetic theory; thermodynamics). In each instance, the first method of approach requires a detailed knowledge of the mechanism of the system, while the second requires no specific model but only information as to the initial and final conditions. In both fields, there are many instances where the two points of view usefully supplement each other.

Finally, it may be pointed out that most of the great principles in science, such as Newton's laws of motion and the laws of thermodynamics, are not capable of direct verification in their general form. They have no mathematical proof but are generalizations of our experience that have shown themselves to be universally trustworthy. As might be expected, ideas of such wide scope have had profound influence in all branches of philosophical thought.

SUMMARY

Temperature is the physical characteristic of an object that we associate with our perception of relative hotness or coldness.

The *centigrade scale* of temperature fixes the freezing and boiling points of pure water, under standard conditions, at 0° and 100°, respectively.

Absolute zero is the temperature at which a confined gas, under ideal conditions, would no longer exert pressure or occupy volume. At this temperature the KE of molecular motion would also become zero.

General gas law: $pv = KT$; temperature T must be on absolute scale.

Heat equation: $\Delta Q = sm \, \Delta t$. The specific heat s is a property of the material. For water, s is taken to be unity.

The unit for measuring ΔQ is the amount of heat (energy) transferred when unit mass of water changes in temperature by one degree. In the metric system, this is 1 *calorie;* in English units, 1 *Btu.*

A given quantity of mechanical energy is always equivalent to a fixed amount of heat energy (*first law of thermodynamics*).

Conservation of energy: The total amount of all kinds of energy in a closed system remains constant, no matter what transformations from one form to another take place.

The *second law of thermodynamics* expresses the universal tendency of mechanical and other forms of energy to degenerate into the less available form of heat energy. It also denies the possibility of converting, by any means, a quantity of heat *completely* into useful mechanical work.

READING REFERENCES

1. Mott-Smith, M.: "The Story of Energy," Appleton-Century-Crofts, New York, 1934. Read Chaps. X–XIII inclusive, on the work of Mayer, Joule, and others.
2. Dingle, H.: "The Scientific Adventure," Philosophical Library, New York, 1953. Chapter 1 presents an authoritative sketch of the history of the thermometer and other topics in heat.
3. Moulton, F. R., and J. J. Schifferes: "The Autobiography of Science," Doubleday, New York, 1945. Read pp. 240–246 (Rumford) and 292–299 (Joule).
4. Chalmers, T. W.: "Historic Researches," Scribner, New York, 1952. Read Chap. II on the mechanical equivalent of heat.
5. Ruhemann, M.: "Power," Sigma Books, London, 1946. An excellent popular account of energy and engines. Read especially Chaps. 8 and 9 on heat engines.

FILM

"Thermodynamics," Encyclopaedia Britannica Films. 16 mm, sound, 1 reel.

EXERCISES

1. A human being can withstand such temperature differences as those between northeastern Siberia ($-90°F$) and Death Valley ($+125°F$). What does this difference amount to in centigrade degrees? If normal body temperature is $99°F$, how does the above temperature interval compare with the body temperature expressed on the absolute scale?

2. Air at $-5°C$ is drawn into a heater, emerging at a temperature of $30°C$. Assuming the pressure to remain constant, by what factor is the volume of the air increased?

3. An automobile tire is inflated to a pressure of 30 lb/in² in a garage where the temperature is $20°C$. What will the gage pressure be when the tire is outdoors on a day when the temperature is $-15°C$? Assume that the volume of the tire remains constant, and remember that the gage reads pressure *above* that of the air (15 lb/in²).

4. On a winter day, the radiator in a previously unheated room is turned on, raising the temperature of the room from 10 to $25°C$. As the air is warmed, some of it escapes from the room but the pressure remains constant. If the air in the room originally weighed 120 lb, what weight of air escaped in the heating process?

5. A sample of hydrogen is confined at constant pressure in a gas thermometer. It is found to occupy a volume of 82.0 cm³ at $0°C$ and 112 cm³ at $100°C$. Find the value of the absolute zero as determined by these observations.

6. Five hundred calories of heat is supplied to a 300-gm sample of porcelain, and its temperature is found to be raised 6.40 centigrade degrees thereby. What is the specific heat of this material?

7. An engine, while idling, expends energy at the rate of 120 watts. If 20 per cent of this energy goes into heat developed in the bearings, at what rate (in calories per minute) is heat being lost through friction?

8. A floor clock is driven by the descent of two 4-kg weights, each of which travels a vertical distance of 1.3 m in 24 hr. Assuming that all the initial PE of the weights is transformed into heat, how many calories are produced in the clock mechanism each hour?

9. An average adult when resting produces about 65,000 cal of heat per hour (basal metabolism). To how many watts is this equivalent?

10. Diesel locomotive fuel oil produces 100,000 Btu/gal when burned and costs 2 cents per gallon. The over-all efficiency of the locomotive is 20 per cent. The work done against all resistances while bringing the train up to its running speed amounts to 4.8×10^7 ft-lb. How much heat is produced when a 600-ton train, traveling at a speed of 90 ft/sec on a level track, is brought to rest? About how much extra fuel cost is incurred if this train makes an unscheduled stop? Do the answers depend on how quickly the train is brought to rest? State the reason.

Chapter 9

ROTATION AND VIBRATION

Up to this point our discussion of mechanical questions has confined itself almost entirely to linear motion of particles of matter or of bodies which for our purposes could be thought of as particles. Now we find it useful to consider rotational motion as well and to inquire what happens when a particle moves in a curved path, or a body of finite size rotates about an axis. The effects in such cases are in general less familiar or intuitive, but they are of considerable interest, and their practical consequences are great.

Another special type of motion is that in which a particle or extended object oscillates back and forth, or *vibrates*. This kind of motion also will be described in the present chapter.

9·1 Angular Motion

When we talked of the translatory motion of a particle—the motion along a path in space—we specified the position of the particle

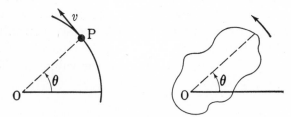

Fig. 9·1   Angular distance.

at any instant by giving its distance from some fixed point. In the same way, if we wish to state the exact position of a particle that repeatedly travels around a circle or of a rigid body that rotates about a given axis, we can do so by giving the angle turned with respect to a fixed line. In Fig. 9·1 the Greek letter θ (theta) denotes the angular distance between a fixed line and the radius drawn to the moving particle P. Similarly, the position of a rotating body is specified by the angle between a fixed reference line and a radial line that turns with the body.

Ordinarily we would measure an angle in degrees, there being arbitrarily 360 deg in a full circle. In analytical work, however, angles are always measured in *radians.* To measure an angle in radians, draw a circle whose center is at the vertex of the angle. The size of the angle, in radians, is the length of the arc cut off, divided by the radius of the circle. With reference to Fig. 9·2, this says that

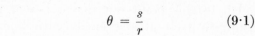

$$\theta = \frac{s}{r} \tag{9·1}$$

An angle of 1 rad is one that cuts off an arc just equal in length to the radius of the cir-

Fig. 9·2   Radian measure of angle.

cle that was drawn. Since the circumference of a circle is $2\pi r$, the radius will fit around the complete perimeter 2π times, so that there are 2π rad in a complete circle (360 deg). Thus π rad $= 180$ deg, $\pi/2$ rad $= 90$ deg, $\pi/4$ rad $= 45$ deg, etc. One radian is $360/2\pi$, or about 57.3 deg.

9·2   Angular Speed and Acceleration

The particle in Fig. 9·1 may be thought of as moving around its circle with an instantaneous linear speed v. Instead of stating its rate of motion in terms of v we could do this by using the *angular speed* instead. Just as the ordinary, or linear, speed of a particle is defined as the *distance* covered per unit of time, so the angular speed is given by the *angular distance* traversed per unit time and is expressed in radians per second. Using the Greek letter ω (omega) to represent angular speed, we write for the value[1] of this quantity

$$\omega = \frac{\Delta\theta}{\Delta t} \tag{9·2}$$

Engineers usually quote the rate of turning of machinery in revolutions per second. Since each turn is equivalent to 2π rad, the angular speed in radians per second would be found by multiplying the number of revolutions per second by 2π.

How is the linear speed of a particle related to its angular speed? This is not hard to work out. If we are talking about instantaneous values, Eq. (9·1) is written $\Delta s = r\,\Delta\theta$. Substituting the value of $\Delta\theta$

[1] In the limiting case (Δt approaching zero) this will give the *instantaneous* angular speed.

from (9·2) gives

$$\Delta s = r\omega \, \Delta t \qquad \text{or} \qquad \frac{\Delta s}{\Delta t} = r\omega$$

But $\Delta s/\Delta t$ is merely v, the linear speed, so that (passing to the limiting case of Δt very small) we have for the relation between linear and angular speed

$$v = r\omega \tag{9.3}$$

Notice that all particles of a *rigid* rotating body have the **same** angular speed. The *linear* speed of any particle, however, depends on its distance from the axis of rotation, as stated by the last equation. A particle halfway out to the rim of a wheel has a linear speed half as great as one on the rim.

If the rate of motion of a particle in a circle or of a rotating rigid body is not constant, we could properly speak of **accelerated angular motion,** defining the angular acceleration by analogy with the linear case (where we had $a = \Delta v/\Delta t$) as

$$\alpha = \frac{\Delta\omega}{\Delta t} \tag{9·4}$$

where the Greek letter α (alpha) is used for angular acceleration. We may even have occasion to discuss motion with **constant** angular acceleration and would find that we could write down relations between angular distance, angular speed, and time which would be exact counterparts of the equations for the corresponding linear case [Eqs. (4·6) and (4·10), page 63]. Force, mass, momentum, and kinetic energy also have their rotational counterparts, but a full discussion would carry us too far at this time.

9·3 Dynamics of a Particle Moving in a Circle

According to Newton's first law the natural path of a particle that is subject to no outside forces is a straight line, pursued at constant speed. Consider a ball rolling along a smooth, level floor. At the present moment it is at the point P (Fig. 9·3a), and if no forces are applied it will continue to move in the direction PN with the constant speed v. Suppose it is desired to change the direction of motion of the ball suddenly. The required external force might be brought to bear by rolling another ball in from the upper right-hand side of the figure so that the two collide. The effect on the first ball is to give it an additional velocity, say, Δv, directed as shown. It now has two component velocities, the original v and the additional Δv, and as a consequence the first ball now moves with the velocity V, which is the resultant of the two components. After a short time another ball, coming from the right, may now be allowed to hit the original ball, repeating the process. At each collision the first ball experiences a sudden change in velocity, and it describes the broken path shown in the diagram.

If the impacting balls are rolled in more frequently and at regular intervals and if they are always projected toward a fixed point O, the changes in direction of the original ball will be more frequent and it can be made to describe a regular polygon that fits very closely to a circle (Fig. 9·3b). In the limiting case, if the blows are applied continuously, the polygonal path of the first ball will shrink

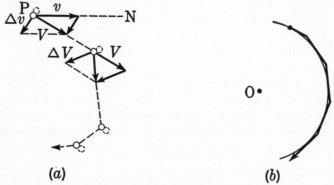

(a)   (b)

FIG. 9·3   Path of a ball subjected to repeated blows.

down to coincide exactly with the circle. We have made the ball follow a circular path by exerting on it a force that acts always toward the center, just as if we had tied it to the fixed center by means of a thread. Moreover, if the only acting force is toward the center, it must at all times be perpendicular to the path of the ball and so can have no component along that path. Thus there is nothing to alter the *speed* of the ball along the circle, and it moves over this path with constant speed.

The force exerted by the thread (or the average force exerted by the impacts of the other balls), which makes the original ball move in a circle rather than in its "natural" straight-line path, is called the **centripetal** (meaning "toward the center") *force.*[1] According to the second law, if there is a force acting on the ball and directed

[1] The term is due to Newton.

toward the center, there must be an acceleration directed also toward the center. This is actually the case, for we saw that as a result of the blows the ball was continually receiving additional velocity toward the center. Hence we must conclude that despite the fact that the speed along the circle is constant the ball moving around the circle is being continuously *accelerated toward the center*. This does not mean that it *moves closer* to the center; in following the circle it moves toward the center only in the sense that it curves away from the tangent—the path it would follow in the absence of a centripetal force.

The centripetal force in the example of the ball whirled in a circle on the end of a thread was the pull of the thread on the ball. According to the third law there must exist an equally large but oppositely directed reaction force, and this would be the pull exerted by the ball on the thread. It is called the *centrifugal* ("fleeing the center") *force.* If the thread happens to break, the centripetal force suddenly ceases and its reaction, the centrifugal force, passes out of existence just as suddenly. The body, now subject to no force, reverts at once to its natural straight-line path. As we correctly express it, the body "flies off on a tangent." But the centripetal force—the pull of the thread—is, in a sense, the primary action. Without it the body would not have moved in a circle in the first place, and the question of centrifugal force would not have arisen.

9·4   Magnitude of Centripetal Force; Applications

The frequent occurrence of rotating parts in all kinds of machines makes it important to know how to compute the amount of the centripetal force in a particular case. It is comparatively simple (see the Appendix, page 480) to calculate that the centripetal force required to hold a particle of mass m moving with a speed v in a circular path of radius r amounts to

$$f_c = \frac{mv^2}{r} \tag{9·5}$$

where f_c is given in absolute force units.[1] The dependence on v to the second power is noteworthy. This means that if the speed is

---

[1] Thus f is in dynes if m is given in grams, r in centimeters, and v in centimeters per second. In the English system, f would be in poundals, m in pounds, r in feet, and v in feet per second.

doubled (mass and radius remaining unchanged) the required force becomes *four* times its former value—a fact that often accounts for accidents to high-speed rotating machinery.

If the revolving particle is part of some rigid rotating system, it is more convenient to express the centripetal force in terms of the angular speed of the whole system rather than using the linear speed of a particle part. If ωr is substituted for v, Eq. (9·5) becomes

$$f_c = mr\omega^2 \tag{9·6}$$

Equations (9·5) and (9·6) are alternative forms of the same relation, giving the force in terms of either linear or angular speed.

Many situations arise in practice where centrifugal force must be taken into account. The curves on a railroad or highway are "banked," or raised at the outer edge. The downhill component of the weight then furnishes the centripetal force needed to hold the vehicle in its curved path, and sideward pressure of the rails or friction with the roadway need not be depended upon to supply this force. A cyclist leans toward the inside of a curve in order to counteract the overturning tendency of centrifugal force.

Chemists and biologists make use of the **centrifuge** to separate suspended matter from a liquid. When the mixture is whirled rapidly, the difference between the centripetal force on the suspended particles and on the lighter liquid causes the former to collect toward the outside of the vessel. Using special experimental arrangements, centripetal accelerations of over 100 million times gravity have been attained.

In testing airplane performance it is customary to speak of the centripetal acceleration registered during a maneuver as "$3g$," "$5g$," etc. A 150-lb pilot pulling out of a dive at $6g$ is being pressed into his seat with a force of 6×150, or 900, lb, in addition to his static weight.

The centrifugal force due to the rotation of the earth operates to decrease the weight of bodies on the earth's surface. This lightening effect is zero at the poles and is easily calculated to be about 0.3 per cent of the true weight for a body at the equator. The equatorial bulge of the earth and other planets is probably a consequence of the action of centrifugal force when the planets were still plastic billions of years ago.

Two examples will show how the centripetal-force relations can be applied:

1. An airplane traveling 600 ft/sec describes a horizontal turn having a radius of 2500 ft. To how many g's is the pilot being subjected? To find the centripetal acceleration a_c, equate the value of f_c in Eq. (9·5) to ma_c, obtaining $a_c = v^2/r$, as in the deduction of this relation (page 480). If a_c is wanted as a multiple, k, of g, put $kg = v^2/r$, or $k = v^2/rg$. Substituting: $k = (600)^2/(2500)(32)$, or $k = 4.5$.

2. An ultracentrifuge is to whirl a small sample of matter in a circle of 2 mm radius with a centripetal acceleration of $10,000g$. What rotational speed is required? This time, using the form (9·6) of the centripetal-force equation, we have $\omega^2 = (10^4)(980)/0.2$, yielding a value of $\omega = 7000$ rad/sec $= 1100$ rev/sec.

9·5 Rotational Momentum

In previous chapters we have made much use of the idea of linear momentum as a measure of "quantity of motion." Now, extending our considerations to include rotational motion, we may speak of the *rotational* (or angular) *momentum* of a body about some axis. In Sec. 6·7 (page 106) it was seen that the linear momentum of a particle is a measure of how long the particle will continue to move against the action of a constant opposing force. In exactly the same way the rotational momentum of a system about a specified axis is a measure of the length of time that the motion will persist against a constant opposing twist, or *torque* as it is called.

The expression for the angular momentum of a single particle of mass m moving in a circle of radius r with a linear speed v is found to be

$$A = mvr \qquad (9·7)$$

For a finite body this product would have to be computed for each of its particles and the results added to give the over-all value. In a general case, this procedure requires advanced methods and will not be attempted here. Even so, it is easy to see that the angular momentum of a finite body will depend not only on its total mass but on how that mass is *distributed* with respect to the axis of rotation.

Just as there is a principle of the conservation of linear momentum, so a similar statement can be made for angular momentum. *If a rotating system is not subjected to any external torque, its total angular momentum remains constant.* This generalization is amply supported by experience. For example, a figure skater will execute a pirouette by first giving himself a moderate rotational speed while holding his arms and perhaps one leg extended; when he now draws in his limbs, his rotational speed increases many times. By decreasing the effective r for part of his mass, v has to increase if A is to remain constant. In the same way, a star or planet that contracts as a result of cooling must increase its rotational speed.

Try the experiment suggested by Fig. 9·4. A weight is swung in a vertical circle by means of a cord passing through a smooth tube, the motion being maintained by a very slight circular movement of the tube. Now if the cord is pulled in somewhat, decreasing r, the motion of the

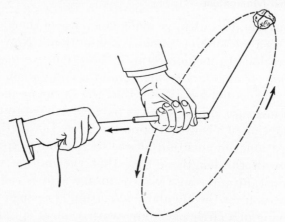

FIG. 9·4   Conservation of angular momentum.

weight will speed up considerably. The pull of the string is always perpendicular to the path and hence can have no direct effect on the speed of the weight; the increase in speed is a result only of conservation of angular momentum.

9·6   Rotational Inertia; the Gyroscope

A body capable of rotating about an axis shows rotational inertia, just as a particle does translational inertia. If no torque (twist) is applied from the outside, the body will maintain its condition of rest or of uniform rotation. The purpose of the flywheel of an engine is to smooth out, by means of its rotational inertia, any irregularities in the driving force. When the engine is first started, it takes some time to counteract the considerable rotational inertia of the flywheel and get it up to running speed; when the power is shut off, rotational inertia of the wheel tends to make the engine continue to turn until frictional and other retarding torques succeed in bringing it to rest.

One of the most striking characteristics of a spinning body is its ability to maintain the *direction* of its axis of rotation. A spinning top does not fall over, although it is unstable when at rest. The fact that the spinning earth maintains the direction of its axis in space while moving around its orbit is the cause of the seasons (Fig. 9·5)

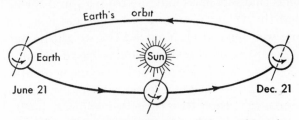

Fɪɢ. 9·5   Constancy of direction of the earth's axis.

A *gyroscope* is a wheel of large rotational inertia that is kept spinning at high speed. Its ability to maintain the direction of the axis of spin has many important applications. Heavy gyroscopes installed in a ship can reduce the rolling motion. The gyroscope of an automatic pilot on an airplane keeps the airplane in steady flight on a set course by responding to changes in its orientation. In the gyro compass the rotation of the earth reacts on the instrument in such a way as to bring its axis into parallelism with that of the earth, after which the gyro maintains this position and so continues to indicate true geographic north.

VIBRATORY MOTION

A special type of motion that we have not yet examined but that is encountered in many familiar situations is *vibratory,* or *oscillatory, motion.* Any sufficiently strong disturbance of an elastic body such as a spring, a violin string, a steel structure, or even the earth's crust will set up internal forces that result in a to-and-fro motion of the body. Each particle of the vibrating body will move back and forth on a given path, and in most instances the motion is observed to repeat itself at perfectly regular intervals of time. In this case the vibration is said to be *periodic.*

Every source of musical sounds is a mechanically vibrating body of some kind, and part of the energy of vibrational motion is handed on to the surrounding air and carried off in the form of sound waves (Chap. 10). Vibration is not confined to mechanical systems. Later we shall discuss electrical oscillations, such as those occurring in a radio set, and light vibrations whose source is in the atoms and molecules of matter.

9·7 Weight Hanging from a Spring

One of the best examples to contemplate in learning about vibratory motion is that of a mass hanging from a spiral spring (Fig. 9·6). Suppose that the weight is originally hanging at rest, with the coils of the spring well separated. Now, let the weight be pulled down a short distance and released. It will be observed to move upward, reaching a point as far above its original rest position as it was pulled below, then to return to its lowest position, repeating this sequence of events at regular intervals until, with gradually shortening excursions, it finally comes to rest when all of the elastic potential energy given to it by the starting pull has been dissipated.

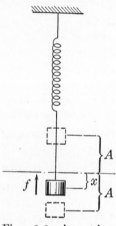

Fig. 9·6 A spring-oscillated mass.

During the vibration, there is a continual interplay between the *elasticity* of the spring and the *inertia* of the hanging weight. When the mass is below its normal rest position, the spring is stretched and in acting to return to its original length it gives upward motion to the weight. The inertia of the latter prevents it from stopping as its initial position; instead, it moves upward, allowing the spring to slacken relative to its normal condition until the weight comes to rest. The weight now exceeds the pull of the spring, and the mass descends. Finally, when the mass reaches its lowest point, the spring has been stretched again as before and everything repeats.

9·8 Simple Harmonic Motion

It is characteristic of any elastic deformation that the *force* needed to produce the change, whether it be one of stretching, compression, twisting, bending, or any combination of these *is proportional to the displacement* as long as the displacement is not too great. For example, if one end of a long strip of metal is clamped in a vise and it is found that the free end can be pulled aside 3 mm by a force of 100 gm, then a force of 200 gm will pull it aside a distance of 6 mm and one of 300 gm a distance of 9 mm.

Hooke's law, formulated by the gifted English experimenter Robert Hooke, who was a contemporary of Newton's, states this simple proportionality between cause and effect in elastic deformations. The relation is strictly valid only if the displacements are kept within the so-called *elastic limit.* Figure 9·7 is characteristic of the relation between the stretching force and the displacement of the end of a metal bar or a spiral spring. Hooke's law is valid over the initial straight portion of the elastic curve. If the stretching is carried beyond the elastic limit, the test specimen will acquire a permanent "set" and fail to return to its original length when the stress is removed.

At any instant during deformation the elastic body must react on whatever is causing the displacement with a force equal and opposite to that applied. The elastic system always tends to return to its initial form, and the return force acting on any particle is at every moment proportional to the departure from the initial position. *Any vibration in which the return force, or restoring force, is proportional to the displacement is called simple harmonic motion* (SHM). Below you will learn that, besides all elastic bodies, certain other types of systems can have SHM.

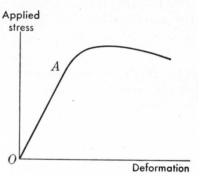

Fig. 9·7 Stress-deformation curve of an elastic body.

The condition of a vibrating system at any time can be specified by a single number if the system is simple. Thus the momentary location of the mass oscillating at the end of the spiral spring is given by stating the displacement of, say, its center of gravity from its normal rest position. This amounts to replacing the entire mass by a single particle that moves back and forth in a straight line. The instantaneous distance from the normal position is called the *displacement.* Then the proportionality between restoring force f and displacement x may be stated in symbols as

$$f = -kx \tag{9·8}$$

where k is called the *force constant* of the system. In the case of the weight hanging from a spring, k is a measure of the stiffness of the spring—the extra force needed to stretch the spring an additional unit of length. The minus sign merely indicates the fact that f and x are always **opposite** in direction: When the particle is above the center (Fig. 9·6), the resultant force acting on it is directed downward; when it is below, the force acts upward. At all times it is a **restoring** force, tending to bring the particle back toward the center. Only under such circumstances would the motion repeat itself.

The maximum displacement attained by the particle, on either side of the center, is called the **amplitude** A of the vibration. The time required for a complete cycle of events is called the **period** T of the motion. It is usually expressed in seconds. In speaking of a rapid vibration, such as that of a clarinet reed, it is often more convenient to specify the **frequency** of vibration n, which is the reciprocal of the period. Thus, if the period of oscillation is 0.02 sec (really seconds per vibration), the frequency would be 1/0.02, or 50, vib/sec. In general, we have

$$n = \frac{1}{T} \tag{9·9}$$

9·9 Reference Circle for SHM

Imagine a wagon to be moving down the street, going directly away from you at constant speed. If there is a lump of mud at one

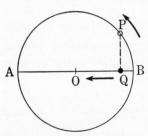

place on the side of the wheel, you will see the motion of this object as if it were projected on a vertical plane and the lump will appear to move up and down in a straight line. It can be shown that this motion is simple harmonic; that is, the projection, onto a diameter, of the motion of a point that goes around a circle at constant speed is accurately SHM. In Fig. 9·8, P is the particle moving around the circle, and Q

Fig. 9·8 Reference circle for SHM.

is its projection on the diameter AB. The motion of Q is simple harmonic. While P goes once around its circle, Q completes 1 vib. The amplitude of the SHM is equal to the radius of the so-called reference circle.

With the aid of the reference circle, useful relations governing SHM are easily obtained (Appendix, page 481). In particular, it is found that the period of any SHM is given by the following equation,

$$T = 2\pi \sqrt{\frac{m}{k}} \qquad (9 \cdot 10)$$

where, as before, T is the period, m the mass of the oscillating particle, and k the force constant expressed in **absolute units** of force per unit length.

Suppose, as an example, that a certain spring can be stretched 2 cm by pulling on it with a force of 50 gm. What will be the period of oscillation when a 500-gm mass is hung on the spring? The force constant of the spring, in absolute units, is $k = (50 \times 980)/2 = 24{,}500$ dynes/cm. Substituting what is known in Eq. (9·10) and neglecting the mass of the spring itself, $T = 2\pi \sqrt{500/24{,}500}$, or 0.90 sec.

It is evident that a particle describing SHM is continually undergoing complicated changes in direction and speed. We can follow these changes by considering what happens to the point moving around the reference circle. At any instant let the point moving in the circle be at P (Fig. 9·9) and the vibrating particle be at Q. The velocity vector of P is V, and hence the velocity of Q is represented by v, the projection (or component) along the diameter. From this we can see how the velocity of Q changes as the motion proceeds. It will equal V when Q passes through the center, for then V and its projection are parallel. It will be zero when Q is at either end of its path; for then V is vertical,

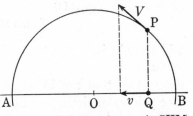

FIG. 9·9   Velocity changes in SHM.

and hence its projection on AB vanishes. At in-between points, v will have intermediate values. Thus the speed of a particle in SHM is a maximum when it passes the center; it is zero at the ends of its path, as it must be if the particle is to reverse its direction at these points.

The acceleration of the particle is also variable, since the acting force is variable. From Eq. (9·8) it is seen that f, and hence the acceleration, has its greatest numerical value at the ends of the path of vibration (where the spring is stretched to its greatest point) and is zero when the particle is passing the center (where the spring has its normal length). To summarize: The speed is greatest at the center and zero at the ends, while the acceleration is zero at the center and greatest at the ends. The speed and acceleration are thus out of step by a quarter of a period, or by the time taken for the point on the reference circle to go 90 def. Technically, we say that the two quantities differ in *phase* by 90 deg. The *phase angle* is merely the part of a vibration already completed, measured from some fixed place. If two SHM's have the same period, they

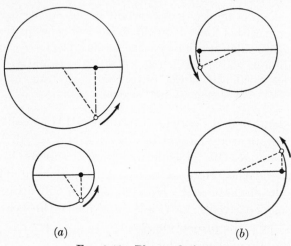

(a)   (b)

Fig. 9·10   Phase relations.

will remain in a constant phase relation with each other. Figure 9·10a shows two particles vibrating in the same phase; Fig. 9·10b shows two that are in opposite phase (phase difference 180 deg). The reference circles are also shown.

9·10   The Simple Pendulum

There are certain mechanical systems which vibrate with SHM but in which the restoring force is not due to an elastic body. By far the most important of these is the *simple,* or *ideal, pendulum*— a particle hanging from a weightless thread and allowed to swing in a vertical plane.[1] In order to convince ourselves that the vibration of such a pendulum is simple harmonic, we must show that the pendulum bob is acted upon at all times by a return force which is proportional to the displacement from the rest position. In Fig.

---

[1] "Simple" as distinguished from a *compound,* or *physical, pendulum,* where the mass is distributed along the length, as in a clock pendulum, rather than concentrated in a single particle. This greatly complicates the analysis, and hence the physical pendulum is not treated here.

9·11 the return force tending to bring the bob back to the center is seen to be the component of the weight in a direction tangent to the arc of swing. If we agree to let the pendulum swing only through a small arc, then the displacement may for all practical purposes be measured in the horizontal direction instead of along the arc itself.[1]

The two right triangles in the figure are similar, and thus their sides are proportional: $f/mg = x/l$, or $f = (mg/l)x$. This last relation says that f is a constant times x. Besides f is obviously directed always toward the center; hence there is a restoring force proportional to the displacement, and we have the condition for simple harmonic motion. Substitution of mg/l for k in the general equation (9·10) leads to an expression for the period of a simple pendulum: $T = 2\pi \sqrt{m/(mg/l)}$ or

$$T = 2\pi \sqrt{\frac{l}{g}} \qquad (9·11)$$

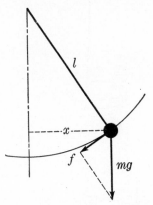

Notice that the amplitude of swing does not appear in this equation. Hence *the period of such a pendulum is independent of the amplitude.* Galileo is said to have observed the swinging of a hanging lamp and, timing the swings with his pulse, to have found that the period remained constant despite the fact that the amplitude

Fig. 9·11 Simple pendulum.

decreased as time passed. It is just this fact of constancy of period that makes the pendulum usable for controlling a clock. The pendulum, of course, does not drive the clock—it merely regulates the rate of the mechanism. The driving energy is furnished by the springs or by descending weights. The clockwork imparts regular pushes to the pendulum, but no mechanism is so perfect that these impulses are all of equal strength. Nevertheless, even with the resulting variations in amplitude, the period remains almost perfectly constant.

Another important fact is that the **mass** has canceled out of the last equation. Making this cancellation, we tacitly assumed that

[1] The error in the period, resulting from this approximation, amounts to only a few hundredths of a per cent if the swings are not allowed to exceed 5 deg on each side of the center.

the m in Eq. (9·10) and that occurring in the expression for k were the same quantity. Actually, the former m represents the **inertial** effect of the bob, while the latter denotes its **gravitational** effect. The fact that Eq. (9·11) correctly predicts the period in every instance with great accuracy is definite evidence of what was mentioned on page 91—that the same number m which we call the

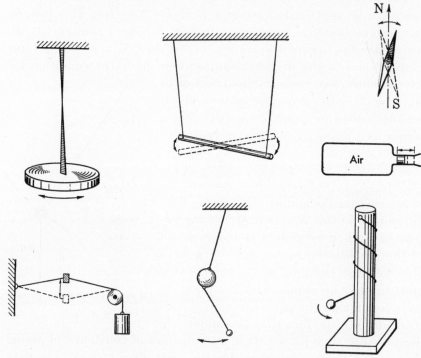

Fɪɢ. 9·12   Vibrating systems.

"mass" represents both the inertial and the gravitational effects of a piece of matter.

Galileo also proved by experiment that the period of the pendulum does not depend on the kind of material used for the bob.

If the length and period of a simple pendulum are measured, Eq. (9·11) may be used to find the value of g at any locality. The pendulum provides the simplest and most accurate way of determining the acceleration of gravity. By means of special pendulums, mineral deposits may often be located by the very slight variations of g caused by their presence.

9·11 Complex Vibrations

Simple harmonic vibration is extremely important and will be encountered again in connection with other topics in this book, but it must not be concluded that *all* vibrations are necessarily of this type. The motion of a violin string while it is being bowed or the vibration of a screeching brake shoe is not simple harmonic. *Nonharmonic* vibrations are found in certain mechanical, acoustical, and electrical systems. In such cases, however, it is possible to analyze the motion as a combination of simple harmonic components.

Figure 9·12 shows a number of mechanical vibrating systems. All but the last two have simple harmonic vibration, provided that the amplitude is not too large.

SUMMARY

Angular motion: Angular displacement is measured in **radians.** An angle in radians is equal to the arc divided by the radius. The **angular speed** is the angular displacement per unit time. Relation between angular and linear speed: $v = r\omega$.

Centripetal force: The force to hold a particle of mass m, moving with a speed v, in a circle of radius r is $f = mv^2/r = mr\omega^2$. The equal and opposite reaction force is called the **centrifugal** force.

Angular momentum: Defined as $A = mvr$. In the absence of external torque, A remains constant (**conservation of angular momentum**).

Vibratory motion: The **period** is the time for a complete vibration. The **frequency** is the reciprocal of the period. The **amplitude** is the largest displacement of the particle from its rest point. The **phase** of a vibrating particle at any instant is a measure of the part of a vibration already completed.

SHM: Return force proportional to displacement. Period given by $T = 2\pi \sqrt{m/k}$, where k is the **force constant** of the system.

Simple pendulum: Period is $T = 2\pi\sqrt{l/g}$, provided the amplitude is small.

READING REFERENCES

1. Freeman, I. M.: "Invitation to Experiment," Dutton, New York, 1940. Chapter 8 describes rotational motion and its effects.
2. Cajori, F.: "A History of Physics," Macmillan, New York, 1929. Galileo's investigation of the pendulum is described on p. 42. The Foucault pendulum experiment is discussed on p. 157.
3. Harsányi, Zsolt: "The Star Gazer," translated by Paul Tabor, Put-

nam, New York, 1939. Pages 17–19 present an exciting account of how Galileo may have discovered the law of the pendulum.

4. Moulton, F. R., and J. J. Schifferes: "The Autobiography of Science," Doubleday, New York, 1945. Hooke's description of his law of elasticity is found on pp. 169–171.

5. Taylor, Lloyd W.: "Physics, the Pioneer Science," Houghton Mifflin, Boston, 1941. Read Chap. 15 on harmonic motion.

FILMS

"Simple Harmonic Motion," McGraw-Hill (AAPT Physics Films). 16 mm, sound, 1 reel.

EXERCISES

1. Through how many radians does the minute hand of a clock turn between the hours of 3:00 P.M. and 5:45 P.M.? The hour hand?

2. A pipe wrench 3 ft long is turned through an angle of 1.5 rad. How far (in feet) does the end of the handle move?

3. What is the difference in meaning between the terms *rotation* and *revolution?* Consult a dictionary. Is the motion of the earth one of revolution or rotation, or both? Explain.

4. Calculate the angular speed of rotation of the earth. If the radius at the equator is 4000 mi, what is the linear speed (miles per hour) of a point on the equator? Of a locality at latitude 60°?

5. A wheel has a constant rotational speed of 30 turns per second. Over how many radians is the image of each spoke blurred if the wheel is photographed with an exposure of 0.001 sec?

6. Give an accurate description of the rotational motion of the wheel of a car moving along a road with constant linear acceleration. Assume that the wheel turns without slipping.

7. What agency furnishes the centripetal force that keeps a planet moving in a closed path around the sun? Since the orbit of a planet is observed to be an ellipse rather than a circle, the centripetal force will not be perpendicular to the path at all points. What do you conclude about the constancy of the linear speed of the planet in its orbit?

8. Compute the magnitude of the average centripetal force holding the moon in its orbit, using the following data:

Mass of moon = 1.6×10^{23} lb

Distance from center of gravity of earth-moon system = 1.3×10^9 ft

Time of one complete trip around its orbit = 2.4×10^6 sec

9. Why does the rotational speed of motion of water running out of a circular washbowl increase as the water nears the opening in the bottom of the bowl?

10. In performing a pirouette (page 145) the rotational kinetic energy ͭᶠ the skater increases, since each portion of his mass moves with increased

speed. Where does the required energy come from? (Consider the fact that a centripetal force acts on each part of his body. Must he do work in drawing in his limbs?)

11. Look up the Foucault pendulum in Ref. 2.

12. What is meant by saying that a certain radio station broadcasts at a frequency of 660 kc?

13. An iron ball of mass 200 gm vibrates with a frequency of 4 vib/sec when suspended from a certain spiral spring of negligible mass. When the ball is hanging at rest, how much of a downward pull is required to stretch the spring an additional 1 cm?

14. A chandelier hanging by a relatively lightweight chain is effectively 20 ft long. If it starts to swing in a vertical plane with small amplitude, what will be the period of this motion?

15. A simple pendulum of length 327 cm is observed to take 363 sec to complete 100 vib. What is the value of g at the place where the observations were made?

16. Show that the right-hand side of Eq. (9·10) has the dimensions of time. (Use $f = ma$ to express the dimensions of force in cgs units.)

Chapter 10

WAVES

A stone dropped into a quiet pond gives rise to a set of circular ripples or waves spreading outward over the surface at constant speed. A floating chip of wood encountered by the waves will be set into oscillation, indicating that energy has been transferred from the source of the disturbance to other parts of the water surface. The chip merely makes small excursions about its original position; it does not move forward with the set of waves.

Leonardo da Vinci, the versatile fifteenth-century Italian genius, watched waves move across a wind-swept field of wheat and realized that the forward motion of the grain was an illusion—that each stalk simply vibrated back and forth as the wave passed. In any wave, it is only the *form* of the disturbance that moves along as one part after another of the surrounding medium receives energy and hands it on.

Besides waves on water, on grain, on a fluttering flag, there are other types. A sudden explosion will compress the air in its immediate neighborhood, and when this layer of air expands again it will, in turn, compress the adjoining layers, so that a *wave of compression,* or *sound wave,* is propagated outward from the source.

It has been found that light, too, travels in the form of waves—waves of a much more subtle nature, which require no material substance to carry them. Because of the universal occurrence of waves of various types as a means of transferring energy, some of the more important features of wave motion deserve study at this point.

10·1 The Nature of Wave Motion

In the case of the stone dropped into a pond, the succession of disturbances at the point where the stone enters is duplicated at later and later times for parts of the pond's surface farther and farther from the source. At any instant, all points on any circle

158

drawn with its center at the source are in the same *phase,* or state of vibration (page 152). If the water surface is not uniform—as would be true, for instance, if there were patches of oil on it—the parts having the same phase will lie, not on circles, but on curves of some other kind (Fig. 10·1). In any case, the lines connecting places that are in the same phase are called *wave fronts.*

The impact of the stone on the water in the example above produced a limited number of oscillations, after which the surface was again quiet. Such a disturbance of short duration is called a *pulse.*

If, instead of dropping a stone at a given place, we dip a stick into the surface at regular intervals of

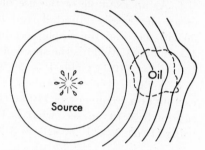

Fig. 10·1 Wave fronts of ripples on a nonuniform surface.

time, a continuous *wave train* will result (Fig. 10·2). Looking at the entire train of waves at any instant, it is seen that a given phase recurs at exactly equal distances along the wave train. The distance between any two successive particles that are in the same phase is called the *wavelength* and is denoted by the Greek letter λ (lambda). In particular, this would be the distance between two adjoining crests or between two adjoining troughs.

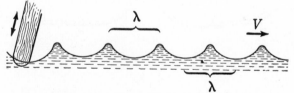

Fig. 10·2 Train of water waves.

Evidently, in order to produce a continuous train of waves, the source must be a constantly vibrating body, such as the stick in the above case. Each time the source makes one complete vibration, one complete wave is sent out and incorporated into the wave train, which continues to move outward at a constant speed if the surrounding medium is uniform. If the wave train, moving at the wave speed V, goes a distance λ in a time T (the period of vibration of the source), then $λ = VT$, or, in terms of the frequency n ($= 1/T$) of the source,

$$V = n\lambda \tag{10·1}$$

This relation holds for *any* type of continuous wave in a uniform medium and is merely a result of the constancy of both the wave speed and the period and the way in which the three quantities were defined.

1. As an example of the use of the wave equation, consider the case of an electrically vibrated reed that dips into water. The reed makes 50 vib/sec, and the ripples produced are observed to have their crests 1.5 cm apart. What is the speed of the ripples on the surface of the water? Use of Eq. (10·1) yields $V = 50 \times 1.5 = 75$ cm/sec.

2. A radio receiver is tuned to receive signals from a station broadcasting at a frequency of 710 kc (kilocycles). If radio waves travel at the rate of 3×10^8 m/sec, what is the wavelength of these waves? Again using (10·1), $\lambda = V/n$, or $\lambda = 3 \times 10^8/7.1 \times 10^5 = 423$ m.

10·2   Direction of Particle Motion

It has already been mentioned that a particle involved in a wave motion does not move on with the wave but oscillates about its normal position as the disturbance passes. The character of this oscillation depends on the type of vibration of the source and on the nature of the medium. Ripples on the surface of a pond may be thought of as waves progressing in two dimensions.|

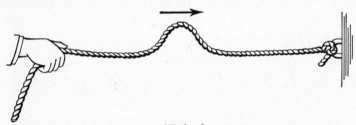

FIG. 10·3   Pulse in a rope.

A simpler case that might well be considered first is that of waves in a rope—waves in one dimension. One end of a heavy rope is tied to a hook in the wall. The other end is held in the hand, and the rope is pulled fairly taut in a horizontal position. If, now, the hand is moved suddenly upward, a pulse—in this case a "hump"—will travel down the rope at constant speed (Fig. 10·3). One particle after another is lifted by the passing hump, falling back as the pulse passes on. This pulse may be called a *transverse wave,* since the particles of the rope move in a direction *crosswise* to the direction of progression of the wave. In a sound (or compressional) wave, on the other hand, the air particles move longitudinally, or *in* the line of travel of the wave, as described more fully below. Waves on the surface of water represent an intermediate case in which the individual particles move in circular or nearly circular paths and thus have both transverse and longitudinal components of motion.

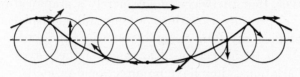

FIG. 10·4   Surface wave on water.

In Fig. 10·4 the curved line represents the profile of a surface wave on water, and the arrows give successive directions of particle motion as the wave passes. Notice that the particles move *forward* (that is, in the same direction as the wave motion) *at the crests* and *backward at the troughs.*

10·3 Compressional Waves

A brief description was given above of the origin of a sound pulse in air due to an explosion. If continuous sound waves are to be generated, we must imagine the single explosion replaced by a regularly repeated disturbance, a continuous vibration. Every maintained sound can be traced back to some vibrating body, such as a tuning fork, violin string, or column of air in a pipe. For purposes of discussion, imagine the vibrating source of sound waves to be a small balloon connected to an air pump. If a little air is alternately pumped into the balloon and drawn out, the surface of the balloon will pulsate and sound waves or, more generally speaking, compressional waves will be sent out in all directions. The wave fronts will be spheres with the balloon as their common center.

The train of waves produced will consist of alternate compressions and expansions, and the particles (molecules) of the air will move back and forth short distances along the line of advance of the waves at any point. For this reason a sound wave or compressional wave is also termed a *longitudinal wave.* The motion of the particles is *forward* at the points of greatest compression and *backward* toward the source at the places of greatest expansion. Figure 10·5a is an attempt to indicate what occurs in a compressional wave. However, a more satisfactory way to represent such a wave is to make a graph showing the manner in which either the pressure in the medium or the particle displacement varies with time or with distance along the direction of wave travel. Such a graph is given in Fig. 10·5b for a simple wave; this looks more like what we are accustomed to regard as a typical wave picture. You must remember, however, that the wavy line is merely a graphical representation of either pressure variations or longitudinal displacements and does not depict anything wagging sidewise; the particle motions are entirely in the direction of advance of the waves. As for the pressure variations, they have no directional properties at all.

Compressional waves may be sent through any medium that can be at all compressed, and this means any substance whatever—gas,

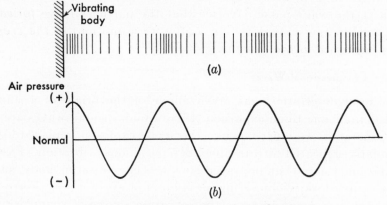

Fig. 10·5   Representation of sound waves.

liquid, or solid. We even speak of "sound waves" in water or in steel, although "compressional" or "longitudinal waves" would be better terms in this case. Such waves are transmitted by the walls and floors of a building. The underwater compressional waves produced by a ship's propellers can be "heard" by a suitable receiver. An approaching train may be heard by waves carried through the rails some time before the wave in the air is audible.

The speed of a compressional wave depends on two properties of the medium—its elasticity and its inertia (density). In air at ordinary temperatures the speed of sound is about 1100 ft/sec. If you watch the firing of a gun from a considerable distance, you will see the smoke of the discharge before the accompanying sound is heard. The delay represents the time required for the sound waves to travel from the gun to the observer (the light waves that enable you to see the smoke arrive almost instantly). The early determinations of the speed of sound in air were made by this direct method. There are indirect methods, too, which are generally more convenient, particularly for substances other than air. The speed of compressional waves in water is about 4700 ft/sec; in steel, about 16,000 ft/sec.

10·4 Wave Frequency; Doppler Effect

What is called the *pitch* of a simple musical tone, or its position in the scale, is judged largely by the *frequency* of the sound waves striking the ear. A normal human ear can respond to frequencies ranging from about 20 to 18,000 vib/sec. Below this range the separate pulses are heard, and if the frequency goes above the upper limit the sound becomes entirely inaudible. Frequencies lying above this range are referred to as *ultrasonic* and have valuable special properties (Ref. 4).

The frequency of a train of waves remains the same as that of the vibrating source even if the waves pass from one medium into another. In such a case, in Eq. (10·1) both V and λ would change, but n would remain the same.

There is an important special case in which the frequency of the waves as received may differ from the frequency of vibration of the source, and that is when the source and the observer are *moving* relative to each other. For example, if the whistle of an approaching train is blowing, its pitch will seem *higher* than normal while approaching, will drop abruptly as the train passes, and will remain *lower* than normal as it recedes.[1]

The explanation of these effects is fairly direct. If the source and observer are approaching each other, more waves strike the ear each second than if everything were at rest; if they are receding, fewer waves strike in 1 sec. The apparent pitch of the sound depends entirely on the frequency of the received sound. In Fig. 10·6 the spherical sound waves shed at regular intervals by the moving source are spaced more closely in the forward direction, more widely toward the rear. Consequently a stationary observer at A receives waves at a greater frequency than normal, while one at B receives them at a correspondingly lower rate. An observer moving along with the source or a stationary observer who happens to be

---

[1] There will, of course, be concurrent changes in the *loudness* of the sound due to the changes in *distance,* but this is a separate effect (see p. 166).

at any point lying in the directions C from the source will receive the normal frequency.

This phenomenon is called the **Doppler effect,** after the investigator who first worked out its theory. The effect is also observed in the case of light waves, where it has important applications (page 236).

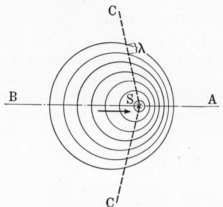

FIG. 10·6　Doppler effect.

If the relative speed of source and observer is small compared with the wave speed, which is usually the case, the apparent change in frequency is given approximately by the relation

$$\frac{\Delta n}{n} = \frac{v}{V} \qquad (10\cdot2)$$

where Δn is the apparent change in frequency, n the true frequency of the source, v the relative speed, and V the speed of the waves. The change Δn represents an **increase** for approach and a **decrease** for recession. Thus, if source and observer are approaching each other at a speed equal to one-twentieth the wave speed, the frequency of the waves as received will be about one-twentieth greater than the true value.

10·5　Intensity of Waves

Sound waves may in a sense be made visible by several methods. One means is to reflect a narrow beam of light from a small mirror attached either to the vibrating source or to a diaphragm, which receives the sound produced (Fig. 10·7). In order to spread the vibration out laterally so that the form of the wave can be seen, the beam is reflected also from a rotating mirror and then to a screen.

Modern sound-wave analysis is more often carried out by allowing the sound to strike a microphone, where the oscillations of the air particles produce corresponding oscillations of an electric current. This current is then applied to a cathode-ray oscilloscope (page 351), which is much like the tube in a television receiver, and the vibration is finally traced out visually on the end of the tube.

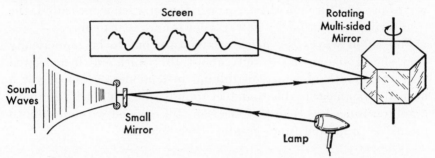

FIG. 10·7   Apparatus for showing the form of a sound wave.

If a tuning fork, for instance, is placed near the microphone and struck gently, the pattern on the screen will resemble Fig. 10·8a; if the same fork is then struck more vigorously, the sound will be louder and the pattern will look like Fig. 10·8b. Each curve is really a graph of the way in which the air vibrations vary in time, but the louder sound corresponds to a wave of greater amplitude. Thus an

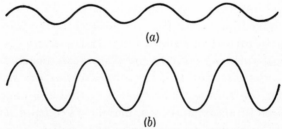

FIG. 10·8   Waves of different amplitude.

increase in the amplitude of motion of the source and the corresponding increase in amplitude of vibration of the air particles go in general with an increase in the perceived loudness; but the response of the ear is not simple, and other factors contribute to the loudness as judged by the human hearing mechanism.[1]

There is, however, an objective physical quantity called the *intensity* of the wave motion that can be measured in terms of the

[1] If these questions interest you, consult Ref. 3.

amplitude. Earlier it was pointed out that a wave disturbance involves motion which is handed on from one particle to the next. Motion implies kinetic energy, and thus energy is transmitted with and by the waves. The *intensity* is the amount of energy carried each second through a unit of area of a surface held broadside to the waves. In Fig. 10·9, if the energy in joules delivered by the waves passing through the 1-cm² window in 1 sec is measured, the result will be the intensity in watts per square centimeter.

For sound waves the figure would turn out to be numerically very small, amounting to only about 10^{-9} watt/cm² if measured near the mouth of a person talking in a moderate voice; yet a normal human ear is able to detect sounds whose intensity is about a million times less than this and can still respond without pain to intensities a million times greater! (See below.)

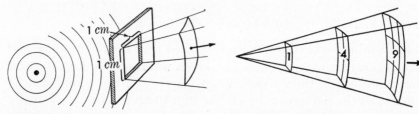

FIG. 10·9 Measuring the intensity of waves.

FIG. 10·10 Spreading of waves from a point source.

Besides the amplitude of vibration of the source, another circumstance determines the intensity of received waves—the *distance* of the receiver from the source. If the source is small and there are no disturbances due to reflection from nearby surfaces or other causes, *the intensity will vary inversely as the square of the distance from the source.*[1] The reason is that the energy carried by a given area of an expanding spherical wave front continues to spread over a larger and larger area as the front moves away from the source, and this area increases as the square of the distance (Fig. 10·10).

A given amount of wave energy will be spread over four times the area at twice the distance, over nine times the area at three times the distance, etc., with the result that the amount of energy flowing each second *through unit area* will decrease with the square of the distance. This statement about the rate of falling off of the intensity

[1] If you are not perfectly clear as to the meaning of this statement refer to p. 475 again.

is strictly valid, however, only for an isolated "point source." If the source is not small compared with the distances being considered, the contributions of all parts of the source must be summed up to get the total effect at a distant place. Reflected sounds usually contribute to the intensity also, especially indoors. Dissipation in the wave-carrying medium must be allowed for as well.

In place of specifying the intensity of a sound in terms of energy carried, it is more common to state this quantity in terms of the minimum amount the average ear can detect—about 10^{-16} watt/cm^2. Since the ear is capable of responding to so large a range of sound intensities, it must in a sense be self-protecting by reacting, not in direct proportion to the stimulus, but at a more moderate rate. It happens that the ear judges one sound to be about *twice* as loud as another of the same frequency when the actual mechanical power of the second sound is *ten* times that of the first. It is therefore usual to give the amount by which the loudness of a sound exceeds the minimum audible value by stating the exponent to which the number 10 must be raised in order to equal the ratio of the two intensities. This exponent is expressed in a unit called a *bel*.[1]

A smaller unit, the *decibel* (equal to 0.1 bel), is of more convenient size in practice. If one sound is 1 db louder than another, its intensity on an energy scale is 1.26 ($= \sqrt[10]{10}$) times as great. On this basis the rustling of leaves in a light breeze has a loudness of 20 db; ordinary conversation, 60 db; the noise inside a subway car, 100 db; etc.

The pressure changes and amplitudes of motion in ordinary sound waves in air are surprisingly small. In a sound wave of minimum audibility (10^{-16} watt/cm^2) the pressure departs from normal by only about 10^{-9} atmosphere (atm), and the amplitude is around 10^{-9} cm—less than molecular diameters! Even for sounds approaching the level of pain, the pressure variations are only 10^{-3} atm and the amplitudes a few hundredths of a millimeter.

10·6 Reflection of Waves

If the spreading circular wave fronts produced by dropping a stone into a pool of water strike the side of the pool or any straight obstacle such as a floating board, it is observed that a second set of circular wave fronts comes off the obstacle, moving in the reverse direction. The new wave fronts have their common center as far

[1] After Alexander Graham Bell, American patentee (1876) of the telephone and an outstanding investigator in the field of sound. Today, too, much important research on the acoustics of speech and hearing is conducted in connection with the telephone industry (see Ref. 3).

behind the obstacle as the source of the original disturbance was in front (Fig. 10·11). The waves are said to be *reflected* from the surface in question.

The set of reflected waves passes right through the initial set of waves without any mutual dependence; each group moves exactly as it would if the other were not present. We know by experience that this is true also for sound waves, for the air in a room can convey the sounds of several independent conversations with no effect of one wave motion upon the other.[1] The actual disturbance existing in the air at any point in the room, however, is a combination of the separate disturbances and may be quite complicated. This is discussed more fully below.

A transverse pulse started along a rope, as described on page 160, will be reflected from the fixed end. If the original pulse is a

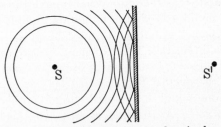

FIG. 10·11   Reflection of circular ripples.

"hump," the reflected one is observed to be a "hollow." This is a result of the action of the boundary (the fixed hook) on the rope. As the hump reaches the hook, it tends to move the entire wall suddenly upward; since this is impossible, the reaction snaps the cord downward and a hollow starts (is reflected) back along the rope. This pulse may be similarly reflected when it meets the experimenter's hand at the far end, and several reflections usually result before the energy is completely dissipated.

If now, in place of giving it a single snap, the end of the rope is shaken up and down in regular succession, two continuous wave trains travel along it, the direct set going down the rope and the reflected set coming back. The displacement of any particle of the rope is, at any instance, the vector sum of the displacements due to these two wave trains. It is exactly as if an inverted wave were

---

[1] For very intense sound waves, such as those produced in the vicinity of an explosion, this is no longer the case. The direct and reflected waves have a mutual influence.

coming out of the wall to meet the direct wave and reminds us of
what was happening in Fig. 10·11. At the two fixed ends of the rope
the displacement is always zero.[1] This means simply that the displacements which the direct and reflected wave trains would produce separately are always equal and op-
posite at these two points. Intermediate
parts of the rope will in general undergo a
succession of configurations such as those
shown in Fig. 10·12.

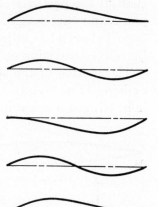

10·7 Stationary Waves in a String

At a definite rate of shaking, all appearance of progressive motion along the rope
will disappear, and it will vibrate as a single arch swinging back and forth across
the line representing its rest position. This
condition is an example of a *stationary
wave.* Figure 10·13 shows successive positions of a rope vibrating in one segment.

FIG. 10·12   Composite vibration of a rope.

Each configuration of the string is merely a crosswise magnification
or reduction of any of the others.

If the frequency of shaking is exactly doubled, this pattern gives
way to a new steady state in which the rope vibrates in two equal
segments. Besides the fixed ends there is now a stationary point

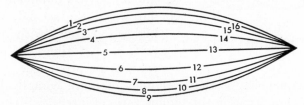

FIG. 10·13   String vibrating in one segment.

midway between them, and this point remains fixed despite having
no constraint from the outside. It is simply a place where the two
traveling waves conspire always to produce zero resultant displacement. Similarly, for vibration rates exactly 3, 4, 5, . . . times the

---

[1] This seems to contradict the statement that the end held in the hand is being
shaken up and down. However, this end is approximately fixed; its slight motion
is due only to the fact that it must be moved somewhat in order to feed energy
into the rope by the method described.

original the rope breaks into steady patterns shown as "time exposures" in Fig. 10·14. Points where the rope remains motionless at all times are called *nodes,* places halfway between the nodes, where the amplitude is a maximum, are called *loops,* or *antinodes.* Notice that all the particles of the rope in any one loop are in the same phase and that neighboring loops are in opposite phase. The distance between two adjacent nodes or loops is half the wavelength of the waves traveling on the rope.[1]

The motion of the stretched rope which we have just been examining is of exactly the same nature as that of a wire or string in a stringed musical instrument such as the violin, harp, or piano.

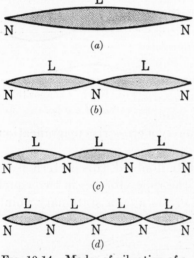

FIG. 10·14   Modes of vibration of a string.

If the string is bowed, plucked, or struck at its center, it will vibrate in one segment as in Fig. 10·14*a,* giving off the lowest pitched tone it is capable of producing—its so-called *fundamental.*

By temporarily touching the string at its middle and stimulating it at the quarter point it can be made to vibrate in two loops, as in Fig. 10·14*b.* It is then said to give off its *first overtone,* which in this case has exactly *twice* the frequency of the fundamental. In similar ways, the second, third, and higher overtones with frequencies 3, 4, 5, . . . times the fundamental may be produced.

The frequencies of the overtones of more complicated sound sources do not stand in this simple ratio of integers. Strings and air columns (described below) are the only common sources whose overtone frequencies are exact integral multiples of the fundamental frequency. In this case we speak of *harmonic overtones,* or simply *harmonics.*[2] In practice, the form of a vibrating string is usually a

---

[1] Try these experiments yourself.

[2] The overtones of most *percussion instruments,* which involve the vibration of plates, bars, membranes, etc., are not harmonic. For instance, the frequencies of the first two overtones of a reed clamped at one end and set into vibration are 6.267 and 17.55 times that of the fundamental.

combination of the fundamental along with smaller amounts of several of the harmonics.

10·8 Stationary Waves in an Air Column

Just as the operation of stringed musical instruments depends on the production of stationary waves along the string, so wind instruments like the flute, trumpet, and pipe organ employ stationary compressional waves in the air within a tube. If a single compressional pulse is sent down a tube, it will be reflected from the far end and return along the tube. Here, unlike the situation with a string, there are two possibilities. If there is a fixed wall at the far end of the tube (as in a "closed" pipe), the compression arriving at this end will have no room for further motion and so will react by compressing the air it has just passed through, with the result that a compression will be reflected back along the pipe.

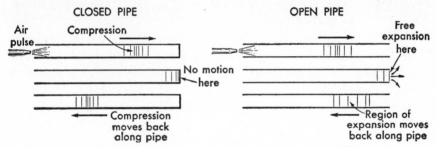

FIG. 10·15 Reflection of a pulse at the end of a tube.

On the other hand, if the far end of the tube is *open* to the surrounding air ("open" pipe), the compression arriving there expands into free space. In doing so, the inertia of the moving air makes it "overshoot"; instead of merely lapsing back to its normal value, the air pressure at the mouth of the tube becomes lower, causing the air particles just inside the end of the tube to flow toward this end. This motion in turn causes the neighboring air particles to shift in a similar way, with the result that a region of local *expansion* moves back up the pipe. These effects are pictured in Fig. 10·15, which you should examine closely.

Now, if the single pulse is replaced by a *regular succession* of air vibrations, say, from a vibrating tuning fork, and if the frequency of the source and the length of the tube are properly related, you can readily see that a system of stationary waves will result inside the tube with certain points as nodes and others as antinodes of displacement of the air particles. In an ordinary flue-type organ pipe (Fig. 10·16) the vibrations are started and maintained merely by blowing a thin stream of air against the edge of an opening at one end of the pipe. This air stream has a highly irregular motion, which can be looked upon as a mixture of a great number of frequencies of vibration. In the absence of a pipe the air jet itself would emit only a noisy hiss— the mixture of a great many unrelated frequencies. The pipe, however, selects from this jumble a single frequency and rejects all others.

The process is an example of *resonance*—the strong response of a system when stimulated in the tempo of its own natural frequency of vibration. Thus a swing, for instance, may be given a motion of large amplitude by a succession of very weak pushes, provided that they are applied at intervals equal to the swing's own period of vibration.

Air

FIG. 10·16 An open flue-type organ pipe.

In the case of the organ pipe, the result of this resonance process is that a strong system of standing waves builds up in the air within the tube. Part of the energy is radiated to the surrounding air in the form of sound waves of definite pitch.

As in the example of the string, the air in a pipe can be made to vibrate in any one of several different modes, particularly if driven

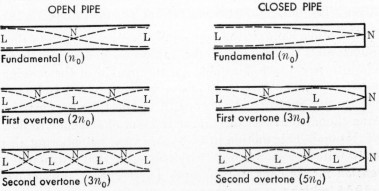

OPEN PIPE

Fundamental (n_0)

First overtone ($2n_0$)

Second overtone ($3n_0$)

CLOSED PIPE

Fundamental (n_0)

First overtone ($3n_0$)

Second overtone ($5n_0$)

FIG. 10·17   Modes of vibration of the air in a pipe.

by a source whose frequency can be adjusted to different values. Here again the frequencies of the overtones will be harmonic, or integral multiples of the fundamental frequency.

Some of the possible modes of vibration of open and closed pipes are shown in Fig. 10·17, where in each instance the wavy line is a graph of the displacement of the air particles at various places along the pipe. At an open end there is always a displacement loop, and at a closed end a displacement node, with intermediate loops and nodes in the case of the overtones. Upon remembering that the distance between two adjacent loops or nodes is half the wavelength of the tone produced, it is evident from the figure that the open pipe can produce harmonics whose frequencies are 2, 3, 4, . . . times the fundamental. The closed pipe, on the other hand, gives only the *odd* harmonics of frequencies 3, 5, 7, . . . ; for its two ends are unlike, and there must be an odd number of segments along it. This figure should be studied carefully.

10·9 Wave Form and Tone Quality

It has been explained how a string or an air column can vibrate with its fundamental frequency or with any one of a set of harmonic overtones whose frequencies are integral multiples of the fundamental. In almost every practical case of tone production

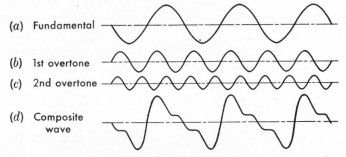

(a) Fundamental

(b) 1st overtone

(c) 2nd overtone

(d) Composite wave

Fig. 10·18   Complex wave form.

the overtones as well as the fundamental are present to some extent in the vibration of the source. A *pure tone,* involving a single SHM, is seldom produced. A tuning fork struck gently with a soft hammer or a flute blown softly gives approximately pure tones. It was such waves that were represented by the graphs of Figs. 10·5 and 10·8, for example.

If overtones are present, the air will in a sense have to vibrate in several different ways at once. Actually the vibrations due to the various overtones will combine to give a single complex disturbance. Suppose that a certain complex wave consists of a fundamental of given amplitude (curve a in Fig. 10·18) plus lesser amounts of the first and second overtones (curves *b* and *c*). What will the composite wave look like? This can be seen by adding the ordinates of the three separate curves at each point, paying attention to whether a given curve is above or below the axis at that place. If below, its ordinate must be subtracted from the sum of the others. In this way the complex wave represented by curve *d* is obtained. This is just as much a wave as any of the simpler ones, for it represents the periodic repetition of a certain form of disturbance. Its wavelength is that of the fundamental.

By means of certain mechanical or electrical methods, separate wave forms can be combined to produce complex waves; conversely it is possible to analyze any complex periodic disturbance into a

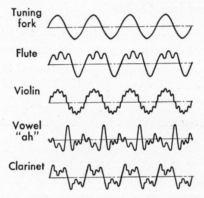

FIG. 10·19   Wave forms of various musical sounds.

series of simple harmonic waves. It is found that the perceived difference in character of two tones of the same pitch and loudness sounded on two different instruments is due to a difference in wave form, or—in terms of the analysis into simple tones—to a difference in the *relative prominence of the fundamental and the various overtones*. This attribute of musical tones is called *quality*. The difference in quality of tones from various sources is evident from an inspection of the wave forms (Fig. 10·19), but the ear is not able to analyze a tone into its component frequencies.

It must be said that there are other circumstances besides the distribution of energy among the overtones that determine the auditory impression produced by a musical tone. Such factors as the method of starting or stopping the tone or the way in which its volume changes have some effect on our identification of the instrument producing the sound, but their exact role is not well understood at the present time.

10·10 Other Wave Phenomena

The present chapter has attempted to describe some of the more important characteristics common to all types of waves. These general attributes, though introduced and described by talking specifically about water waves or sound waves, are possessed in common by waves of all types. It is in connection with light waves in particular that many of the results arrived at will prove most useful to you in your further study.

Water waves are directly observable. Sound waves are not, though they may be made so by indirect means. But even if they could not be made evident in this literal sense, we should not question their reality, for the *assumption* that sound is propagated in the form of waves accounts in a complete and exact manner for the many observed features of sound that you have studied in these pages as well as for others not explicitly mentioned. When, in what follows, you come to learn about the phenomena of light, you will find that a wave explanation is again indicated—and justified—despite the fact that light waves are even less evident than those of sound.

Phenomena that you will come to know under such names as "interference," "diffraction," and "refraction" might equally well have been discussed in the present chapter; but since our primary concern with them is their application to light waves, their explanation is deferred to later chapters.

SUMMARY

Wave: A form of disturbance that travels out through the surrounding medium from a vibrating source. The waves are said to have the same period and frequency as their source.

Wavelength: The distance, in a wave train, from any particle to the next one that is in the same phase. For any continuous wave train, $V = n\lambda$.

Direction of particle motion: Longitudinal in sound (compressional) waves; *transverse* in light waves or waves in a cord. In water waves the particle motion has both longitudinal and transverse components.

Doppler effect: Relative motion of source and observer alters the received frequency—an *increase* if *approaching,* a *decrease* if *receding.*

Intensity of a wave motion is measured by the rate of energy transfer through each unit area of a surface held normal to the waves. Intensity of a directly received sound depends on strength of the source and its distance away.

Stationary waves: Result from combination of direct and reflected waves, as in strings or air columns. They represent a resonance effect.

Complex waves: Relative prominence of fundamental and overtones determines form of the composite wave or *quality* of the corresponding tone.

READING REFERENCES

1. Jeans, J. H.: "Science and Music," Macmillan, New York, 1938.
2. Mills, John: "A Fugue in Cycles and Bels," Van Nostrand, New York, 1935. Items 1 and 2 are excellent books that should be read by everyone who is interested in the physical basis of music.
3. Fletcher, Harvey: Pitch, Loudness, and Quality of Musical Tones, *Am. Jour. Phys.*, Vol. 14, p. 215, 1946. A good summary of recent work at the Bell Telephone Laboratories on the behavior of sound, particularly phenomena connected with tone production and hearing.
4. Henry, G. E.: Ultrasonics, *Sci. American*, Vol. 190, pp. 54–63, May, 1954. An excellent summary of principles and applications of this field.
5. Bragg, W. H.: "The World of Sound," G. Bell, London, 1925. A well-written popular exposition, clear and interesting.

FILMS

"Sound Waves and Their Sources," Encyclopaedia Britannica Films. 16 mm, sound, 1 reel.

"Fundamentals of Acoustics," Encyclopaedia Britannica Films. 16 mm, sound, 1 reel.

"Progressive Waves," "Stationary Transverse Waves," "Stationary Longitudinal Waves," McGraw-Hill (three AAPT Physics Films). 16 mm, sound, 1 reel each.

EXERCISES

Where the speed of sound in air is required, assume it to be 1100 ft/sec or 330 m/sec.

1. Compute the wavelength, in air, of the lowest and of the highest frequency sound that can be heard by an average ear.

2. A man standing some distance from a cliff fires a shot. The sound of the report comes back to him 4.2 sec later. How far is he from the cliff?

3. At a certain place on a phonograph record the speed of the groove, with respect to the needle, is 100 cm/sec. If the frequency of the tone produced is 384 vib/sec, what is the distance between crests of the wavy indentations of the groove?

4. A diaphragm vibrating with a frequency of 940 vib/sec is placed in water. What is the frequency of the compressional waves produced in the water, and what is their length? If these waves, striking the surface, set up compressional (sound) waves in the surrounding air, what is their frequency and wavelength? The speed of sound waves in water is 4700 ft/sec.

5. A car traveling 55 ft/sec sounds its horn as it passes a man standing beside the road. If the effective pitch of the horn, as heard by the driver, is 120 vib/sec, what will the frequency appear to be to the stationary observer?

6. Does the music of a symphony orchestra appear one-fourth as loud to a man in the twentieth row of the hall as it does to one sitting in the tenth row? In answering, consider such factors as size of source and presence of nearby walls.

7. Assuming that the opening of the human ear is effectively a circle 8 mm in diameter, how long would you have to listen with both ears to a sound at the lower limit of audibility in order to take in 1 erg of energy?

8. The loudest sound the ear can tolerate without damage is rated at 120 db. The sound level in an average restaurant measures 50 db. How do these two sound levels compare in terms of energy?

9. One end of a rope 12 ft long is tied to a hook in the wall. With what frequency must the free end of the rope be shaken back and forth in order to make it break into exactly three loops if the speed of transverse waves in the rope is 28 ft/sec?

10. A tuning fork whose frequency is 440 vib/sec is held near the mouth of a narrow jar 10 in. deep. To what depth must water be poured into the jar before the sound of the fork will be strongly reinforced?

Chapter 11

THE NATURE OF LIGHT

The greater part of our information about the surrounding universe is brought to us through the sense of sight. It is the light sent out from or reflected by the objects around us that produces the sensation of vision. Light is our only perceptible connection with distant astronomical bodies.

The ancients speculated about the true nature of light. Some believed it to consist of small particles shot out from luminous objects at high speed. Plato and others thought of light as some sort of emanation from the eye that made bodies visible when they were struck by it. Aristotle, on the other hand, preferred to think of light as something nonmaterial occurring in the space between the eye and the object seen.

This last interpretation did not take on a more definite form until the seventeenth century, when Hooke and Huygens separately made the suggestion that light is a *wave motion.* Newton himself entertained both the ideas of light as a stream of particles shot out from luminous bodies and as a train of waves, but he seemed to lean more to the particle theory, or *corpuscular theory* as it was called. His great authority and prestige kept this notion alive for nearly a century after his time, in spite of the fact that certain features of the behavior of light to be described below are almost impossible to explain on a corpuscular basis but have a ready interpretation in terms of waves.

If light is thought of as a wave motion, the question immediately presents itself, "Waves in *what?*" A medium—the "ether"—was invented to serve as the carrier of these waves; but no experimental evidence has ever been obtained for the existence of such a medium, and the concept is considered unnecessary in modern physics. As a result of the theoretical work of Maxwell and the experiments of Hertz, during the latter part of the last century, we now know that what is propagated in a light wave is a *change of electric and magnetic stress.* This originates in the motion of electricity in the atoms or molecules from which the light is emitted (Chap. 20).

In our study of light in this book, one of the primary aims will be to examine the main phenomena with regard to their bearing on our conception of the nature of light.

11·1 Light Travels in Straight Lines

One of the most immediately evident features of light is the fact that it advances in straight lines—a circumstance that seems to favor the idea of corpuscles. You are familiar with the appearance of shafts of sunlight coming through a rift in the clouds or with the practice of sighting along the edge of a board in order to determine whether or not it is straight. Almost instinctively we recognize the impossibility of "seeing around a corner." On the other hand, water waves striking an obstacle are observed to bend around it into the space beyond. Sound waves, too, quite obviously deflect around barriers; you do not have to be in line with an open window in order to hear noises from the street.

If light is alleged to consist of waves, we might then expect bending to be observed in this instance, too. For a long time the failure to observe such deviation in the case of light prevented the acceptance of the wave theory. Later, it was recognized that if waves are extremely short their deflection will be inappreciable. This turns out to be true for waves of light; delicate experiments are needed to reveal their departure from straight-line travel. Detailed evidence will be presented later (Chap. 14).

11·2 Light Rays

Another item of evidence for the straight-line travel of light is the sharpness of the shadow of an opaque object illuminated by a small, concentrated source. The boundary of the shadow is determined by lines drawn outward from the source and passing through the edge of the obstacle casting the shadow (Fig. 11·1). These lines, called light *rays,* may be drawn outward from the source in any number and in all directions. The ray drawn through any point gives the direction in which the light disturbance is traveling at that place. For an object to be seen, rays of light from it must enter the eye. The rays, of course, have no physical reality; they are merely constructions that give the direction of advance of the waves, just as stream lines may be drawn in flowing water to show the direction in which the particles of the liquid are moving. A great virtue of the ray concept is that it does not restrict us to any particular interpretation of the nature of what is being sent out along the rays. In the next chapter you will see how the basic features of many optical instruments can be explained in terms of rays without troubling at all about the existence of waves.

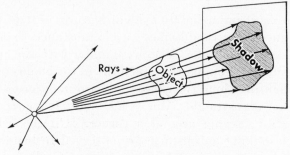

FIG. 11·1   Rays of light define the shadow.

It probably occurs to you that in our discussion of waves in Chap. 10 we might well have made use of the ray concept. Rays are seldom used in connection with sound waves and water waves, our two most frequent illustrations in that chapter, probably because in almost all practical cases sound waves and water waves are observed to bend around corners, as mentioned above, while for light waves this occurs under less usual conditions.

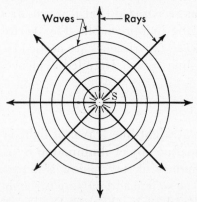

FIG. 11·2 Spherical waves and some associated rays.

For a medium in which the speed of travel of the waves is the same in all directions the wave front (page 159) and the ray at any point are perpendicular to each other. For example, in the case of spherical waves coming from a point source, the rays would be lines drawn radially outward in all directions from the source. A plane section of this situation is represented by Fig. 11·2.

Another illustration of the straight-line travel of light is provided by the **pinhole camera.** This is a lighttight box having a small hole in the front face. If a lamp or a brightly lighted object is placed in front of the box, an *image* of the source will appear on the inside back surface of the box (Fig. 11·3). This image will be inverted as well as reversed sidewise. If a piece of photographic film is put on the inside rear face of the box, a surprisingly good picture can be obtained. Each point of the object acts as a source of light, and rays from any point that come through the pinhole fall at a given spot on the wall of the box. Rays from an adjacent point fall next to this spot, and in this way, point for point, a complete reproduction or image of the object is outlined on the rear of the box. Since the image of any point will be a small circle of light, the pinhole must be small if the image is to be sharp. You will find it instructive to

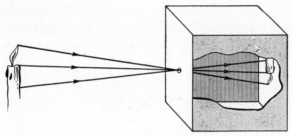

FIG. 11·3   Pinhole camera.

make a pinhole camera or at least to view such an image directly in a darkened room by putting a lighted candle in front of a cardboard having a small hole in it and catching the image on a sheet of white paper held a few inches beyond. Notice that an image is formed regardless of the distance of the luminous object from the pinhole, but that the greater the distance, the smaller the image.

11·3   Early Measurements of the Speed of Light

On the basis of almost any reasonable view of the nature of light the disturbance would be expected to take an appreciable time to go from one place to another; yet in the early days of science there were many differences of opinion as to whether the speed of light is finite or not. Certainly, common observations such as the interval noted between a flash of lightning and the arrival of the sound of the accompanying thunder indicate that the speed of light, if not infinite, is much greater than that of sound.

Galileo was the first to try to measure the speed of light. In his experiment, one observer uncovered a lantern, which could be seen by a second observer several thousand feet away. As soon as the second experimenter saw the flash of light, he uncovered a similar lantern and the first observer attempted to note the total time that elapsed for the two-way passage of light. Needless to say, these attempts gave no definite result, since the reaction times of the experimenters were much larger than the interval they were trying to measure. But it should be mentioned that Galileo's experiment was in principle the method used in some of the later successful determinations.

The first indication that the speed of light is finite was obtained in the latter part of the seventeenth century by the Danish astronomer Römer. He observed that one of the satellites (moons) of the planet Jupiter appeared to emerge from behind the planet at successively later and later times when the earth was receding from Jupiter and at correspondingly earlier times when the earth was approaching (Fig. 11·4). The actual period of motion of the satellite is,

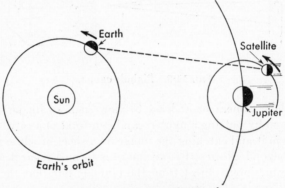

Fig. 11·4   Römer's method.

of course, constant, and these apparent changes are due to a kind of Doppler effect (page 163) resulting from the relative motion of source and observer. The total delay was found to be very nearly 1000 sec, and Römer correctly interpreted this as the time taken by light to cross the earth's orbit. However, since the diameter of the orbit was not well determined at that time, a numerical evaluation of the speed was not forthcoming.

At the present time the best value deduced from the results of several methods appears to be

$$c = 299{,}790 \text{ km/sec} = 186{,}262 \text{ mi/sec} \qquad (11\cdot1)$$

c being the standard symbol for the speed of light in a vacuum. The speed in any transparent material medium is found to be *less* than that in a vacuum. In air the speed is only 0.03 per cent less than c, but the speeds in water and in glass are considerably smaller—respectively about ¾ and ⅔ of c.

11·4 Fizeau's Method

The first successful measurement of the speed of light carried out entirely on the surface of the earth was made by the French experimenter Fizeau in the middle of the nineteenth century. His method was a direct mechanization of Galileo's experiment, using instead of the first lantern shutter a revolving toothed wheel and replacing the second observer by a mirror, which returns a light signal without any delay. Figure 11·5 shows a schematic diagram of Fizeau's apparatus. Light from an arc lamp S is reflected from an

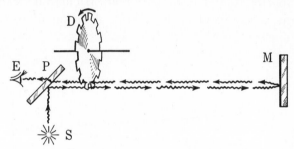

FIG. 11·5   Fizeau's apparatus.

inclined glass plate P and sent through the openings of a toothed disk D to a distant mirror M, which was over 5 mi away in this instance. The light is reflected back along its original path and goes through the edge of the disk once more and through the plate P to the eye of the observer.

The function of the rotating disk is essentially to chop up the light beam into a series of equal portions as shown in the diagram. If the speed of the disk is just right, these limited flashes, or wave trains, will return to the disk at just the right times to slip entirely through the openings and a maximum of illumination will be seen at E. The light will also be a maximum for 2, 3, 4, . . . times this disk speed. However, if the speed is exactly *half* the original value, a returning train of waves will be stopped completely by the presence of the succeeding tooth and no light will get through. The same thing will happen for any odd multiple of half the original disk speed. At intermediate speeds, part of each wave train will get through, and intermediate illumination will result.

By noting the speed of rotation of the disk when the light is first cut off completely, the time taken for a tooth to turn to the position formerly occupied by an opening is easily computed; it is the same as the time required by light to go to the distant mirror and return. In this way Fizeau obtained a value for c; it turned out to be slightly higher than that given in Eq. (11·1).

11·5   Modern Methods

About a year after Fizeau's experiment another French scientist, Foucault, refined the method by replacing the toothed disk by a rotating mirror; but it was in the hands of Michelson[1] and his associates that this direct mechanical method attained its highest precision—better than 1 part in 10,000. Michelson's experimental arrangement is sketched in Fig. 11·6. A beam of light from an

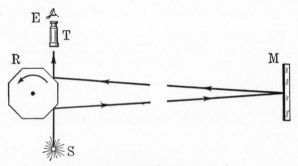

Fig. 11·6   Michelson's method.

intense arc source S is reflected from one face of an octagonal mirror R rotating at high speed. The light goes to a distant mirror M, located in this instance about 22 mi away, and on its return is reflected from another face of the eight-sided mirror to the observing telescope T. If R is stationary and in the position shown in the diagram, the light will be seen in the telescope. If the mirror R is now set into rotation, the light will not be seen in the field of view until the octagon is spinning at just the right speed to bring one of its faces into the exact position of the next in the time taken by light to go to the distant mirror and back.

The precision of the result obtained was made possible by the

[1] Albert A. Michelson (1852–1931), extraordinarily ingenious and careful experimenter, chiefly in the field of optics; first American physicist to receive the Nobel prize.

extreme accuracy with which the various factors were determined. The distance of about 22 mi to the mirror M had been measured by direct surveying methods to within about 1 in., or 1 part in a million. The angles between the faces of the rotating mirror had been made equal to about this same relative precision, and great pains were taken to see that the rate of rotation was held constant during a run. Measurements were also made by this method by reflecting the light back and forth in a partly evacuated pipe about 1 mi long. The final values for c were very close to the number quoted in Eq. (11·1).

Later methods give even higher accuracy than Michelson's experiment. One of these more recent procedures uses an electronic shutter in place of a mechanically rotated mirror, and the higher rate of interruption of the beam makes it possible to keep the experiment within the confines of the laboratory. In an even newer method, electric waves of the kind used in radar—microwaves—are employed. According to theory, electric waves should have the same speed as those of visible light (see Chap. 13). The results show that this is the case.

11·6   Significance of the Speed of Light

In reading the preceding account of the more important methods of measuring the speed of light you may have wondered why so much effort and time have been given to the determination of this quantity, to the point where its value can be considered known to within a few parts in a million. The reason is that modern physics ascribes to the velocity of light a fundamental significance far beyond the field of optics itself. In the first place, c represents the speed in a vacuum not only of visible light but of all other radiations of this nature, from the largest radio waves down to the shortest waves produced in subatomic processes. Maxwell (footnote, page 332) was led to his electromagnetic theory of radiation by noticing that the ratio of two electrical units was numerically equal to c. Again, both theory and experiment indicate that c is an upper limit for the speed with which any material object can move. Finally, the two most fundamental physical concepts, mass and energy, are found to be equivalent, and the theory of relativity shows that the factor connecting these two interconvertible quantities is the square of the number c. These ideas will be amplified later in this book.

11·7　Electrical Sources of Light

One of the more practical aspects of the subject of light is concerned with illumination. The most commonly used source is the *filament lamp,* in which the light is produced by passing a current of electricity through a fine wolfram (tungsten) filament placed in a glass bulb containing an inert gas or a vacuum. The function of the electric current is to raise the temperature of the metal filament to the point where it emits essentially "white" light—around 2500° abs.

The *carbon arc* is a very intense source of light and is used in motion-picture projectors, searchlights, etc. It consists of two carbon rods connected one to each terminal of a battery or other source of direct current. The tips of the rods are brought together and then drawn apart, producing a flame of burning carbon, which conducts the current across the gap. Most of the light comes from the incandescent tips of the carbons, particularly the positive one, which attains a temperature of about 3500° abs. The negative carbon operates at about 3000° abs.

Another type of widely used light source employs the discharge of a current of electricity through a gas or vapor at low pressure. This type of lamp is best known in the form of tube-type lighting used for advertising and display purposes. The tubes are filled with some permanent gas such as neon or helium or with a mixture of such a gas and an easily vaporized metal such as sodium or mercury. The apparent color of the emitted light depends on the substances present. Unlike the filament lamp or the arc, the light in a gas-filled tube originates, not in a substance at high temperature, but in a more direct conversion of electrical energy into light by atoms of the gas. The study of the complex processes occurring in such a tube has contributed much to our understanding of the structure of the atom. These phenomena will be treated in more detail in Chap. 18.

In the *fluorescent lamps* now widely used the passage of current through a mixture of mercury vapor and argon at low pressure produces ultraviolet radiation (page 234), which is itself invisible but which causes a suitable chemical coating on the inside of the tube to emit an intense visible glow. The color of the glow depends on the mixture of fluorescent materials used; in particular, a mixture giving a good approximation to daylight can be prepared.

The efficiencies of most light sources are discouragingly low. Ordinary filament lamps convert only a very few per cent of the electrical energy supplied to them into visible light. Fluorescent lamps, however, are now made that are more than five times as efficient.

11·8 Luminous Intensity; Illumination

The strength of a lamp or other source of light is specified by a quantity called its *luminous intensity*. This is measured in **stand-ard candles**—a unit that goes back to the ordinary wax candle as a source of light. In modern work this unit is fixed by means of standard filament lamps kept in laboratories such as the Bureau of Standards. The luminous intensity of a filament lamp of moderate size is about one candle for each watt rating. For example, the intensity of a 60-watt lamp is very nearly 60 candles.

The amount of light falling on each unit area of a surface exposed to a concentrated source depends on the luminous intensity of the lamp, its distance from the sur-face, and the inclination of the rays to the illuminated surface. Since luminous energy from a point source, like sound-wave en-ergy, spreads out on the surface of an expanding sphere, the illumi-nation as measured by the energy falling on each unit area will vary inversely as the square of the dis-tance (see page 166). Thus the illumination E of a surface held perpendicular to the rays from a point source of intensity C at a distance d will be given by

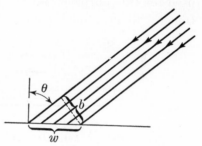

FIG. 11·7   Oblique illumination of a surface.

$$E = \frac{C}{d^2} \qquad\qquad (11\cdot2)$$

If C is measured in candles and d in feet, E is expressed in *foot-candles;* a corresponding metric unit, the meter-candle, is some-times used. While it is not customary to specify illumination directly in terms of energy passing through unit area in unit time, as was done on page 166, it is interesting to notice that an area ex-posed directly to 1 ft-c of illumination is receiving energy at the rate of about 10^{-5} watt/cm^2. The eye can be stimulated by an illumina-tion as small as 10^{-10} ft-c, equivalent to the light of a single candle nearly 20 miles away.

Equation (11·2) will not give accurate results unless the distance to the receiving surface is fairly large compared with the dimen-sions of the light source. For a bare, frosted 60-watt filament lamp, for example, this relation will not give dependable results at distances less than about 1 ft. Also, if the light does not strike perpendicular to the surface, the result computed according to Eq. (11·2) must be reduced by a factor equal to the ratio of the breadth of the beam to the width of the illuminated area (Fig. 11·7), both being measured in a plane that is normal to the surface and parallel to the rays.[1]

11·9 Photometry

The intensity of a source of light is commonly determined by matching the illumination it produces with that from a standard lamp. There are many experimental arrangements that may be used for this purpose, but the general principle is that of the photometer diagrammed in Fig. 11·8. A standard lamp S and the lamp

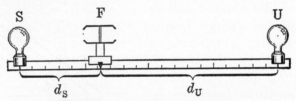

FIG. 11·8 A laboratory photometer.

U of unknown intensity are held in suitable mountings at the ends of a long graduated bar. A white screen F may be moved to any desired point between the lamps. Some arrangement of mirrors or other optical parts, not shown in the sketch, is provided to allow the experimenter to view both sides of the screen at the same time. With all light excluded except that coming directly from the two lamps, the screen is moved back and forth between the lamps until both sides of the screen appear to have the same brightness. When this is realized, the illumination must be equal on the two sides. Then, according to Eq. (11·2), $C_U/d_U^2 = C_S/d_S^2$, or

$$\frac{C_U}{C_S} = \frac{d_U^2}{d_S^2} \tag{11·3}$$

This equation expresses the fact that when the illuminations produced by the two lamps have been matched the more distant lamp is the more powerful. A competent operator, using the best form of such an instrument, can match illuminations to well within 1 per cent, provided that the two sources have about the same quality (color).

[1] This ratio is, in trigonometric notation, simply cos θ.

Other instruments, called *illuminometers* or foot-candle meters, are used by lighting engineers and architects to measure illumination directly. Modern portable meters of this kind (Fig. 11·9) employ the photoelectric effect (page 386) and are similar to the exposure meters extensively used by photographers. A foot-candle meter placed on a given surface measures the total illumination produced on that surface by all sources present, regardless of their locations, sizes, etc.

Based on experience, lighting engineers have arrived at certain standards of illumination for various purposes. While universal agreement is lacking, the present tendency is to use higher illumination levels than in the past.

11·10 Reflection of Light

In Sec. 10·6 it was pointed out that waves striking a boundary are *reflected*, or turned back into the space from which they come. In particular, we are now interested in the reflection of light waves and in arriving at an exact description of how this takes place. Instead of describing reflection solely in terms of what happens to the waves, as was done

FIG. 11·9   Photoelectric foot-candle meter.

above, we can often represent conditions more simply by using rays. This will be done not only for reflection but for certain other light phenomena where the ray method proves to be convenient and useful.

It is found by experience that when light or any other wave motion is reflected from a surface *the reflected ray* at any point *makes the same angle with the normal,* or perpendicular, to the surface *as does the incident ray.* Also, the reflected ray lies directly on the opposite side of the normal from the incident ray—that is, *the two rays and the normal all lie in one plane.* These features of the law of reflection are represented in Fig. 11·10. Angle i is called the *angle of incidence,* angle r is the *angle of reflection,* and the plane com-

mon to both rays and the normal is called the **plane of incidence.**[1]
The law of reflection, then, is a general description of what happens
to any ray. By applying this law to particular sets of rays, the way
in which light is reflected from any
surface can be worked out.

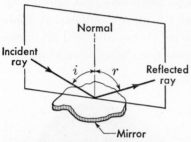

FIG. 11·10   Reflection of a ray.

While the law of reflection is
most commonly used in connection
with light, it is valid for the reflection of certain other disturbances,
whether they consist of waves or of
something else. In particular, a perfectly smooth and elastic ball will
rebound from a surface in accord-
ance with the reflection law given above. This implies that the phenomenon of the reflection of light is as readily explainable on a
corpuscular theory of the nature of light as on the wave theory.

11·11   Plane Mirror

A limited portion of a spherical wave coming from a distant small
source is essentially plane, and the associated rays are practically
parallel. Thus we speak of sunlight as consisting of **plane waves** or
as having parallel rays. If such a beam of light strikes a plane mirror, the law of reflection tells us that the reflected rays will also be

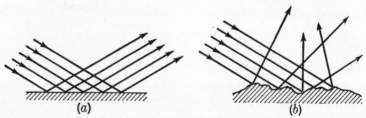

FIG. 11·11   Regular and diffuse reflection.

parallel (Fig. 11·11*a*). Contrasted with this so-called **regular reflection** is the **diffuse reflection** that takes place when a beam of light
strikes a rough or irregular surface (Fig. 11·11*b*). At each point on a
rough surface the angles of incidence and reflection are equal, but

---

[1] It may seem more natural to measure the directions of the rays with respect
to the surface itself rather than with the normal, but the latter procedure turns
out to be simpler mainly because the normal provides the most direct way of
specifying the plane of incidence.

the normals at various points have different directions, and so do
the reflected rays. Since all but self-luminous objects are seen by
light which they reflect, a rough surface will be visible by means of
diffusely reflected light from almost any position, while in order to
receive light from a mirror the observer must be in the particular
direction in which the illuminating beam is reflected. It is the effect
of the surface texture of the object on light reflected from it that
makes the object visible. A perfectly smooth, clean reflecting surface is not visible; what is seen is the source of light rather than the
reflecting surface.

We usually say that we look *into* a mirror in order to see our reflection there. Of course, nothing actually occurs behind the reflecting surface, but it is true that the light coming originally from any
point in front of the mirror *appears to come,* after reflection, from
a point on the normal an equal distance behind the mirror (Fig.
11·12). The latter point is said to be the *image* of the source S.

The truth of this statement is proved by simple geometry. Angles
SPN and NPQ in Fig. 11·12 are equal by the law of reflection, and $N'PS'$

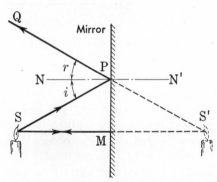

and NPQ are equal because they
are opposite angles formed by the
intersection of the lines NN' and
QS'. As a result, angles PSM and
$PS'M$ are equal, and the two right

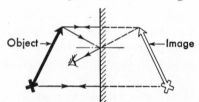

Fig. 11·12 Location of reflected image
of a point.

Fig. 11·13 Reflected image of an
extended object.

triangles are equal. This makes $SM = MS'$. Inasmuch as PQ was any
reflected ray, all reflected rays will appear to come from S'.

The image in a plane mirror of an extended source or object is
found by taking one point after another and locating its image. The
familiar result is that the complete image is the same size as the
object and is placed symmetrically with regard to the mirror (Fig.
11·13). It is a common misconception that a mirror must be at least
as large as the object in order to form a complete image. No matter

how small the mirror may be, the entire image can be viewed in it, although it may be necessary to move the eye about in order to see all parts of the image. The situation is exactly as though the mirror were a sort of window permitting the observer to look into the space beyond, where the image is located (Fig. 11·14). Thus the eye must be placed at A to see the (reflected) head of the arrow and at B to see the tail.

Because of the circumstance that light rays do not actually originate there but merely *appear* to do so, the image in a plane mirror is called a *virtual image*.

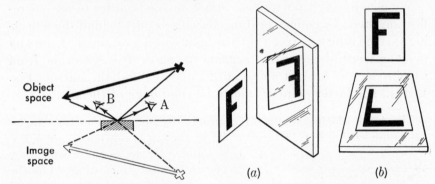

Object
space

B A

Image
space

(a) (b)

Fig. 11·14   Mirror of limited size.   Fig. 11·15   Reversal of the image.

11·12   Reversal Due to Reflection

The image that you see of yourself in a plane mirror is not identical with the appearance you present to other persons or the way you look in a photograph but is turned left for right. Each of your features has an image identical with it, but the parts are arranged in reverse order. Why is there not also an inversion—an interchange of up and down? The sketches of Fig. 11·15 show a vertical card bearing the letter F as seen by reflection, first in a mirror placed in a vertical plane and second in a horizontal mirror. In the first case the image is sidewise *reversed* but *erect;* in the second case it is *unreversed* but *inverted.* The explanation for the existence of only a *one-way* interchange is to be found in the fact that in order to bring the object into the position of its image it must be imagined turned about a *single* axis—the line in which the card and the mirror meet. This is a vertical line in the first instance sketched, a horizontal line in the second.

Two reflections, however, can be arranged to yield an unreversed image. If you look into a pair of plane mirrors arranged like the covers of a book opened at right angles, so that part of your face is seen on each side of the dividing line, your image will have the features disposed as they appear to other people. What do you observe when you touch your right ear while looking into the mirrors? The explanation of what happens can be found by examining Fig. 11·16. The final image of any point—the right ear, for instance—formed by both mirrors can be looked upon as the image in the second mirror of the image formed by the first mirror. The actual rays that enter your eyes appear to come from the final image D, but their course is as shown in the figure.

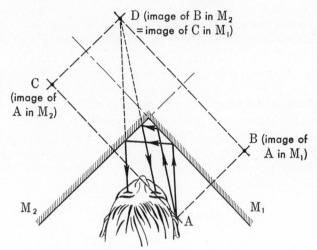

Fɪɢ. 11·16   Image in a pair of mirrors.

11·13   Intensity of Reflected Light

The bounding surfaces of a transparent material such as glass reflect light even if they are not silvered, as is the ordinary mirror. In riding in a train at night the interior of the car is seen strongly reflected in the windows. The amount of light reflected at the front surface of ordinary glass is usually small—only about 4 per cent at normal incidence—so that if appreciable light is coming from behind the glass this may escape notice. Light is also reflected from the rear surface of a sheet of glass. Of the 96 per cent entering the glass at normal incidence, another 4 per cent is turned back at the rear surface. This reflection from the glass-air boundary corresponds to the reflection occurring when a sound wave moving down a pipe reaches the open end (Fig. 10·15, page 171). Altogether, then, about 8 per cent of the light striking a glass plate at normal incidence is turned back; the remainder, except for a slight loss due to absorption in the glass, gets through. At large angles of incidence, however, most of the light is reflected at the front surface.

SUMMARY

Light ray: A line representing the direction of advance of light waves.

Speed of light: In a vacuum the speed is very nearly 300,000 km/sec, or 186,000 mi/sec. In a material medium the speed is less.

Luminous intensity of a lamp: The strength of the lamp in terms of the standard candle. Filament lamps rate about 1 candle per watt of power consumed.

Illumination of a surface: Defined by $E = C/d^2$ if the source is small and the light falls at right angles to the surface. Illumination is given in foot-candles if C is in candles and d in feet.

Photometer: An apparatus for comparing the luminous intensities of two lamps.

Law of reflection: Incident and reflected rays make the same angle with the normal to the surface, and both rays and the normal lie in the same plane.

Plane mirror: An image in such a mirror is virtual and of the same size as object. Point for point, the image is at the same distance from the mirror as the object.

READING REFERENCES

1. Bragg, W. H.: "The Universe of Light," Macmillan, New York, 1933. A clear, simple presentation of many phenomena relating to light. Chapters 1 and 2 should be read at this point.
2. Jaffe, B.: "Men of Science in America," Simon and Schuster, New York, 1944. The biography of Michelson is of interest in connection with the present chapter.
3. Rush, J. H.: The Speed of Light, *Sci. American*, Vol. 193, p. 62, August, 1955. A summary of the results of a variety of methods. The interesting question of the possible variation of c with time is discussed.
4. Taylor, Lloyd W.: "Physics, the Pioneer Science," Houghton Mifflin, Boston, 1941. Read pp. 397–404, 410–421, and 423–428.

FILM

"Measurement of the Speed of Light," McGraw-Hill (AAPT Physics Films). 16 mm, sound, 1 reel.

EXERCISES

1. In a certain pinhole camera the back surface is 6 in. from the pinhole. How tall will the image of a 6-ft man be when he stands 18 ft from the camera?

2. If a beam of light could be made to go around the earth along the

equator, how long would a complete circuit take? Radio waves can make such a trip.

3. Express, to three figures only, the distance in miles traveled by light in 1 year. This is used in astronomy as a unit for stating stellar distances and is called one *light-year*.

4. A radar signal sent from the earth and reflected back from the moon was found to take 2.52 sec for the complete trip. How far is the moon from the earth's surface, assuming that the signal traveled with the speed c?

5. In one of the trial runs of the Michelson method the octagonal mirror was running at a speed of 530.0 rev/sec when reflection was observed from an adjoining face of the mirror. If the distant mirror was 22.02 mi away, what result was obtained for the speed of light in air under the prevailing conditions?

6. At the surface of the earth, the noonday sun produces an illumination of about 10,000 ft-c. If 20 ft-c is considered proper illumination for reading, would an inhabitant of Pluto find daylight sufficient for this purpose? The distance of Pluto from the sun is about 40 times the earth's distance.

7. How far from a wall must a 75-c lamp be placed to produce the same illumination as that now obtained by means of a 100-c lamp 10 ft away together with a 50-c lamp 5 ft away?

8. At what point on the line joining two lamps located 3 m apart, one of 5 c and the other of 20 c, must a screen be placed in order to be equally illuminated by each source? Account for the fact that there are *two* answers.

9. Why is it recommended that in reading the light should come from over one shoulder? In this case, is the page seen by regularly or diffusely reflected light? Where does any regularly reflected light go?

10. A man 10 ft from a plane mirror wishes to take a picture of his image, using a camera standing next to him. For what distance should the camera be focused?

11. How tall a mirror, mounted on a vertical wall, is needed in order that a man 6 ft tall may just be able to see himself head to foot? How must the mirror be placed? Does it make any difference how far away the man stands? Draw a diagram.

12. A good way of drawing an accurate perpendicular to a given line is to stand a small mirror on edge astride the line and rotate the mirror around a vertical axis until the image of the line in the mirror is seen as an unbroken continuation of the line itself. Explain.

Chapter 12

REFRACTION OF LIGHT

As pointed out in the preceding chapter, light traveling in a homogeneous material is observed to advance in straight lines. If the properties of the medium differ from place to place, this is no longer true; the rays will be bent rather than straight. This change of direction that occurs in a nonuniform transparent substance is called *refraction*.

12·1 Refraction at a Plane Surface

When light strikes a plane boundary separating two transparent substances, part of it is reflected in accordance with the law of reflection already described, while the remainder enters the second medium. Except in the special case where the original light happens to be traveling along the normal to the boundary plane, the part that enters the second medium experiences an abrupt change of direction on going through the boundary.

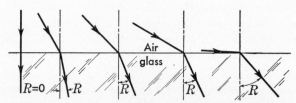

Fig. 12·1 Refraction at a plane surface of glass.

The refracted ray lies in the same plane as the incident ray and the normal to the surface. As might be expected, the reflected ray is also in this plane. The angle R (Fig. 12·1) is called the **angle of refraction.** Rays incident on glass at various angles are refracted as shown. In a case like this where the light goes from a rarer medium such as air into a denser medium such as glass, the refracted ray is bent **toward the normal.** When light goes from a denser to a rarer medium, the bending is in a direction **away from the normal.**

196

Familiar observations are readily explained by the general state-ments made above. Aristotle described the broken appearance of an oar dipped in water—the apparent bending upward of the im-mersed part. Any point P of an underwater object (Fig. 12·2) is seen by light coming from it and passing upward through the surface. Rays from such a point are bent as in the dia-gram, appearing to originate at a point P' that lies higher than P. The result is that the entire immersed part of the oar ap-pears to be swung upward as in the sketch. Light passing com-pletely through a parallel-sided piece of glass (Fig. 12·3a) is re-

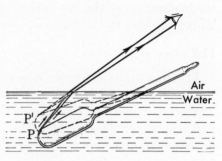

FIG. 12·2 Apparent bending of a partly immersed object.

fracted at each surface, the bending being of the same amount at each surface but toward the normal in one case and away in the other, so that the emerging beam has the same direction as the incident one. However, the passage through the plate results in a

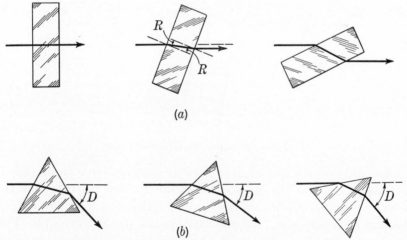

(a)

(b)

FIG. 12·3 Refraction by a parallel plate and by a prism.

sidewise displacement of the ray as shown.[1] Evidence for such dis-placement is provided by viewing a pencil through a thick piece

[1] This displacement is absent only in the case shown in the first drawing, where the ray goes along the normal.

of glass held obliquely to the line of sight. The part of the pencil seen through the glass appears to be moved to one side.

Figure 12·3*b* shows the course of a ray through a triangular prism, or wedge-shaped piece of glass. In this instance, because of the inclination of the two refracting surfaces the emerging ray is no longer parallel to the incident one but has an angular deviation *D*.

12·2 Law of Refraction

Through many centuries a large number of investigators, including Kepler, had looked for a quantitative description of refraction. The correct relation was discovered by the Dutch astronomer and mathematician Snell early in the seventeenth century. A geometric description of the law of refraction may be given as follows: Figure 12·4 shows a parallel beam of light incident obliquely on the plane

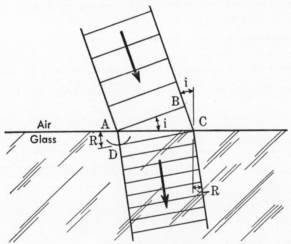

Fig. 12·4 Tracing the refracted beam.

surface of, say, a piece of glass; *AB* is a plane wave front that is just about to enter the glass at the point *A*. Now the course of the refracted ray is determined by a number that is a characteristic of the *pair* of substances—air and glass in the present example. This number, denoted by the Greek letter μ (mū), is called the ***index of refraction*** of the second medium with respect to the first. Usually the first medium is air (more strictly, a vacuum), in which case we speak of μ merely as the index of refraction of the second medium. The numerical value of μ is always greater than 1, being about 4⁄3 for water and 3⁄2 for common glass.

The direction of the refracted ray is found by means of the following construction: Divide the distance BC by μ. Set a compass for this distance, and with A as a center draw an arc in the lower medium. From C draw the line CD tangent to this arc; CD is then one of the wave fronts in the second medium, and the refracted rays have the direction AD. The important fact to remember is that μ is a characteristic constant of the second medium (vacuum above) which, with the help of the above construction, determines the course of the refracted light whatever the direction of the incident light may be.[1]

The passage of light from a denser to a rarer medium may be traced by means of the same construction. It is a fact of experience that when a ray of light passing between two points is reversed it retraces its path exactly. This so-called *reversibility of light rays* is self-evident for reflection; an examination of Figs. 12·1 to 12·4 with the above construction in mind will show its validity for the case of refraction, also.

Snell's law of refraction is best stated in the language of trigonometry. Referring to Fig. 12·4, the index μ was described as the ratio of BC to AD. This means we can write

$$\mu = \frac{BC}{AD} = \frac{BC/AC}{AD/AC} \qquad (12\cdot1)$$

But the angle BAC is the same as i, the angle of incidence of the beam, and angle ACD is the same as R. Hence, in the small triangles, $BC/AC = \sin i$, and $AD/AC = \sin R$. Substituting in Eq. (12·1), we have

$$\mu = \frac{\sin i}{\sin R} \qquad (12\cdot2)$$

which is Snell's law.

12·3 Critical Angle; Total Reflection

Imagine a point source of light S located under water (Fig. 12·5a), sending rays to the surface in various directions. A ray such as SA will be refracted away from the normal on emerging. There will also be an internally reflected ray AR, which does not especially concern us. Another incident ray SB, approaching the surface at a greater angle of incidence, will be closer to the surface than AA' after

---

[1] The value of the index for a given substance depends slightly on the color of the light used. This will be discussed later (p. 221). Tabulated values of μ are usually for yellow light.

emerging. Finally, there will be some ray SC for which the emerging ray will lie exactly along the surface; that is, for this particular angle of incidence the angle of refraction will be 90 deg. Any ray whose angle of incidence is greater than i_c will not be able to emerge at all but will be entirely reflected as shown by SDD'. The beam is said to undergo **total internal reflection,** and the angle of incidence i_c for which this just occurs is called the **critical angle.** It amounts to about 49 deg for water and 42 deg for ordinary glass.

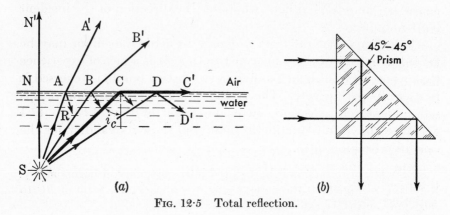

FIG. 12·5   Total reflection.

Total-reflection prisms, having two 45-deg angles and one right angle, are of great use in a variety of optical instruments. Figure 12·5*b* shows one way in which such a prism may be used. Since the incoming rays meet the normal to the back surface at 45 deg, which is greater than the critical 42 deg, no light can escape—it is all reflected internally.

12·4   Corpuscular Explanation of Refraction

How is the phenomenon of refraction to be explained? Does it provide any evidence as to the nature of light? Consider first the possibility of explaining the observed features of refraction on the basis of a corpuscular theory of light. Newton reasoned somewhat as follows: A beam of light is incident on the refracting surface of a dense medium (Fig. 12·6). Let the vector u represent the velocity of the light corpuscles before entering the lower substance. This substance will attract the particles, but the force of attraction will be negligible until the particles are very close to the surface. The net effect, then, of the attraction will be to give the corpuscles an additional velocity v directed straight down into the second medium as soon as they cross the boundary. As a consequence, the velocity of the light particles in the second medium will be V, the vector resultant of u and v. The diagram indicates that the refracted ray will lie closer to the normal than the incident ray, as required by observation. As a matter of fact, the application of trigonometry to the figure shows that the angles of incidence and refraction are related precisely as described by Snell's law of refraction discussed above.

It would be tempting to conclude on this evidence that the corpuscular theory adequately explains the phenomenon of refraction and to consider the matter settled. However, it must always be remembered in scientific work that no theory may ever be considered final, since it may conceivably fail to meet the test of the very next experiment that is performed. Moreover, there always exists the possibility that an entirely different theory, not resembling in the least the one in vogue, may be devised and that the new theory may be equally successful in accounting for the known facts. It may even turn out that the new theory ultimately succeeds in accounting for facts later discovered, where the earlier

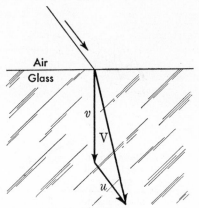

Fig. 12·6   Refraction according to the corpuscular theory.

theory does not. This has happened many times in the history of science; it happened in the case of the theory of light, as you will see.

Notice from the figure that the corpuscular idea requires the speed of light to be greater in the dense medium. This seems to be a good feature of the theory because it suggests new experiments. But in Newton's time the facilities for measuring the speeds in air and in water or glass did not exist. The crucial test was made by Foucault at the middle of the nineteenth century. The outcome will be discussed presently.

12·5   Wave Theory of Refraction

A different theory of the nature of light was championed by Huygens,[1] who preferred the view that light consists of a wave

---

[1] Christian Huygens, famous Dutch physicist, mathematician, and astronomer; contemporary of Newton. His studies in dynamics led him to the invention of the pendulum clock.

motion. In connection with the types of waves with which we are familiar—sound waves and surface waves on water—we know for one thing that reflection takes place according to the law observed to hold for light. The phenomenon of refraction—the swerving aside of sound waves when they enter air of a different temperature or of ripples when they come to a place where the water depth changes—is also known by experience (Fig. 12·7). Huygens suggested that refraction is readily explainable on a wave theory, provided that the speed of light in a dense medium is *less* than in

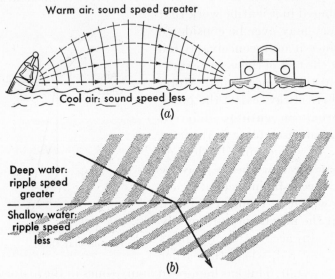

Warm air: sound speed greater

Cool air: sound speed less

(a)

Deep water: ripple speed greater

Shallow water: ripple speed less

(b)

FIG. 12·7   Refraction of sound waves and of ripples.

air. Again, in Fig. 12·4, *AB* is a wave front that is about to cross the boundary at the point *A*, while *DC* is the wave front that has just crossed completely. Thus in the same time that light traveled the distance *AD* in glass, say, it went the greater distance *BC* in air; this means that the speed must be *less in glass.* Here, then, is a clear point of issue between the two theories, the corpuscular requiring that the speed of light be greater in glass, the wave theory demanding that the reverse be true. Unfortunately, as mentioned above, the means for an experimental test were not developed until nearly two centuries later. During the intervening time, Huygens' suggestion was almost completely ignored, overshadowed by the great authority of Newton.

12·6 Speed of Light in Matter

When Foucault actually measured the speed of light in a long tube of water, he found it to be about three-fourths of the speed in air. There could no longer be any doubt that the wave theory offered a truer picture of refraction than the corpuscular. In the meantime, additional triumphs (described below) were scored by the wave theory, and it was not until the present century that any occasion arose to modify and extend that view.

The wave theory, together with direct measurements of the speed of light in matter, gives us an interpretation of the index of refraction of a substance as the ratio of the speed of light in a vacuum to the speed in the material in question. Thus the speed of

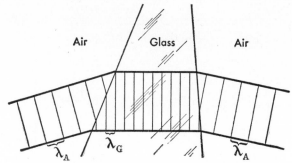

FIG. 12·8   Change in wavelength on refraction.

light in a vacuum is four-thirds as great as that in water and three-halves that in ordinary glass. The general wave relation $V = n\lambda$ (page 159) holds for light as well as for other kinds of waves. Moreover, when a wave passes from one medium to another the *frequency* remains the same, being determined only by the vibration of the source and not by what happens to the waves subsequently. As a result, a change in wave speed on going into a new medium implies a corresponding change in wavelength. Thus light waves become *shorter* when they enter a medium where μ is greater. They resume their former length if the beam again emerges into the original medium (Fig. 12·8).

Our discussion of the bearing of the phenomenon of refraction on the theories of light has been somewhat lengthy, principally because the story furnishes such an apt illustration of the way in which scientific ideas evolve. Here we have a tangible example of the fact that science is a creation of human beings and that the course of its development is often greatly influenced by human fallibilities, traits, and weaknesses; that there is no such thing as a theory that is "right" to the exclusion of all others; that a theory which can be guaranteed to be permanent or final does not exist.

12·7 Huygens' Principle

It is known by experience that in a uniform substance a spherical wave front coming from a point source moves onward as a sphere of constantly increasing radius and that a plane wave continues as a plane parallel to itself. A logical way of explaining these facts and of predicting the future course of *any* wave front was given by Huygens in the statement that *every point on a wave front may be regarded as a new source of waves.*

To see how this works out for an expanding spherical wave, let the innermost solid circle in Fig. 12·9*a* be the cross section of such a wave

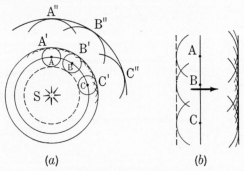

(a)   (b)

Fig. 12·9   Huygens' principle.

at any instant. Considering any points on it, such as A, B, C, $\ldots$, to be new sources of light, we have wavelets spreading out simultaneously as sketched. A very short time later the enveloping curve $A'B'C'$, which is also a circle if the medium is uniform, is the new wave front. A little later the wave front is the circle $A''B''C''$, and so on. Similarly, sketch *b* of this figure shows the propagation of a plane wave in terms of the elementary wavelets originating at various points on it. It can be proved mathematically that the possible enveloping curve that might be drawn on the *backward* side of each set of wavelets (shown as a broken line in each sketch) does not exist, so that only the forward-moving wave is propagated, as observed.

This brief statement of Huygens' principle hardly conveys an idea of its wide usefulness in optics. Later you will see that the idea proves of greatest value in handling cases where the wave speed varies from place to place or where parts of a wave front are held back altogether, but at this time we can profitably apply the principle to reflection and refraction at a plane surface. In Fig. 12·10 suppose that an incident plane wave front AB is just striking the glass surface at the point A. A Huygens wavelet immediately starts from this point, reaching M one wave period later. At this time the foot of the incident wave front is at C, and a wavelet is about to spring into being there. The reflected wave front is then MC. Similarly, the first wavelet from A gets to N at the same instant that the one from C gets to P, making NPD the next of the reflected

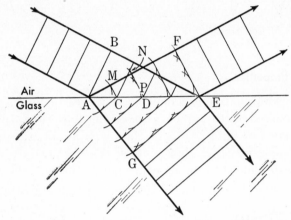

Fɪɢ. 12·10   Reflection and refraction according to Huygens' principle.

fronts, and so on. The law of reflection follows at once from the symmetry of the figure. A similar process accounts for the refracted beam, except that the elementary waves inside the glass are spaced only ⅔ as far apart as in air because $\mu = \frac{3}{2}$ for glass.

12·8   Lenses and Their Function

There are indications that crude lenses were made and used as far back as 25 centuries ago. In modern times, lenses constitute an essential part of many indispensable optical devices such as microscopes, projectors, eyeglasses, cameras, telescopes, and range finders.

The purpose of a lens is to change the curvature of wave fronts by means of refraction, usually in order to form an image. In practice, a lens consists of a portion of some transparent material bounded by two spherical surfaces. In particular, one of the surfaces may be plane. Cross sections of typical lens shapes are shown in Fig. 12·11. Those which are thicker at the center than at the edge are called *converging lenses,* those thinner at the center are called *diverging lenses,* for reasons to be explained presently. The line joining the centers of the two spheres that determine the surfaces is called the *principal axis* of the lens. It is the line of symmetry of the lens itself.

Converging   Diverging

FIG. 12·11   Lenses of various forms.

12·9   Focal Properties

Consider what happens when plane waves of light, advancing along the axis, strike a typical converging lens (Fig. 12·12a). Because the speed of light is less in glass than in air, the part of the wave front passing through the thick central portion of the lens will be retarded more than the other parts, the retardation diminishing as we go outward toward the edge. As a result, the emerging

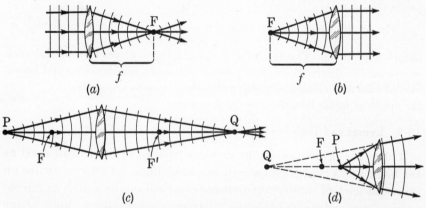

FIG. 12·12   Action of a converging lens.

wave front will be concave, and it turns out that if the glass surfaces are spherical the wave front is nearly spherical and closes down approximately to a point. After passing through this point, called the *principal focus* of the converging lens, the waves again expand as they continue onward. If the plane waves were to pass through the lens in the reverse direction, it would be found that they would come to a focus at a point lying the same distance on the other side of the lens.

There are **two** principal foci, at equal distances f from the lens; f is known as the (principal) *focal length* of the lens.[1] Thus, the principal focus on either side of a converging lens is the point at which light waves moving along the axis and coming from a very distant point source will converge (or the point where the corresponding rays will cross) after passing through the lens.

If a point source is placed at the principal focus of a lens (Fig. 12·12b), the waves diverge from it, strike the lens, and are just made plane on emerging—obviously the reverse of the previous situation. On the other hand, if the source is at a point P (Fig. 12·12c) located **beyond** the principal focus, the lens will be able to reverse the curvature of the wave fronts and they close down to a point Q that lies beyond the other focus. To an observer some distance to the right of the lens the origin of the waves appears to

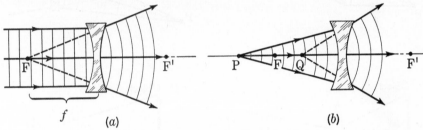

FIG. 12·13   Action of a diverging lens.

be Q rather than P. Finally, if the point source is placed **closer** to the lens than its principal focus (Fig. 12·12d), the lens reduces the curvature of the wave fronts somewhat but is not able to reverse them or even to make them plane. To an observer on the right-hand side of the lens they appear to have come from some point Q that is more distant from the lens than their actual source P. The point Q is appropriately called a *virtual focus*.

The behavior of a diverging lens is much simpler to describe. Waves originating at any point, no matter what its distance from the lens, will have their divergence increased on passing through the lens, as may be seen from Fig. 12·13. If parallel rays strike the lens, the point from which the light **appears** to diverge after passing

[1] Our discussions will be restricted to thin lenses, where the central thickness is small compared with the focal length, so that it does not matter to any great extent whether the distances are measured from the face or from the center of the lens. The behavior of thick lenses is more complicated and will not be treated here.

through the lens is the (virtual) principal focus on the side of the lens from which the light comes. The focus Q is virtual in every instance where the light originates at a point.

12·10 Image Formation by Lenses

If the light falling on a lens makes an angle with the axis, the action of the lens will be as indicated in the last two figures, except that the foci will no longer lie on the principal axis of the lens. This behavior is sketched in Fig. 12·14a and b. Now suppose that we have, in place of a point source of light, an extended object placed

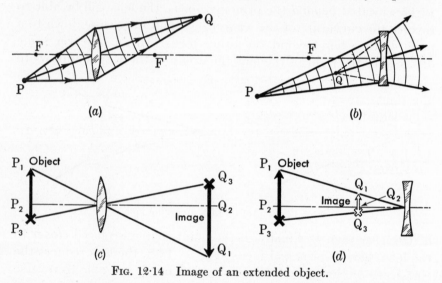

FIG. 12·14   Image of an extended object.

before a lens. Let this object (Fig. 12·14c and d) be located entirely in a plane perpendicular to the principal lens axis. The image may be found by regarding each point of the object as a source of spherical waves.

Although not at once obvious, it turns out that the *image points* will, to a good approximation, *all lie in a plane perpendicular to the lens axis.* This is called the image plane or *focal plane.* It is, for instance, the plane in which the film of a camera must be placed in order to receive the image of the object to be photographed. In this case, and in any case where the waves from points on the object actually converge to points after passing through the lens, the image can be received on a screen and can be viewed in that way. It is called a *real image.* Examples of the formation of real images are given by Figs. 12·12a and c and 12·14a and c. Examine these sketches carefully, and be sure you understand their meaning.

On the other hand, if the waves diverge after passing through the lens, the image is not of the type that can be received on a screen directly. In such an instance the image is said to be *virtual*. A virtual image can be observed by the eye, however, since the waves emerging from the lens travel onward as though they had come from the virtual image. Examples of virtual-image formation are shown in Figs. 12·12d, 12·13b, and 12·14b and d. Notice that a diverging lens produces only virtual images of light coming from a point, while a converging lens may form either real or virtual images, depending upon the location of the object.

12·11 Image Determination by Means of Rays

Any point of an object placed before a lens may be thought of as the origin of spherical waves or, more simply for diagrammatic representation, of rays. While both the waves and the rays have been indicated in many of the figures above, it is usually simpler to deal only with the rays. Moreover, by choosing two special rays from each object point we can determine the corresponding image point uniquely, since an image point is always given by the actual intersection of rays (real image) or by their apparent intersection (virtual image).

The one thing that must be known in order to find an image by such a graphical method is the location of the principal focus of the lens. This may be determined in a number of ways. For example, for a converging lens the focus can be found experimentally by moving a card back and forth beyond the lens until the image of a very distant object is seen to be sharply "in focus." The distance between card and lens is then the focal length of the lens.

Suppose that we have a converging lens (Fig. 12·15a), with an object, represented by the arrow, placed some distance in front of it. Consider a ray coming from the tip of the arrow and proceeding toward the exact center of the lens. This ray will continue onward and go through the lens with no change of direction. It is as if this ray had gone through a parallel-sided plate (compare Fig. 12·3a). Also, since we are dealing with thin lenses exclusively, the small sidewise displacement of the ray can be neglected entirely.

Now trace another ray coming from the tip of the arrow—this time, the one that travels parallel to the lens axis. What is its path after going through the lens? You see from Fig. 12·12a that all rays parallel to the principal axis which strike a converging lens pass through the principal focus after emerging. Thus after refraction by the lens the ray PA in Fig. 12·15a must pass through F'. As long as the object is farther from the lens than F (as in this sketch), the two transmitted rays must intersect at some point Q, which is the image point corresponding to the tip of the arrow. The other image points, corresponding to additional points of the object, will all fall in the focal plane through Q. Specifically, the image of P', the foot of the arrow, will be on the axis if P itself is so placed. An inverted real image of the arrow will actually be seen if a card is held in the

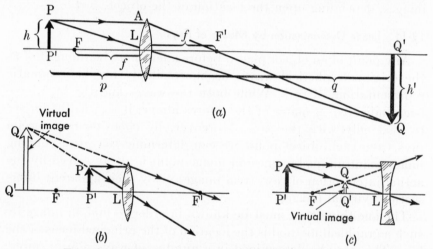

FIG. 12·15   Use of ray constructions to determine images.

plane QQ'. Because the whole figure is symmetric about the lens axis, inversion of the image takes place in the sidewise direction also. Hence, if the object has any extent in a direction perpendicular to the plane of the figure, right and left will be reversed, as well as up and down.

Figure 12·15b shows how to locate the image when an object is placed closer to a converging lens than the focal distance. You already know, from Fig. 12·12d, that this results in a virtual image. From the point of view of the ray construction the reason is that the ray through the lens center and the one passing through F' do not cross on the right side of the lens but diverge instead. However, they *appear* to come from some point Q located by projecting them backward until they cross. This point is the virtual image of the tip of the arrow, and the entire image is represented by the white arrow. It may be viewed by looking into the lens from the right.

In a similar way, the formation of an image (always virtual) by a diverging lens is sketched in Fig. 12·15c. Notice that in the situation represented by sketch a the object and image may be interchanged, while this is not true in b or c. If this is not evident to you, find the image of QQ' in each of the latter two cases, using the method described.

12·12   Lens Formulas; Examples

In every case of image formation described, we see from the similar triangles $PP'L$ and $QQ'L$ in the figures that

$$\frac{\text{Size of image}}{\text{Size of object}} = \frac{\text{distance of image from lens}}{\text{distance of object from lens}}$$

The first ratio is called the lateral magnification or simply the *magnification*. In symbols, using M to represent the magnification, p the object distance, and q the image distance,

$$M = \frac{h'}{h} = \frac{q}{p} \tag{12·3}$$

It is possible to put the method already described into algebraic form, so that the image position may be calculated rather than constructed graphically. In Fig. 12·15a the triangles ALF' and $QQ'F'$ are similar, and thus $h'/h = (q - f)/f$. Upon making use of Eq. (12·3), this relation becomes $q/p = (q - f)/f$. Cross-multiplying, dividing each term through by pqf, and transposing give, finally,

$$\frac{1}{p} + \frac{1}{q} = \frac{1}{f} \tag{12·4}$$

This relation can be shown to hold for *any* case of image formation by a thin lens, either converging or diverging, provided that the following conventions are observed:

1. Consider *f positive* for a *converging* lens and *negative* for a *diverging* lens.

2. The standard arrangement is taken to be object, lens, image, going from left to right in the diagram. If q is *negative,* the image lies to the *left* of the lens rather than to the right and is therefore virtual.

Examples: 1. The lens system of a certain portrait camera may be considered equivalent to a thin converging lens of focal length 12 in. How far behind the lens must the plate be located in order to receive the image of a person seated 5 ft in front of the lens? How large will the image be in comparison with the object?

Substituting in Eq. (12·4) gives[1]

$$\frac{1}{60} + \frac{1}{q} = \frac{1}{12} \qquad q = \frac{60 \times 12}{60 - 12} = 15 \text{ in.}$$

From Eq. (12·3), $M = {}^{15}\!/\!_{60} = \frac{1}{4}$; the image is one-fourth as large as the object.

2. When an object is placed 18 cm from a certain lens, its virtual image is formed 8 cm from the lens. What is the nature of the lens, and what is its focal length?

The fact that the image is virtual means that q is negative. From the lens equation

$$\frac{1}{18} - \frac{1}{8} = \frac{1}{f} \qquad f = \frac{8 \times 18}{8 - 18} = -14.4 \text{ cm}$$

The negative sign resulting for f shows that the lens is diverging.

12·13   Optical Instruments; Microscopes

Before concluding our survey of ray optics, a brief description of the operation of a few important and widely used optical instruments will be given.

Since the eye is the final element in many optical instruments, we consider first the use of a single converging lens in increasing the ability of the eye to examine the details of an object. The object to be studied is brought just within the focal distance of the lens, and the eye is placed as close behind the lens as convenient, in order to have a large field of view. An enlarged, erect virtual image of the object is formed by the lens (Fig. 12·15b). The optical system of the eye, acting like a converging lens, forms a final real image on the retina. A lens used in this way is called a *simple magnifier* or simple microscope. Because of the fact that a normal eye is able to see the details of an object most distinctly when its distance is about 10 in., the magnifier is usually adjusted so that the virtual image falls at this distance from the eye. The magnification will then be approximately $10/f$, where f is the focal length of the lens in inches. In effect, the magnifier enables one to bring the object close to the eye and yet observe it comfortably. Because of the distortions produced by a simple lens, magnifications exceeding about 30 are not practicable with such a magnifier.

Whenever high magnification is desired, the *compound microscope* is used. This instrument, invented at the close of the six-

[1] In connection with numerical examples using the lens equation, see the footnote on p. 304.

teenth century, consists of two converging lenses, a so-called *objective* of very short focal length and an *eyepiece* (or *ocular*) of moderate focal length. In practice, each of these consists of a combination of several lenses in order to reduce distortions and defects of the image. The object to be examined is placed just beyond the principal focus of the objective, producing a somewhat enlarged real

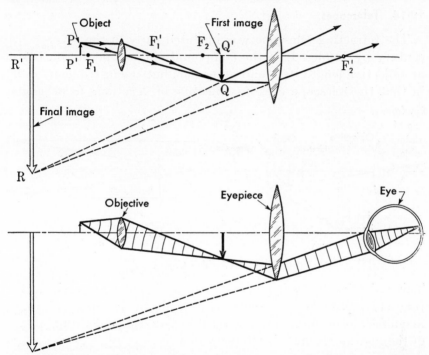

FIG. 12·16 Ray diagram (*above*) and path of waves (*below*) for compound microscope.

image within the tube of the instrument. This image is then examined with the eyepiece, the latter being used as a simple magnifier. Figure 12·16 shows both the ray diagram and the path of the waves for determining the image. The real image QQ' is, of course, not caught on a screen but is merely formed in space, the light going on to meet the eyepiece. The eyepiece is moved up until QQ' lies just within the principal focus F_2. The final image RR' is virtual, enlarged, and reversed with respect to the object. It is possible to show that, with the instrument adjusted to put the final image at a distance of 10 in., the magnifying power is approximately

$$M_{\text{micro}} = \frac{q}{p}\frac{10}{f} \tag{12·5}$$

where p and q are the distances of object and first image, respectively, from the objective and f is the focal length of the eyepiece, all distances being measured in inches. In practice, the largest magnifications employed are about 2000. Much larger magnification may be obtained by means of the electron microscope (page 353).

12·14 Telescopes

The refracting telescope was invented early in the seventeenth century by Kepler. Like the compound microscope, it consists of an objective lens system and an ocular; but the instruments differ in that the telescope uses an objective of very long focal length.

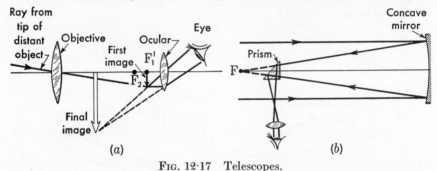

FIG. 12·17   Telescopes.

This objective forms a real image of a distant object within the tube (Fig. 12·17a). The ocular, used again in the role of a simple magnifier, forms an inverted virtual image. The magnifying power of the instrument may be shown to be

$$M_{\text{tele}} = \frac{f_o}{f_e} \tag{12·6}$$

where f_o is the focal length of the objective and f_e is that of the eyepiece. This relation suggests that M may be made as large as desired by choosing a very long focus objective and a very short focus ocular. The Yerkes telescope has an objective whose focal length is about 760 in.; with an ocular of focal length 0.2 in. a magnification of nearly 4000 would result. Other factors, however, drastically limit the values employed in practice, and magnifications exceeding 1500 to 2000 are seldom used in astronomy.

Besides its function in magnifying a distant object, thus making its detailed structure more apparent, there is another feature of the telescope that is often of greatest importance in astronomy. This is the *light-gathering power* of the instrument, one of the main reasons for making telescopes with objectives of large diameter. The brightness of the image formed in a telescope depends on the amount of light collected by the objective. This quantity, in turn, is proportional to the area of the objective. Since the area of a circle is proportional to the square of its diameter, the amount of light energy collected (from a given object located at a given distance) by the objective of the 200-in. telescope at Mt. Palomar is about $(200/0.2)^2 = 1,000,000$ times as much as with the unaided eye (pupil diameter 0.2 in.). Thus stars far too faint to be seen with the eye alone are visible through a large telescope.

Newton seems to have been the first person to construct a *reflecting telescope* in which a concave mirror replaces the objective lens system. One arrangement is shown in Fig. 12·17*b*. A reflector has many advantages over a refractor, including better quality of the image, lower cost, and greater mechanical stability. The optical principle is exactly the same as that of the refractor except that the first image is formed by reflection from the concave mirror.[1] At present, most of the larger astronomical telescopes use concave mirrors.

The remarks made above concerning light-gathering power apply to reflecting as well as to refracting telescopes. In fact, the 200-in. telescope is a reflector.

SUMMARY

Refraction is the change in direction of waves occurring when they pass through a nonuniform medium. On going obliquely from one medium into another, a ray is bent *toward* the normal to the dividing surface if the second medium is *denser*. It is bent *away* from the normal if the second medium is *thinner*.

Law of refraction: The angles of incidence and refraction are related by the *index of refraction* of the second medium with respect to the first. The index of a single substance is referred to a vacuum (index equals unity) and is numerically equal to the ratio

$$\frac{\text{Speed of light in a vacuum}}{\text{Speed of light in the medium}}$$

For an exact statement of the law of refraction, see page 199.

[1] Curved mirrors are capable of forming images of the same variety as those produced by lenses. A study of the geometry of the ray diagrams shows that a *concave* mirror can serve the same purposes as a converging (*convex*) lens, while a *convex* mirror corresponds to a diverging (*concave*) lens. Equations (12·3) and (12·4) apply to curved mirrors as well as to lenses. For a mirror, f is half the radius of curvature of the mirror surface.

Huygens' principle: Every point on a wave front may be considered a new source of waves. Any subsequent wave front may be determined by constructing a surface that just touches the set of wavelets.

Lenses: A *converging* lens brings rays together; a *diverging* lens fans them out. A converging lens forms a real image of an object placed beyond the principal focus and a virtual image of one located inside the focus. Diverging lenses always form virtual images of light coming from a point source.

The image of an object formed by a lens may be found graphically by means of the ray construction or algebraically by using the lens equation

$$\frac{1}{p} + \frac{1}{q} = \frac{1}{f}$$

An optical instrument is usually a combination of several elements (lenses, mirrors). The image formed by one element acts as the object for the next element. The final image is often formed by the human eye.

READING REFERENCES

1. Cajori, F.: "A History of Physics," Macmillan, New York, 1929. Newton's views on the nature of refraction are briefly outlined on pp. 93–96.
2. Moulton, F. R., and J. J. Schifferes: "The Autobiography of Science," Doubleday, New York, 1945. Huygens' principle, pp. 153–158.
3. Freeman, Ira M.: "Invitation to Experiment," Dutton, New York, 1940. Chapters 17 and 18 present some of the topics of the preceding and present chapters from the point of view of simple experiments.
4. Minnaert, M.: "Light and Colour in the Open Air," Dover, New York, 1954. A fascinating exposition of hundreds of observations which the reader can repeat with little or no equipment other than his eyes. Read Chaps. III and IV at this point.[1]
5. Bowen, I. S.: The 200-inch Camera, in "The Scientists Speak," pp. 41–44, Gaer, New York, 1947.

EXERCISES

1. The corpuscular theory of refraction postulates an **attraction** between the light corpuscles and the denser medium. But some of the incident light is always reflected, implying at the same time a **repulsion** of the corpuscles. Discuss this difficulty of the theory. Did Newton have an explanation for it? Consult Ref. 1.

2. In the mirage effect called "looming," light waves are refracted by

---

[1] This will provide helpful information for answering questions raised in some of the exercises below.

the air in the same way as the sound waves in Fig. 12·7a. Explain. In what direction will the source of the waves appear to be with respect to the observer? See Ref. 4.

3. If the atmosphere decreases in density with distance above the earth's surface, how will this affect the path of light coming to us from a star? Will the star seem to lie above or below its true position in the sky? Look up the magnitude of this correction.

4. Explain the "pools of water" seen on a hot day in approaching a slight rise in the road.

5. An object seen under water or through glass appears to be closer to the surface. It can be shown that this apparent depth is equal to the real depth divided by the index of refraction. Check this roughly by looking straight down into a pail or jar of water, placing your finger at a point on the side of the vessel that seems to be at the same level as the bottom, and measuring the two depths.

6. A beam of light whose wavelength in air is 7×10^{-5} cm enters a block of dense glass whose index of refraction is 1.68. What is the wavelength inside the glass?

7. Tell why a total-reflection prism is preferable to a silvered mirror in performing reflections in an optical instrument. What effect has the presence of dirt on the total-reflecting surface of a prism?

8. Does a lens have to be as tall as the object in order to form a complete image of the object? (Think of the relative sizes of a camera lens and a person who is to be photographed.) Refer to page 191, where the corresponding question was raised concerning the plane mirror.

9. What would be the optical properties of a double convex lens made of a material having a *smaller* index of refraction than the surrounding medium—say, a convex lens-shaped cavity in a block of glass?

10. With the aid of ray diagrams similar to Fig. 12·15 fill in the remainder of the following table:

	Location of object	Location of image	Character of image	Size of image
1. Converging lens	Beyond F	Beyond F'	Real, inverted	Enlarged if p is less than $2f$ Diminished if p exceeds $2f$
	Within F			
2. Diverging lens	Beyond F			
	Within F			

11. A lantern slide 2 in. high is projected onto a screen 18 ft away, a lens of focal length 5 in. being used. How tall must the screen be in order to accommodate the entire image?

12. An erect image formed by a certain lens is one-fourth as tall as the object and is located 16 in. from the lens. Find the focal length of the lens.

13. Find graphically the position of the image formed by a diverging lens of focal length 20 cm of an object placed 40 cm from the lens.

14. The first astronomical telescope, devised by Galileo, was really an opera glass. Look up the optical description of the opera glass, or Galilean telescope, and draw a ray diagram.

15. An object and a screen are placed 100 cm apart. At what *two* points between them can a converging lens of focal length 9 cm be placed to form a sharp image on the screen? Compute the lateral magnification in each case.

16. A diverging lens of focal length -10 in. forms a virtual image of an object 1 in. high. The object is placed 30 in. from the lens. Compute the position of the image and its height.

17. A refracting telescope has an objective of focal length 90 cm and an ocular of focal length 3 cm. How far apart must these lenses be placed when the instrument is focused (*a*) on the moon, (*b*) on a house 20 m away?

18. The brightness of the image formed by a camera lens is directly proportional to the area of the lens aperture (which determines the amount of light energy entering the camera) and inversely proportional to the area of the image (the surface over which this light energy is spread). In terms of lens aperture diameter d and focal length f the brightness turns out to be proportional to d^2/f^2, and hence the exposure time is approximately proportional to f^2/d^2 or to R^2, where $R = f/d$ is the relative aperture. If a certain picture can be taken by a lens of maximum $R = 3.5$ with an exposure of 0.01 sec, what exposure time will be needed when the lens is "stopped down" to $R = 11$?

Chapter 13

DISPERSION AND SPECTRA

The ancients were aware of the brilliant colors produced when sunlight passes through various transparent gems and crystals. In refraction experiments such as those described in Chap. 12 the refracted light is usually found to be colored. Newton, troubled by the objectionable fringes of color surrounding images in a refracting telescope, was led to perform a series of crucial experiments that not only cleared up the question of the nature of color but initiated one of the most important and useful branches of physics.

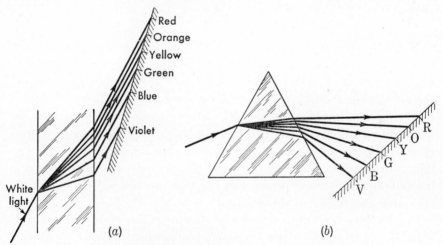

FIG. 13·1   Dispersion by a plate and by a prism.

13·1   Newton's Experiments on Dispersion

If a narrow beam of white light is incident obliquely on a thick plate of glass (Fig. 13·1a), the patch of light produced where the transmitted beam strikes a card is found to be colored. In the order in which they fall, the colors are red, orange, yellow, green, blue, and violet, one merging imperceptibly into the next. The spot of light, in fact, resembles a cross section of a rainbow. Inside the glass the rays fan out as shown in the figure, red being deviated least, violet most. In the figure the angle between the extreme rays is exaggerated for clarity; actually it amounts to only about ½ deg.

The spreading out in angle of the colors produced is called *dispersion;* the colored band of light observed is called a *spectrum.* In Newton's experiments, performed when he was twenty-four and a student at Cambridge, he used a prism to obtain a larger angular spread of the rays. In the case sketched in Fig. 13·1b the angle between the red and violet rays amounts to less than 2 deg, but by casting the spectrum on a screen that is highly inclined to the refracted rays a spectrum of considerable width can be produced.

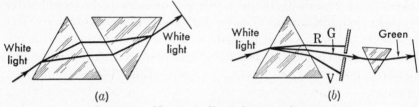

(a)   (b)

Fɪɢ. 13·2   Newton's dispersion experiments.

Next Newton placed another similar prism behind the first, but reversed in position, and found that the rays were reunited into a colorless patch of light (Fig. 13·2a). Again he cast a spectrum on a screen having a small hole in it and placed a second prism just behind this opening (Fig. 13·2b). His intention was to see whether or not a single color, passing through the hole, could be dispersed further by the second prism. Nothing of this kind occurred; green light, for example, coming through the aperture was deviated (refracted) by the second prism, but the transmitted light was still of the same green hue as the original.

Finally Newton showed that the various colors composing white light do not in any way react with each other but simply contribute to the resulting mixture. He did this by inserting a narrow obstacle in the spectrum formed by a prism in order to hold back a single color, say red. When the remaining light was allowed to pass through a second prism, red was found to be completely absent in the resulting spectrum.

13·2   Nature of White Light

From the experiments mentioned and a number of refinements and extensions of these which he carried out[1] Newton concluded that *white light consists of a mixture of colors,* the various colors being refracted different amounts in a transparent material. This means that the index of refraction of a given substance is really slightly different for each color—least for red and progressively greater for orange, yellow, green, blue, violet. It follows, according to the wave theory, that *the various colors travel with different speeds in matter,* red having the greatest speed and violet the least. The difference is not large, however: in glass the speed of red light is only about 1 per cent greater than that of violet.

The adherents of the corpuscular theory attempted to explain dispersion by assuming that each spectral color consists of corpuscles of a given size—an assumption that could not be checked by observations. It was established later that what the eye perceives as the *color* of a particular part of the spectrum is physically represented by the *wavelength* of that radiation. The wavelength is greatest for light at the extreme red end of the spectrum, amounting to about 7×10^{-5} cm and decreasing progressively through the sequence of colors to about 4×10^{-5} cm at the extreme violet. Thus, although Newton did not talk of wavelength, what he found is essentially that white light consists of a mixture of a great many different wavelengths and that the index of refraction of an ordinary transparent substance is slightly different for the various wavelengths. In general then, the meaning of *dispersion is the variation of the speed of waves with their wavelength.*

In a vacuum there is no dispersion of light waves whatever—all colors (or wavelengths) travel with the same speed. This is proved observationally by the fact that when the moon passes in front of a distant star, cutting off its light from our view, the occultation is sudden and shows no color effects. If the various colors constituting the light of the star were to travel with different speeds in empty space, this would not be the case—the star would appear to change color as it disappears. Sound waves ordinarily show no disper-

---

[1] Newton's brilliant work on dispersion is a model of original, well-considered scientific investigation. You will find it highly interesting to read his own account of some of this work (his first scientific publication), for example, in Ref. 3 at the end of the chapter.

sion, as proved by the fact that musical sounds of different pitch coming from a distance arrive exactly in their proper time sequence. On the other hand, waves on the surface of water exhibit dispersion, for their speed is found to depend on the wavelength.

13·3 Chromatic Aberration of a Lens

At the beginning of the chapter it was mentioned that Newton was led to his dispersion experiments when he noticed the annoying fringes of color surrounding the images in a refracting telescope. This difficulty, usually noted when any simple lens is used, is called *chromatic aberration* (literally, "color abnormality"). It results from the fact that a lens not only changes the curvature of wave fronts but at the same time acts like a prism, producing dispersion as well. To see this, consider rays of white light passing through the

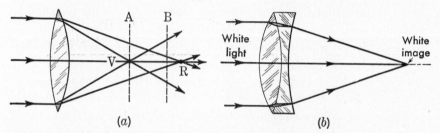

(a)   (b)

Fig. 13·3   Chromatic and achromatic images.

outer parts of a simple lens (Fig. 13·3a). The inclined sides of the lens make it act in every respect like a prism, and dispersion takes place as shown. As a result, there is a slightly different focus for every color, and there is no position where a screen can be placed to receive a perfectly sharp image. Besides, the image obtained will always be surrounded with a colored halo—red on the outside if the screen is placed at some point such as A, violet if at B.

Newton believed that it was inherently impossible to get rid of this defect—a mistaken conviction that had its good side because it led him to devise the reflecting telescope as a substitute for the refractor. What he did not realize was that different types of glass may produce quite different degrees of *spreading of colors* (dispersion) and yet have the power to cause about the same *bending* (same index of refraction) and that by combining two lenses made of glasses having different dispersive powers the color defects of one could be made practically to nullify those of the other. Such a combination, called an *achromatic doublet,* was first made available nearly a century after Newton's dispersion experiments.

Figure 13·3*b* shows that an achromatic doublet consists of a converging lens of lower dispersive glass cemented to a weaker diverging lens of higher dispersive glass, the net effect being that of a converging lens. In order to correct chromatic and various other defects inherent in simple lenses, good-quality camera lenses

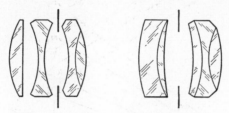

FIG. 13·4   Photographic objectives.

usually consist of combinations of several elements. Two types of well-designed camera objectives are diagramed in Fig. 13·4. It will be noted that both achromatic combinations and simple lenses are used.

13·4   The Rainbow

This is probably the most widely known example of dispersion in all of nature. If, after a shower, the rays of the sun fall upon slowly settling water droplets, the observer will see one or more concentric colored arcs in a direction opposite to the sun. The *primary,* or brightest, bow is red at its outer edge and violet at its inner, the intermediate spectral colors falling in proper order between these places. It is formed by light that is refracted upon entering a drop, internally reflected at the back surface, and refracted again upon leaving. At the same time the light is dispersed within the drop so that rays of the various colors leave at different angles (Fig. 13·5), but there is one angle at which each color emerges most strongly because its rays come out of the drop parallel to each other. The result is that the observer sees a given color in a particular direction with respect to the sun's rays—about 42 deg for the red and 40 deg for the violet. Since this condition can be fulfilled in any plane passing through the line joining the sun and the observer, what is seen is a circular arc lying in a plane perpendicular to this line. Enormous numbers of individual drops contribute to the total effect at any instant.

A **secondary bow,** considerably fainter than the primary and with the order of colors reversed, can often be seen outside the primary. As the diagram shows, this bow is formed by light that has been *twice* reflected inside each drop. The red edge makes an

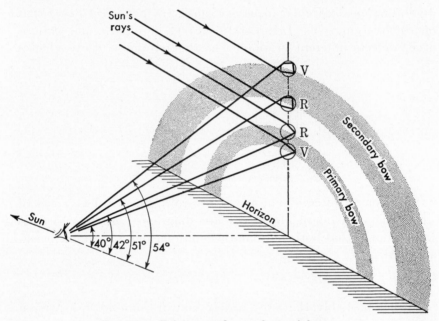

FIG. 13·5　Primary and secondary rainbows.

angle of about 51 deg with the sun's direction, the violet about 54 deg. Additional bows, even fainter than the secondary, are sometimes observed.[1] Their explanation is based on the interference of light (Chap. 14).

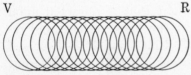

FIG. 13·6　Overlapping of images in a spectrum.

13·5 Prism Spectroscope

In Newton's simple arrangement for producing a spectrum (Fig. 13·1b), what is seen is a series of overlapping images of the round opening through which the original beam of light enters— one such image for each wavelength of light present. Each of these images will have its characteristic color; if the incoming light is white, there will be an infinite number of such circles, as suggested in Fig. 13·6. In all parts of this spectrum there will be overlapping

[1] For a detailed description of rainbow phenomena, see Ref. 4.

and consequent mixing of colors except at the very ends, where "pure" colors will be seen. This overlapping may be avoided by replacing the round aperture by one that is very narrow in the sidewise direction—a *slit* perhaps no more than a thousandth of an inch wide. The addition of two converging lenses serves to form a good image of the slit on the screen.

The entire arrangement, one form of which is diagramed in Fig. 13·7, is called a prism *spectrograph.* It is usually enclosed in a light-tight box, and a photographic film or plate replaces the screen so that a permanent record of the spectrum can be obtained. If only visual observation is desired, the screen or film is replaced by an ocular, as shown in the diagram, and the instrument is then

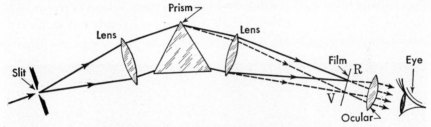

FIG. 13·7   Spectrograph and spectroscope.

called a *spectroscope.* Thus it is the function of a spectrograph (or -scope) to form *an image of the slit for each wavelength* present in the incoming light. Each image of this kind is called a *spectrum line.*

13·6   Continuous Spectra

When sunlight is allowed to fall on the slit of a spectroscope, the spectrum is found to be a continuous band of color (except for a refinement to be described below), with the several colors falling in the order already mentioned. In view of what has been said, this means that the light radiated by the sun consists of an imperceptibly graded set of wavelengths. The spectrum obtained from such radiation is called a *continuous spectrum.* It is found that the light from a filament lamp also gives a continuous spectrum, and so does the glow from a crucible of molten iron or glass or from an arc lamp or even a candle flame.

In general it is found that a *continuous spectrum results when a solid, a liquid, or a gas under high pressure is heated to incandescence.* Thus the glowing tip of an arc-lamp carbon is an incandescent solid object, the filament of a lamp is a piece of solid metal at white heat, and the light from a candle is due to minute particles of solid carbon; molten iron is, of course, a high-temperature liquid, and the body of the sun is a mixture of glowing gases at high pressure. All continuous spectra are *alike* in the sense that there are no gaps or other characteristic markings.

13·7 Bright-line Spectra

If, now, the spectrum of a *gas at low pressure* is examined, the appearance is entirely different. In place of a continuous band of color a characteristic set of distinct and separate spectrum lines is seen against a dark background. In contrast with the continuous spectrum, this is called a *bright-line spectrum*. The occurrence of a line spectrum signifies the fact that the source sends out a limited set of wavelengths of light and no others.

FIG. 13·8 Bright-line spectra. *Above*, hydrogen; *below*, potassium.

The gas may be caused to radiate light by maintaining it at a high temperature (carbon vaporized in an arc or salt in a flame), by passing a spark between metal rods, or by sending a high-voltage electric current through it (neon or other gas-filled tube, page 186).

Two typical examples of bright-line spectra are represented in Fig. 13·8. Hydrogen has one of the simplest spectra, with an obvious regularity in the arrangement of its line. The spectra of other elements usually consist of a number of "series" of lines of this type, often superposed. We return to this topic in Chap. 20. In a given spectroscope, each line always falls at a designated place in the field of view and has the color corresponding to that place in the spectrum. When a spectrograph is used, the negative obtained is, of course, in black and white. The important thing is not the color of a line but its wavelength, corresponding to its position in the spectrum.

The observed radiations are now known to be connected with energy changes on the part of electrons and of atoms in the source of light. In a gas at low pressure the atoms are able to emit their characteristic vibrations unhindered, while in a highly compacted material (solid, liquid, or dense gas), the neighboring atoms disturb this process and a continuous rather than a line spectrum results.

By taking the wavelength of light at about the middle of the visible range to be 5×10^{-5} cm and using the wave relation $V = n\lambda$, the frequency of vibration of the waves is readily found to be $(3 \times 10^{10})/(5 \times 10^{-5}) = 6 \times 10^{14}$ per second. We shall find later that this is not identical with the frequency of motion of the electrons and atoms emitting the light but is connected with their motion in a more complicated way.

In order to avoid inconveniently small numbers for specifying wavelengths of light, a special unit has been adopted. It is named for the Swedish spectroscopist A. J. Ångström, who identified many substances in the sun by means of their spectra.

$$1A = 10^{-8} \text{ cm}$$

Thus the wavelengths of the extreme red and extreme violet ends of the visible spectrum may be expressed as 7000 and 4000A, respectively.

13·8 Spectrochemical Analysis

By studying the spectra produced by vaporizing various substances in a gas flame, Kirchhoff and Bunsen concluded, about 1860, that the presence of a given substance may be recognized by means of its spectrum.[1] They found that each chemical element, when stimulated to give off light, produces a spectrum consisting of a definite pattern of bright lines. This pattern is different for each element and may be used to identify its presence in the source of light. Compare this with the fact, already mentioned, that the continuous spectra of various substances are all alike. A block of iron and a tungsten lamp filament at the same temperature give

[1] Gustav Kirchhoff and Robert Bunsen, professors at the University of Heidelberg, Germany, constituted an ideal research team. The former was a distinguished mathematical physicist and the latter a gifted experimenter in both physical and chemical fields.

continuous spectra that are indistinguishable except perhaps for very slight differences in brightness in certain regions.

In practice, some qualifications present themselves. In a mixture the spectrum of the most abundant element is usually the strongest, and elements present in very small amounts may show only a few lines of their spectra in such circumstances. Also, the nature of the source often determines the extent to which the spectrum develops. In fairly low temperature sources, such as flames, only a few elements show any spectrum whatever, and then only one or two of the strongest lines may appear. The spectra of the same elements when produced in an arc or in a high-voltage spark may contain hundreds of lines.

In spite of such practical difficulties the identification of chemical elements by means of their spectra has become one of the most valuable procedures in experimental science, with applications to industry, medicine, criminology, astronomy (see below), etc.

Techniques have been developed for making *quantitative* spectrochemical analyses, so that a chemist not only can tell the nature of an "unknown" substance from the pattern of lines in the spectrum but can determine within satisfactory limits the percentage composition from the intensities of the lines. Moreover, the analysis by means of the spectrum usually takes much less time than chemical methods. This is especially important in industry. In a steel mill, for example, repeated determinations of the composition of a batch of molten metal may be made while its processing continues.

13·9   Absorption-line Spectra

Almost half a century before Kirchhoff and Bunsen were laying the foundations of spectrochemical analysis, Joseph Fraunhofer, a Bavarian optician and experimenter, discovered that the spectrum of sunlight was not really continuous but was crossed by numerous *dark lines* located in definite positions. He measured the wavelengths of principal dark lines and noted that the same pattern was to be seen in the spectrum of moonlight or of light from the planets. Some of the most prominent of these dark lines, together with the designation given them by Fraunhofer and still used by astronomers today, are sketched in Fig. 13·9. At the present time, more than 20,000 such lines have been mapped in the spectrum of the sun.

The explanation of the dark lines was not forthcoming until Kirchhoff took up his work on spectra. Fraunhofer had noticed that the spectrum of a candle flame contained a bright yellow line (actually two lines close together) which coincided in position exactly with the dark line labeled *D* in his solar spectrum. Kirchhoff identified the yellow line as belonging to the element sodium. But he went further—he sent a beam of white light through a flame heavily charged with salt (sodium chloride) and found that a dark

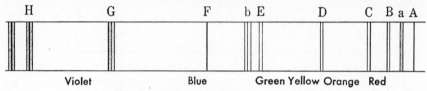

FIG. 13·9 Principal Fraunhofer lines.

line appeared precisely where the sodium flame alone had previously given a bright line (Fig. 13·10).

After experimenting in a similar way with the spectra of other chemical elements, Kirchhoff drew his interpretation of what was happening. When white light enters the flame containing sodium vapor, all the vibrations pass through it practically undiminished except those whose frequency happens to coincide with natural frequencies of the sodium atom—that is, with frequencies that

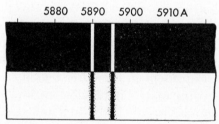

FIG. 13·10 Yellow lines of sodium in emission and in absorption.

this atom can emit. The process, otherwise stated, is one of *resonance* (page 172). The sodium atoms, having absorbed energy from the white light at certain definite frequencies, reradiate it; but since there is an equal chance that this energy will be thrown out again in any direction, the light going in the direction of the original beam is weakened at the particular places in the spectrum corresponding to these frequencies. The result is the observed pattern of dark lines on a bright background—an *absorption-line* spectrum, as it is called. The lines are not absolutely black but appear dark in contrast with the surrounding continuous spectrum. Figure 13·11 gives a schematic representation of the process.

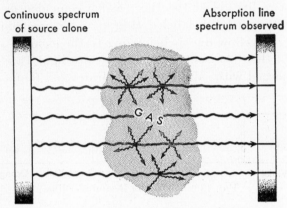

FIG. 13·11   Origin of absorption lines.

13·10   Further Applications to Astronomy

Not only the spectrum of the sun but the spectra of most types of stars are absorption spectra.[1] It is known that the stars, including the sun, consist of incandescent gases—hotter and denser in the interior, cooler and more tenuous near the surface. Light coming from the interior originates in a dense gas at high temperature, and so is continuous radiation. When this passes through the cooler, thinner outer envelope, those frequencies corresponding to atoms present in the outer layers are absorbed and the light coming on to an observer on earth gives an absorption-line spectrum by which the gases present in the outer region can be identified.

Thus the spectrum makes it possible to find out the chemical composition of an inaccessible body such as a star. Over two-thirds of the elements known on earth have been positively identified in the sun and in the stars by means of their spectra, so that on the whole the universe must be made up of familiar materials. In some cases, such as that of helium, the spectrum indicated the presence of a new element in the sun before the substance had been detected and isolated on earth.

---

[1] The spectra are obtained by using the objective of a large telescope to gather light from a star and concentrate it on the slit of the spectrograph, which replaces the ocular of the telescope.

13·11 Band Spectra

In addition to continuous and line spectra, another kind of spectrum often observed consists of an extremely large number of lines that under low resolution give the appearance of fluted bands, as shown in Fig. 13·12a. In high-dispersion instruments each band is seen to consist of individual lines that are progressively brighter and closer together, terminating abruptly at the band "head" (Fig. 13·12b and c).

The spacing of individual lines and of the bands themselves is characteristic of the substance producing them. Bands are found

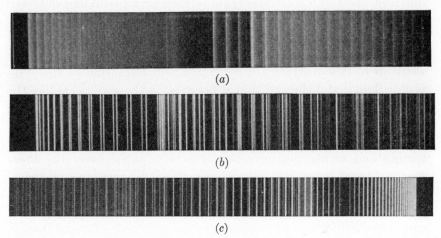

(a)

(b)

(c)

Fig. 13·12   Band spectra. (a) A band system. (b) and (c) Details of individual bands. (From plates by Prof. J. Francis Jenkins.)

only when the light source is known to contain intact **molecules** of one or more chemical compounds, and the source of the bands has been traced to the motion of the atoms constituting the molecules or to combinations of this with the motion of electrons belonging to the atoms. Thus the appearance of its band spectrum indicates the presence of a given compound.

Bands occur both in emission and in absorption—more often in the latter, for many compounds that decompose at the high temperatures prevailing in intense light sources can exist in cooler bodies where absorption takes place. Thus relatively few compounds have been identified in the sun, where high temperatures break most compounds down into their constituent atoms.

In some light sources one may find the band spectrum of a

compound superimposed on the line spectra of some or all of the constituent elements. In such cases the process of identification becomes complicated but not necessarily impossible. The study of band spectra has revealed much concerning the structure of molecules and the nature of the forces holding them together.

13·12   Infra-red Radiation

The radiations emitted by light sources are not confined to the visible range of wavelengths but extend beyond this region on both sides. About 1800, William Herschel[1] placed a thermometer in different parts of a solar spectrum formed by a prism and detected a temperature rise even when the bulb was placed in the dark region beyond the red end. He correctly concluded that radiation was present here as well as in the visible portion of the spectrum; he went on to demonstrate the reflection and refraction of this "invisible light" and showed that it behaved in these respects like the ordinary visible kind. The range of wavelengths beyond the red end of the visible spectrum is called the *infra-red* region.

Later workers had available much more sensitive means for detecting and measuring infra-red radiation, particularly the *thermocouple* and *bolometer,* which detect heat by means of electrical effects. The latter instrument can respond to a temperature change of less than a millionth of a degree. Special photographic plates can be prepared that are able to record infra-red waves as long as 12,000A or more, making photography possible even in complete darkness.

Optical glass will transmit wavelengths only up to about 15,-000A, absorbing all those of greater value. If it is desired to work beyond this point, the prism and any lenses used must be made of quartz or, for the extreme infra-red, of rock salt. It has been found possible to measure waves as long as 1.07×10^6A, or slightly over 0.1 mm, in the light from hot bodies.

13·13   Ideal Thermal Radiation

It has already been mentioned that an incandescent solid body gives a continuous visible spectrum. This spectrum extends beyond the bounds of the visible, particularly into the infra-red, and in almost all cases the greater part of the radiation falls in this latter range. Figure 13·13 shows the type of radiation curve ob-

[1] German-English astronomer; discoverer of the planet Uranus.

tained from a solid or liquid sample of matter—say, a metal—at various temperatures. At high temperatures, all metals are very nearly *ideal radiators*. This means that, at any given temperature, the radiation curve is the same for all.

The amount of energy that is radiated varies markedly with the wavelength, each curve having a *maximum* at a definite place in the spectrum. As the temperature goes up, not only does the total amount of radiation increase as shown by the greater height of the whole curve, but the wavelength at which the maximum

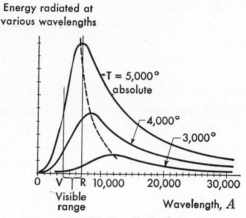

Fɪɢ. 13·13   Ideal radiation curves.

occurs is observed to shift progressively toward *shorter* wavelengths. For an ideal radiator it is known that the product of the wavelength of the maximum radiation λ_M and the absolute temperature T of the body is equal to a constant. Thus, with the wavelength measured in angstrom units and the temperature in degrees absolute, it is found that

$$\lambda_M T = 2.885 \times 10^7 \qquad (13\cdot1)$$

This law provides us with an excellent way of measuring high temperatures, useful not only in the laboratory but in astronomy, also. For example, solar-radiation measurements, after correction for the absorption effects of the earth's atmosphere, are found to fall approximately on an ideal curve whose maximum energy lies at a wavelength of about 5000A. By Eq. (13·1) the temperature of the sun's surface must then be $(2.885 \times 10^7)/5000$, or about 5800° abs. In this way, surface temperatures as high as 20,000° abs have been measured for some of the "blue-white" stars.

In Chap. 20 you will learn how the attempts to explain the form of the energy curve of an ideal thermal radiator led to the development of the branch of scientific thought known as the "quantum theory."

13·14 The Ultraviolet Region

At about the same time that Herschel noted the extension of the spectrum beyond the red, Ritter and others found that photographic materials placed beyond the spectrum at the violet end were affected by a radiation falling there. This radiation, consisting of wavelengths shorter than those of visible light, constitutes the *ultraviolet region.*

Glass prisms and lenses allow wavelengths down to about 3000A to pass, quartz will transmit ultraviolet radiation down to about 1800A, and fluor spar (calcium fluoride) is transparent to nearly 1000A. However, it was over half a century before investigators realized that absorption by the gelatin of the photographic plate and by the air prevented investigation below 2000A. By using special plates and vacuum spectrographs, the range available to experimentation has since been pushed down to about 20A.

In addition to its photographic and other chemical effects, ultraviolet radiation may be detected and measured by its ability to produce *fluorescence* in suitable materials. Numerous substances —petroleum oil, uranium glass, chlorophyll, etc.—have this ability to emit light of their own when exposed to radiation. In this process the atoms of the material absorb certain wavelengths of the incident radiation and reemit the energy, usually at longer wavelengths. The fluorescent lamps in common use are a practical application of this phenomenon (page 186). If the emission of light persists for some time after the stimulating rays have been cut off, the material is said to be *phosphorescent.* The coating materials used in fluorescent-lamp tubes show this effect to some extent (notice that the glow is still faintly visible for some time after the light is switched off). Fluorescence and phosphorescence, collectively called *luminescence,* are forms of radiation not associated with heat.

The biological effects of ultraviolet radiation have been intensively studied in recent decades. At sea level the atmosphere absorbs almost all solar radiations shorter than about 2800A. However, to compensate for this, artificial "sun lamps"—usually mercury arcs in quartz tubes—can be used therapeutically, as in treating rickets. Ultraviolet irradiation also has the ability to produce vitamin D in the skin. The lethal effect of mercury-arc radiations on certain harmful bacteria is utilized in sterilizing foods, or the air in operating rooms.

13·15 The Complete Radiation Spectrum

With the description of the infra-red and ultraviolet we have extended the spectrum over a range about 350 times as wide as the visible region. But this is not the end of the story. Radiations that are 100 million times longer than the extreme red are well known to you in the form of radio waves; others, given off in subatomic transformations, are 10 million times shorter in wavelength than the violet!

In 1888, Hertz succeeded in producing by electrical means waves that could be reflected, refracted, etc., and otherwise made to show all the properties of ordinary light. Their wavelength was found to be much greater than that of the longest infra-red radiation (0.1 mm) described above. Subsequently, others were able to generate electrical waves shorter than 0.1 mm, which could be detected not only by electrical means but by their *heating effect* as well. In principle, there is no upper limit to the length of electrical waves that can be produced. Waves several miles long have been used experimentally.

Below the ultraviolet region we come to the *X rays,* produced by suddenly stopping rapidly moving electrons in a special vacuum tube. X rays, too, were found to have the attributes of light waves. Their unique and important properties warrant a more detailed description later (Chap. 19). Waves whose length is a few hundred angstrom units can be produced either from the optical side by means of an electric spark or from the X-ray side by means of an X-ray tube.

Similar to X rays but more penetrating are the so-called *γ rays*[1] emitted in radioactive and other subatomic processes. These, too, have been shown to be of the same essential nature as light waves.

Because all the types of radiation described here were later shown to be waves of an electromagnetic character (page 332), we speak of the complete spectrum of *electromagnetic waves.* A

[1] To be read "gamma rays."

chart of this spectrum, given in Fig. 13·14, will repay close examination. Note that, while the various ranges are in general produced and detected in different ways and cause widely different effects, all consist of waves of the same fundamental nature; all travel in a vacuum with the speed $c = 3 \times 10^{10}$ cm/sec.

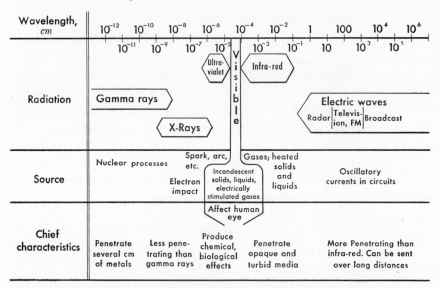

FIG. 13·14   Electromagnetic waves and their properties.

The unification represented by the electromagnetic spectrum is one of the most impressive facts in physics and represents, as has been indicated, an enormous amount of investigation. It must not be concluded that all emanations dealt with in physics are of the nature of electromagnetic waves. Later chapters will describe various types of rays consisting of streams of material particles—β rays, molecular rays, cosmic rays, and many others.

13·16   Doppler Effect for Light Waves

On page 163 it was pointed out that the relative motion of a source of waves and the observer results in an apparent change in the frequency of the waves as received. In the case of sound waves the effect is to alter the pitch of the perceived sound. The corresponding effect may be observed with light waves from astronomical bodies. It manifests itself as a *shift in position* of the lines in the spectrum of a star. Figure 13·15 shows part of the spectrum of a star (center strip). Adjoining, on each side, is the spectrum of a laboratory source producing some of the same lines. The displacement of the lines toward the violet—the higher frequency end of the spectrum—indicates that this star and the earth are approaching each other; a shift toward the red would mean recession.

The approximate formula stated in Eq. (10·2), page 164, holds here, with V replaced by c, the speed of light. Since wavelength rather than frequency is usually measured in spectroscopy, the

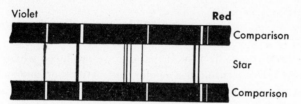

FIG. 13·15 Doppler shift of stellar spectrum lines.

fractional change in frequency appearing on the left-hand side of the equation is conveniently replaced by the fractional change in wavelength, making it read

$$\frac{\Delta\lambda}{\lambda} = \frac{v}{c} \tag{13·2}$$

By measuring the shift in wavelength of any line the relative speed of approach or recession can be computed. The application of Doppler's principle to astronomy was first suggested by Fizeau, and the earliest successful measurements were made by the English astronomer Huggins around 1870. For most stars the relative speeds are less than about 50 mi/sec. The method has been applied to the determination of the rate of rotation of the sun and of double stars, which revolve about each other. The spectra of the distant spiral nebulae ("island universes") show, almost without exception, very large line displacements toward the red; and these displacements are found to increase in proportion to the distances of the nebulae. The Doppler effect seems to be the most straightforward interpretation at this time; if it is responsible for the shift, it must mean that the nebulae are rushing apart in conformance with the idea of an *expanding universe.*

The spectroscope has become in some respects an even more important astronomical instrument than the telescope. For more of the fascinating story of *astrophysics*—the physics of the stars—look up Ref. 5.

SUMMARY

White light, consisting of a mixture of many different wavelengths, may be *dispersed* by passing it through a prism.

Continuous spectra originate in incandescent solids, liquids, or dense gases.

Line spectra originate in gases or vapors at low pressure, and the pattern of lines is characteristic of the atoms of the chemical *element* or elements emitting the light.

Band spectra are characteristic of molecules of chemical *compounds* that are caused to emit light.

Absorption spectra (usually lines or bands) are produced when light from a hot source passes through a cooler gas. Atoms or molecules in the latter absorb energy at their own characteristic frequencies. The process is one of *resonance.*

Infra-red radiation is any optical radiation that has a wavelength greater than that of visible light.

Ultraviolet radiation is any optical radiation whose wavelength is less than that of visible light.

The complete electromagnetic spectrum includes γ radiation, X radiation, and ultraviolet, visible, infra-red, and electric waves (see Fig. 13·14).

The optical Doppler effect is observed as a slight shift in position of spectrum lines from a source that is in motion relative to the observer—toward the *violet* if *approaching,* toward the *red* if *receding.*

READING REFERENCES

1. Bragg, W. H.: "The Universe of Light," Macmillan, New York, 1933. An excellent general reference for this and the following chapter. Read Chaps. III and VII at this point.
2. Freeman, Ira M.: "Invitation to Experiment," Dutton, New York, 1940. Dispersion, color, and related topics are described in Chap. 19.
3. Taylor, Lloyd W.: "Physics, the Pioneer Science," Houghton Mifflin, Boston, 1941. Read pp. 474–477 for Newton's own account of his dispersion experiments.
4. Minnaert, M.: "Light and Colour in the Open Air," Dover, New York, 1954. Read the description of rainbow phenomena, pp. 169–190.
5. Skilling, W. T., and R. S. Richardson: "Astronomy," Holt, New York, 1947; Krogdahl, W. S.: "The Astronomical Universe," Macmillan, New York, 1952; Payne-Gaposchkin, C.: "Introduction to Astronomy," Prentice-Hall, New York, 1954. Three good general texts on descriptive astronomy. Look up such topics as the sun's spectrum, spectra of the stars and nebulae, Doppler effect, expanding universe.

FILM

"The Nature of Color," Coronet Instructional Films. 16 mm, sound, 1 reel, in color only.

EXERCISES

1. Compute the speed of red light and of violet light in a piece of glass for which the values of refractive index are 1.60 and 1.62, respectively, for these two colors.

2. Discuss some advantages of a spectrograph over a spectroscope in terms of such considerations as the desirability of having a permanent record, the possibility of detecting very faint spectra and of observing and measuring spectra of transient sources of light (meteors, lightning, etc.), and any other factors that occur to you.

3. A heated solid first begins to glow visibly when its temperature approaches 1,000° abs. By examining the curves of Fig. 13·13 explain why a heated body appears first a dull red, then orange, yellow, and finally "white-hot."

4. What is the frequency in kilocycles of a radiobroadcasting station sending out waves 455 m long? (1 kc = 1000 cycles = 1000 vib/sec.)

5. An atom radiates a continuous train of light waves of $\lambda = 6000A$ for a time of 10^{-8} sec. How long is the wave train? How many waves does it contain?

6. How would you decide from a study of spectra whether the moon shines by reflected sunlight or by light of its own?

7. A number of the lines in the spectrum of the sun or of a star are really due to absorption by the gases of the earth's atmosphere. This has been confirmed recently by photographing spectra from a high-altitude rocket. Previously, however, this information came from a comparison of spectrograms taken when the source was high in the sky and again when it was near the horizon. Explain how this procedure could lead to the above conclusion.

8. In view of Eq. 10·2, page 164, is the actual wavelength shift (in angstrom units) the same for all the lines in the spectrum of a star receding from the earth? At which end of the spectrum is the actual line displacement greatest? If the star is not moving directly toward or away from the earth, what speed does v, as computed, represent?

9. A line of wavelength 6500A in the spectrum of a star is found to be displaced 1.3A toward the violet end of the spectrum. Is the star approaching or receding from the earth? At what speed?

10. The wavelengths of the two yellow lines in the spectrum of sodium vapor are 5890 and 5896A. How fast would a star containing sodium have to be moving relative to the earth for one of these lines to move to the normal position of the other?

Chapter 14

DIFFRACTION, INTERFERENCE, AND POLARIZATION OF LIGHT

14·1 Evidence for Diffraction

In discussing the nature of light in Chap. 11 it was pointed out (page 179) that, while water waves and sound waves are ordinarily observed to bend around barriers into the space beyond, special experiments are needed to show this effect for light. The Italian experimenter Grimaldi appears to have been the first to observe, around the middle of the seventeenth century, what he termed *diffraction* effects. Examining the shadow cast by an obstacle illuminated by sunlight coming through a pinhole, he discovered that the width of the shadow differed from what it should be according to the straight-line travel of light and that the edges of the shadow were marked by alternate light and dark bands. Newton repeated and refined Grimaldi's tests, but the true interpretation of the effect did not come until the beginning of the nineteenth century.

There are many situations where diffraction effects can be readily observed. You need only look at a distant light through the narrow space between two fingers held lightly in contact to see bands of light appearing behind the fingers where, according to straight-line travel, no light can get. Squinting through the eyelashes or looking through a handkerchief produces similar effects.

Diffraction, then, *is the sidewise spreading of waves after going past the edge of an obstacle or passing through a narrow aperture.* Narrow with respect to *what?* The answer is that the width of the aperture must not be too many times the wavelength of the light used if appreciable diffraction is to result. Thus a doorway acts as a "narrow slit" for sound waves (wavelength of a few feet) but is much too wide to produce appreciable diffraction with light waves.

The pattern of dark and light bands produced by diffraction at a single sharp edge (Fig. 14·1) will be noticeable only for short waves (light) but will be too "flat" to observe if the waves are long.

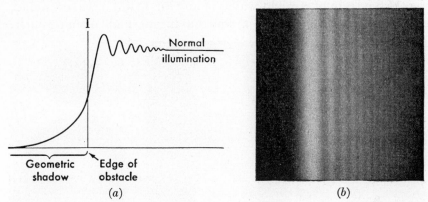

(a)   (b)

FIG. 14·1 Diffraction by a straight-edged obstacle. (*Courtesy of Prof. G. S. Monk.*)

14·2 Diffraction and Huygens' Principle

The principle proposed by Huygens that every point on a wave front may be considered the source of new waves (page 204) was revived by Young[1] early in the nineteenth century to explain diffraction phenomena in terms of waves. His work, to be described below, was received with great distrust, despite the fact that the French physicist and engineer Fresnel added the results of his own extensive diffraction experiments to those of Young to strengthen the case for the wave theory. Fresnel was able to explain in detail the diffraction band patterns observed when light passes through a single narrow slit or through a circular opening. At the same time, it was calculated on the basis of the wave theory that a bright point should be found at the very center of the shadow of a round object. This conclusion was generally doubted, but its correctness was subsequently proved by experiment. Figure 14·2 clearly shows this central bright spot as well as the remarkable diffraction effects observed when objects of various shapes are lighted by a small, concentrated source.

[1] Thomas Young, English scientist, linguist, and archaeologist, was one of the most versatile geniuses in the history of science. He was a professor of physics at the Royal Institution and is known for important work on light, mechanics, vision, etc.

In order to get some idea of how Huygens' principle is used to explain diffraction phenomena, it is worth while to consider a simple example such as the diffraction produced by a single narrow slit. In Fig. 14·3 a train of straight waves of any kind (water waves, sound, light) is advancing toward a wall having a small opening in it.

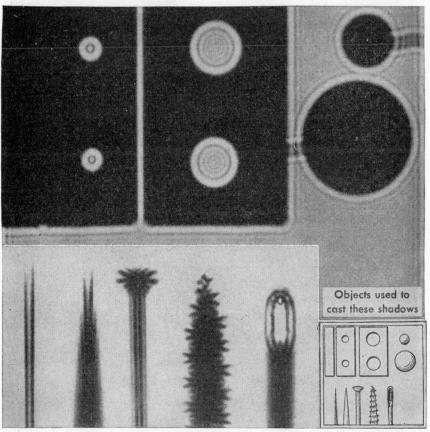

Objects used to cast these shadows

FIG. 14·2   Diffraction effects with various objects. (*From plates by Prof. F. A. Saunders.*)

Assume that the wave fronts extend indefinitely in a direction perpendicular to the page (plane waves) and that the opening does likewise (narrow slit). Any point on one of the wave fronts coming up to the barrier acts as a new source of wavelets, which are in this case cylindrical. For the wave front that is just reaching the barrier, all but the wavelet at S are held back. This gets through and propagates itself on the other side as a series of cylindrical wave fronts as shown.

Were the waves to travel in straight lines through the aperture, the disturbance on the right would be confined to the region between the dashed lines. Actually, because of diffraction a disturbance exists at all points on the right, and it may be said that the slit acts like a new source of waves. However, there is one qualification to this statement. If S were a real point source of waves, we should expect the strength of the disturbance at a given distance from the slit to be the same in all directions. In reality, on any wave front the disturbance is a maximum in the forward direction, falling off rapidly on each side as indicated in the diagram by the shading of the cylindrical wave fronts.

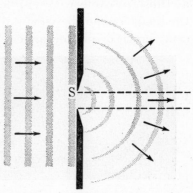

FIG. 14·3   Diffraction of waves by a narrow slit.

14·3 Resolving Power of Optical Instruments

If a point source of light—for example, a star—is viewed through a small circular opening, what is seen is no longer a point of light but a diffraction pattern consisting of a disk surrounded by concentric rings, much as in Fig. 14·2. If the circular aperture is the objective of a telescope or a microscope, each point in the object viewed will produce a ring pattern and the entire image will be made up of such overlapping ring systems. The result is that the instrument will fail to reproduce fine detail, no matter how perfect the lenses or mirrors themselves may be. The instrument is said to have limited *resolving power.*

In the telescope the two components of a double star may not be resolved at all if their diffraction patterns overlap too much, and in order to effect a separation a telescope having an objective of larger diameter must be used (see Fig. 14·4). This is an additional reason for building large-aperture telescopes, increased light-gathering power being the other main consideration (page 214).

The ability to see fine detail in a microscope is limited by the resolving power of the optical system. Theory shows that the resolving power, besides increasing with the aperture, increases also if light of shorter wavelength is used. The ultraviolet microscope, equipped with quartz lenses and using ultraviolet light, has good enough resolution to permit the use of magnifications twice as great as those possible with visible light. Of course, in this instrument the image cannot be viewed directly but must be cast on a fluorescent screen or photographed.

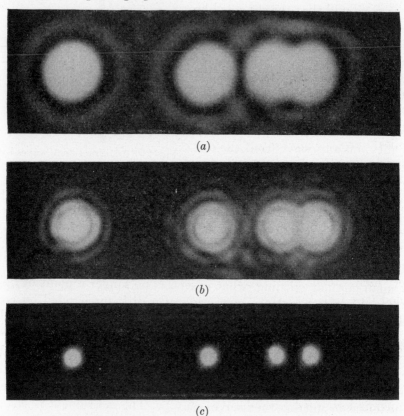

(a)

(b)

(c)

FIG. 14·4 Star images formed by telescopes of various apertures: (a) Small; (b) Medium; (c) Large. (*Courtesy of Sears and Zemansky: "University Physics," Addison-Wesley.*)

14·4 The Diffraction Grating

Fraunhofer, in his work on spectra already described, devised a new instrument for producing spectra by means of diffraction. The size of the diffraction pattern obtained with a given arrangement of apertures or obstacles depends on the wavelength of the light used, coarser patterns resulting for longer waves. If, then, a *mixture* of wavelengths is allowed to fall on a diffracting system, the various wavelengths present will be separated out by this means, which is merely another way of saying that *dispersion* results. Theory shows that a minimum of overlapping can be obtained by using a large number of adjoining, closely spaced slits. The arrangement is called a *diffraction grating*.

Fraunhofer's first crude but ingenious gratings were made by stretching a fine wire back and forth between two parallel screws; there were about 200 openings to each centimeter of width. Later it was found possible to make highly perfect gratings with much finer spacing by building a special machine that draws a fine diamond point repeatedly across a metal plate, the point being moved onward the desired distance between rulings. The "slits" are the untouched strips between such lines and act by reflection, while the roughened lines ruled by the diamond point act like barriers because they throw the light off diffusely.

The ruling of a grating is an almost incredibly ticklish process, requiring elaborate precautions to avoid vibration, temperature changes, or other disturbances that would spoil the uniformity of spacing of the rulings. High-quality gratings several inches wide and having 15,000 to 30,000 lines per inch have been successfully ruled (see Ref. 5 at the end of this chapter).

14·5   How Gratings Form Spectra

In order to understand the operation of a grating, consider the ideal transmission grating represented in cross section in Fig. 14·5 by the broken line. The black parts represent opaque portions of the surface, and the spaces between represent the transparent places. If plane waves of light of a single wavelength

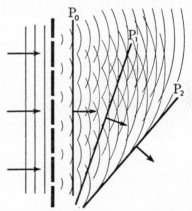

FIG. 14·5 Wave fronts formed by a grating.

strike the grating as shown, each point of every slit will act as a source of Huygens wavelets, which propagate themselves in the space to the right of the grating. The question is what kind of wave fronts exist in this region. According to Huygens' principle the possible wave fronts are given by the sets of lines that can be drawn touching the elementary wavelets. One set is obviously that represented by such planes as P_0—the light that "goes straight through" the grating in the same direction as the original beam. But there are other possibilities. Planes having the direction of P_1 also fulfill the requirements. Each is the common tangent to a wavelet from a given point in one slit, the *succeeding* wave from the corresponding point in the adjoining slit, etc.; each gives rise to a set of plane waves traveling obliquely at a certain angle with the perpendicular to the grating. Further, P_2—the common tangent of a *given* wavelet from one slit, the *second* wavelet *beyond* from the next slit, etc.—represents still another possibility, and so on.

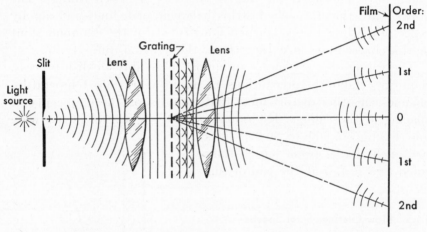

Fig. 14·6   Formation of images in a grating spectrograph.

Corresponding to each of the sets of waves just described there is, of course, another set making an equal angle with the perpendicular but lying on the opposite side. The several sets of plane waves may be brought to a focus at distant points on a screen or photographic film by means of a converging lens, as shown in Fig. 14·6. The whole arrangement constitutes a *grating spectrograph* (or spectro*scope* if the film is replaced by an eyepiece). The various images of the slit are referred to as spectra of different *orders,* the central image being the *zero order,* the first one to each side the *first order,* etc. The image brightness diminishes rapidly with increasing order, a fact that appears reasonable from what has been said regarding Fig. 14·3.

14·6   Determination of Wavelength

The geometry of the grating spectrograph makes it possible to compute exactly where a given order will fall. Figure 14·7a is a simplified diagram of the formation of the first-order image. Any of the first-order wave fronts, such as BC, comes off the grating at an angle θ_1 and is brought to a focus at a distance x_1 from the central image. The right triangles IOM and ACB are similar, and hence their sides are proportional. If the **grating space** is d and the light is of wavelength λ, this means that

$$\frac{x_1}{h} = \frac{3\lambda}{3d} = \frac{\lambda}{d}$$

The angle θ_1 in the sketch is much exaggerated for clarity; usually it is small enough so that h may, without appreciable error, be

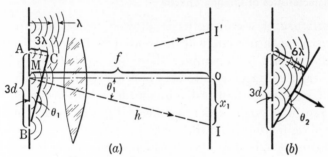

FIG. 14·7   Geometry of the grating.

replaced by f. The last equation then becomes $x_1/f = \lambda/d$, or $x_1 = f\lambda/d$, where f is practically the same as the focal length of the lens used to form the image.

In a similar way Fig. 14·7b shows how the second-order wave fronts are formed. Here the number of waves along AC is just **twice** the number of grating spaces along AB, with the result that the position of the second-order image is determined by $x_2 = 2f\lambda/d$. For the third order it would be $x_3 = 3f\lambda/d$, etc., and in general, for the mth order,

$$x_m = \frac{mf\lambda}{d} \tag{14·1}$$

This is the equation of the plane diffraction grating. The resulting disturbance coming from the grating is practically zero in any direction that differs even slightly from one of those given by the equation. The effect of the large number of slits is to make the diffraction maxima very sharp, as compared, for instance, with those shown in Fig. 14·1.

The grating equation gives us an accurate way of measuring the wavelength of a radiation. If f and d are known and x is measured for any order m, then λ can be computed.

Example: Using a grating having 125 lines per centimeter in conjunction with a lens of 200 cm focal length, the third-order image of a certain radiation is formed at a place 3.00 cm sidewise from the zero-order position. Find the wavelength.

Since the grating has 125 lines per centimeter, the grating space d is 1/125 cm. By substituting the known data in Eq. (14·1), the result is

$$\lambda = \frac{3}{125 \times 3 \times 200} = 4 \times 10^{-5} \text{ cm} = 4000\text{A}$$

14·7 Characteristics of Grating Spectra

If a *mixture* of wavelengths is allowed to fall upon a grating, every wavelength present will be treated as indicated by the diagrams above. If, for example, there are just two wavelengths present, each will give rise to sets of wave fronts as pictured and each will produce a first-order image, a second-order image, etc. The image of a given order produced by the longer of the two waves will lie farther from the central position, as indicated by the diagrams and also by Eq. (14·1), which states that x is proportional to λ. In addition, the separation of the two images will increase in proportion to the order, being twice as great in the second order as in the first, three times as great in the third order, etc. (see Exercise 4).

Separation of lines that are close together in wavelength is often of prime importance, and therefore this suggests the desirability of working with a spectrum of high order. However, since the brightness of the lines decreases rapidly with increase in the order, it is often not feasible to work with orders higher than perhaps the third or fourth, even when strong light sources are used. An additional reason will be given below.

Further characteristics of the spectra formed by a grating may be recognized by considering what happens when white light falls on such a device. A continuous spectrum will be found in each order, with the red end farthest from the center and the violet nearest to this point. The zero-order image, however, will be, not a spectrum, but an image of the entrance slit formed in white light (Fig. 14·8). This, again, is the light that comes "straight through" the grating, to be brought to a focus by the second lens. Equation (14·1) also shows why there is no dispersion in the zero order; for if m is set equal to zero in this relation, then x will be zero regardless of the value of λ. This is simply another way of saying that in the zero order all λ's are brought to the same point on the screen—there is no dispersion.

Another feature of grating spectra is revealed by examining Fig. 14·8. Inasmuch as the separation of the wavelengths in each spectrum *increases* with the order, while the spacing of the various orders is uniform, there must come a point where the succeeding

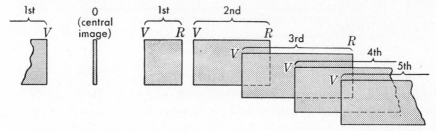

FIG. 14·8   Several orders of the visible spectrum, showing overlapping.

orders overlap. For the visible range this already happens between the second and third orders, as the figure shows. Of course, if a wider range of wavelengths than the visible is being investigated, this troublesome overlapping may occur even between the first and second orders.

14·8   Grating and Prism Compared; Concave Grating

It is interesting to compare the grating with the prism for the production of spectra. The chief advantage of the grating over the prism is the fact that grating spectra have *linear dispersion*—that is, the distances between lines on the film are proportional to their differences in wavelength, as Eq. (14·1) states.[1] This fact makes it possible to determine the wavelength of a spectrum line formed by a grating by computation from the equation or by interpolating simply between two neighboring lines of known wavelength. In a prism spectrum, on the other hand. the dispersion increases in going from red to violet, and the determination of wavelength is more complicated. Figure 14·9 shows the spectrum of a hypothetical set of radiations that are 500A apart in wavelength, as formed by a grating and by a prism.

[1] This is true to the approximation involved in arriving at Eq. (14·1).

A further advantage of the grating is the fact that much higher dispersions can be obtained with it than with any practicable prism, for a prism of very high dispersion would have to be extremely large, with consequent great absorption of the light passing through it.

One disadvantage of the grating is the fact that the light entering is distributed among a large number of orders, so that the spectra are faint, particularly in higher orders. With a prism, on the

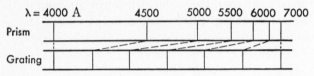

FIG. 14·9   Comparison of dispersion by prism and grating.

other hand, all the light goes into the one spectrum formed. Because it is imperative in working with a grating to conserve as much light as possible, it would be helpful if the lenses used in the spectrograph sketched in Fig. 14·6 could be omitted and the losses due to absorption in the glass and reflection from the lens surfaces thus eliminated. This was first accomplished by Rowland,[1] who ruled high-quality gratings on the surface of *concave* mirrors, which acted both to diffract the light and to focus it.

14·9   Interference

A particular example of the interference of waves was described in Chap. 10 in connection with standing waves in a string and in the air within an organ pipe.[2] It was found that at certain points where the direct and reflected waves arrived always in opposite phase they canceled each other. At these places—the nodes—the resultant disturbance was zero.

In a more general situation, interference will occur whenever two or more sets of waves traverse the same medium. At any instant the disturbance at a given point will be the vector sum of the disturbances due to the separate waves arriving there. If there are a number of sets of waves and if they are of the same frequency and have a *definite phase relation* with each other—that is, if they are

[1] H. A. Rowland, 1848–1901, gifted American experimental physicist noted for his skillful contributions to many fields of physics.

[2] You should review pp. 169–173 at this point.

permanently "locked in step"—a stationary pattern of disturbance results, with nodes (places of minimum disturbance) at certain fixed places and loops (maximum disturbance) at others. This
was the case for the stationary waves you have already studied.

Figure 14·10a shows a snapshot of the interference pattern produced on the surface of a pond when two sets of waves were produced by dipping the two round objects in and out of the water
simultaneously and with constant frequency. Part b of the figure
is a drawing of the same situation. Along certain radial curved lines
the two disturbances cancel each other, and we have "destructive
interference"; in the regions between, the amplitude is doubled

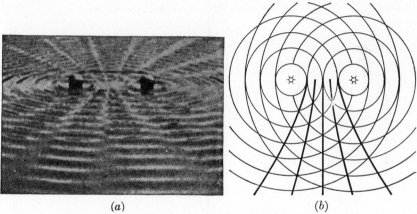

(a)   (b)

FIG. 14·10   Interference of ripples from a pair of sources.

("constructive interference"). An exactly similar phenomenon
may be observed with sound waves. It is perfectly true that "sound
added to sound can produce silence" at certain places.

In no interference experiment is there destruction of energy, for
it can be proved that the total energy of the pattern is the same as
that furnished by both sources. All that happens is that the energy
is redistributed in space, the disturbance being increased at some
places and diminished at others.

The term "interference" is not particularly apt, for the word indicates
a mutual disturbing effect of one set of waves on another, while in reality
it is their complete *independence* (see page 168)—the fact that the resultant disturbance can be computed as the vector sum of the separate
ones—that makes the so-called "interference effects" possible.

14·10 Young's Experiment

Can light added to light produce darkness? The first definitive demonstration of the interference of light was the experiment performed by Young at the very beginning of the nineteenth century. It is the optical analogue of the water-wave situation represented by Fig. 14·10. A source of light is placed behind a slit S_1 (Fig. 14·11); two slits S_2 and S_3, which are very close together, are placed parallel to S_1. In Young's original experiment, pinholes were used, but the effect is much easier to observe if slits are used instead. If light traveled in straight lines under all circumstances, the illumination on a screen W placed some distance beyond the pair of

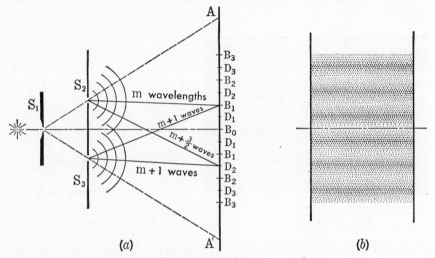

FIG. 14·11   Young's interference experiment.

slits would consist merely of two bright lines at A and A'. In reality, Young found that the illumination on the screen consisted of many alternate light and dark spots. When slits are used, the appearance of the screen is as shown in Fig. 14·11b.

Each of the narrow apertures S_2 and S_3 acts as a source of Huygens wavelets, and the interference of these wavelets produces the pattern observed on the screen. The interference effects exist throughout the entire space beyond the double slit; the purpose of the screen is merely to make the pattern visible. At any point on the screen such as B_1 the two sets of waves arrive exactly in the same phase, and a bright band is observed. This amounts to saying that the distances of any of these bright bands from S_2 and S_3

differ by exactly 0, 1, 2, 3, . . . wavelengths. On the other hand, at points such as D_1, D_2, D_3, . . . , the waves arrive exactly in opposite phase, destroying each other and producing darkness; the distance from the two slits differs by ½, 3/2, 5/2, . . . wavelengths. That the observed pattern is due to an effect of the light coming from *both* slits is easily verified by covering one of them. The appearance of the screen changes, the former pattern being replaced by the much coarser and less conspicuous one due to diffraction by a single slit.

14·11 Conditions for Interference

Could you perform Young's experiment by placing two *separate* light sources behind the respective slits S_2 and S_3 in Fig. 14·11? Do the sound waves from two violins in an orchestra interfere? The answer to such questions is contained in the statement made on page 250—in order to get a lasting interference pattern the two interfering sets of waves must come from a common source so that they have a *constant phase relation* with each other. It is true that at any instant *any* two sets of waves will produce an interference pattern in the space common to them; but unless constancy of relative phase is maintained, this pattern will change so rapidly that it cannot be perceived and only average effects will be observed. Thus for the two violins the disturbance in the air at the listener's ear is sometimes double that of one instrument, at other times zero, according to the momentary phase relationship of the two. But the phase cannot possibly be held constant for the two independent sources, and what is heard is the average effect, which amounts to a steady sound which is twice as intense as that due to a single instrument.

If two sources could in some way be coupled together, like two broadcasting stations joined to the same network, then interference between them would be possible. In the case of light, however, this is entirely out of the question, for the source consists of myriads of independent atoms or molecules emitting their radiations at random. By using a *single* source and splitting the light from each entity into two sets of waves that can interfere, we obtain a single interference pattern from the whole aggregate. There are additional conditions that should be satisfied if an easily visible pattern is to result. The light used should be at least approximately of a single wavelength (this may be realized by using a filter in front of a lamp), and the difference in path between the two beams should not be too great.

14·12 Newton's Rings

More than a century and a half before Young's crucial experiment Newton made certain observations that clearly showed the phenomenon of interference; yet he seems to have stopped just short of recognizing this fact and its bearing on the concept of the nature of light. A very slightly convex piece of glass is placed on a flat piece, and the combination is viewed by reflected light (Fig. 14·12a). Seen from above is a system of circular rings, alternately bright and dark (Fig. 14·12b). The explanation in terms of interference is straightforward. In the figure, $SABCE$ is a ray coming to

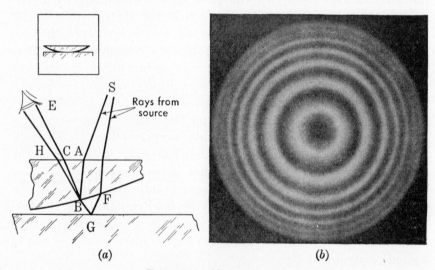

(a)   (b)

FIG. 14·12   Newton's rings.

the eye after reflection from the curved surface, while $SFGBHE$ is a ray coming back through B after reflection from the flat surface. The second ray goes a greater distance than the first. If the thickness of the "air film" at B is such that the two rays emerge from the system exactly *in phase,* this part of the glass will appear bright; if exactly *opposite in phase,* there will be darkness at this point. Intermediate phase relations will correspond to illumination lying somewhere between these two extremes. Going outward from the center, we come alternately to places where constructive and destructive interference occurs. Since the whole setup is symmetric around the central axis, a set of *circular* interference bands results.

If the curvature of the upper glass is known, the thickness of the air film at any point can be found and it is possible to calculate the wavelength of the light used by measuring the diameters of the interference rings. Young actually used some of Newton's data to compute wavelengths in this way.

It was probably the fact that Newton was unaware of the phenomenon of diffraction which kept him from considering the possibility of a wave explanation for the ring experiment. How close he was to doing this is shown by the fact that he recorded the observation that the ring pattern was larger for red light than for blue and that he attempted to theorize about the phenomenon in terms of some kind of *periodicity* inherent in a beam of light (Ref. 2). Certainly the situation is one of the most interesting examples of a "near miss" in the entire history of scientific discovery.

14·13 Examples of Interference Phenomena

A familiar example of interference from a thin film is the rich coloration of a soap bubble or of a film of oil on a wet pavement. As in the case of Newton's rings, the color seen at any point is a *composite* of all the colors in the incident light that are *not* destroyed by interference. The colors are most vivid when the film is between about 3×10^{-5} and 7×10^{-5} cm thick. If the film is thinner, the number of different wavelengths destroyed is small and the remaining mixture is not very brightly colored; if the film is thicker, the wavelength regions removed or weakened by interference are narrow and well spaced through the spectrum so that the remaining mixture appears essentially white.

A carpenter tests the flatness of a board by placing the edge of a ruler in contact with it in various orientations. This crude method would naturally be inadequate for testing the flatness of the glass surface of a prism, mirror, or plate used in accurate optical work, where a surface must often be made truly plane to within a fraction of a wavelength of light. During the process of grinding and polishing such a plate it is repeatedly tested for flatness by inspecting the interference pattern produced by laying it on another plate that is known to be flat. If the interference bands are irregular, the plate requires further polishing (Fig. 14·13).

In a compound-lens system such as a photographic objective, light reflected from the several glass surfaces impairs the efficiency of the unit in two ways: (1) Less light is transmitted, weakening the image. (2) The reflections from curved surfaces give rise to troublesome secondary images. It has been found possible to coat the surfaces with a thin layer of transparent material and thus eliminate the reflected light by destructive interference. By selecting the proper thickness and index of refraction for the coating the light waves reflected from its two surfaces can be made to emerge in opposite phase and destroy each other. The wave energy, instead of being reflected off the surface, is then thrown

FIG. 14-13　Optical testing for flatness, using interference fringes. (*Courtesy of Bausch and Lomb Optical Company.*)

back into the lens. With a compound lens consisting of several units, coating the surfaces may increase the brightness of the image by as much as 25 per cent or more.

14·14　Interferometers

The term *interferometer* is applied to any one of a number of devices that use interference phenomena for purposes of measurement. The quantity measured may be the wavelength of a certain kind of light, a distance (such as the thickness of a film or the diameter of a star), the index of refraction of a sample of matter, etc. One of the most useful forms of interferometer, that devised by Michelson, is shown schematically in plan in Fig. 14·14. Light from the source falls on the lightly silvered surface of a plane parallel plate P, where it divides, part being reflected to the silvered mirror M, which sends it back once more through P and onward into the observing telescope. The other part of the beam is sent to the mirror N, which returns it to P, from which it is also directed into the telescope. The two beams entering the telescope will be in a position to interfere; and if the two mirrors M and N are set not quite exactly at right angles, the interference pattern will consist of equally spaced straight bands perpendicular to the page. This is because, optically speaking, the entire arm PN of the instrument may be considered swung up at right angles into the position PN' and the interference can be looked upon as taking place between the two surfaces of the wedge of air formed by M and N', just as in the case of Newton's rings.

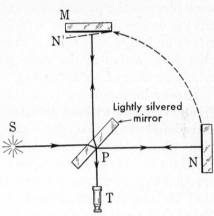

In the actual instrument, M is mounted on guides and may be moved back and forth along the line MP by means of a very accurate screw. As M is moved slowly in one direction, the entire interference pattern moves across the field of view. Obviously, if M is moved a distance equal to just half a wavelength of the light being used, the length of path of the beam re-

FIG. 14·14   The Michelson interferometer.

flected from this mirror will be changed by exactly one wavelength and the phase relation with the beam going to N will be again the same as before. In this process, then, the interference pattern will have moved along by just the distance between adjoining bands. If the number of times this happens is counted while the screw is advanced a given distance, the wavelength of the light can be calculated. Conversely, by using light of known wavelength the motion of M can be computed very accurately. Thus the Michelson interferometer can be used to measure displacements of the order of a millionth of an inch. For other interesting applications of this instrument, see Ref. 4.

14·15   Comparison of Diffraction and Interference

What, if any, is the difference between the phenomenon of diffraction and that of interference? In the early part of this chapter, diffraction effects were discussed in terms of Huygens wavelets. However, the mere production of these wavelets is not in itself sufficient to account for the diffraction patterns observed. It must also be realized that *interference* occurs between these waves and that such interference is an essential part of the phenomenon. In particular it is responsible for the fact that there are no backward-traveling wave fronts (see also page 204). As a matter of fact, once we grant that diffracted light exists, the application of the inter-ference conditions tells us where the maxima and minima of illu-mination will be found and what the relative brightness will be at each place in the pattern. For example, the grating equation (page 247) is easily obtained by noting that, at any point on the screen where an image is to result, the rays diffracted from two adjoining slits must arrive in the same phase (path difference equal to a whole number of wavelengths).

It may be concluded from the above that there can be no dif-fraction effects without interference. However, the examples we considered show that there *can* be interference without diffrac-tion—that is, interference between direct (not diffracted) beams. At the time of Young's experiment the connection between dif-fraction and interference was lacking, and the objection was raised that the observed effects were due to diffraction of the light by the pinholes rather than to an interference effect as such. To meet

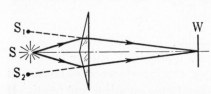

FIG. 14·15 Interference without dif-fraction: the Fresnel biprism.

this criticism, Young and others devised a number of arrange-ments, really interferometers, in which interference effects are produced without diffraction. One of these, the Fresnel biprism, is diagramed in Fig. 14·15. The largest angle of the prism is very nearly 180 deg so that light from the source S is refracted as though it had come from two virtual sources S_1 and S_2, which are very close together. Interference bands are observed on a screen W.

Finally it is interesting to note that interference (including dif-fraction) always comes about through the superposition of two periodicities. Two sets of waves from a common source have the same frequency (periodicity in time); but by arranging that they strike a screen at slightly different angles the effect of two slightly different space periodicities is obtained, and interference results. The result is quite comparable with that observed by looking through two picket fences. Because of a difference in distance or direction the apparent spacing is slightly different for the two sets of pickets, and an "interference" pattern is observed (Fig. 14·16). In the use of the grating, one of the periodic spacings involved is that of the lines of the grating; the other spacing is that of the light waves.

FIG. 14·16   "Picket-fence" effect.

14·16   Are Light Waves Longitudinal or Transverse?

The successful interpretation of diffraction and interference established decisively the wave nature of light and even made possible the measurement of wavelength, but there still remained the important question as to the *type* of waves of which light is constituted. In Chap. 10 you learned that disturbances of various kinds possess wavelike properties. Sound waves are made up of longitudinal motions of the particles of the medium, the waves in a rope are transverse, and waves on the surface of the sea are made up of a combination of these two kinds of particle motion. Does light correspond to one or another of these types? The answer, resulting from a study of what is called *polarized light,* is that *light waves are transverse.* Historically there was widespread objection to the acceptance of this view. Such a state of affairs is understandable, for we invariably form a mental picture of waves only in connection with a material medium; and the difficulty is that the high speed of light would require this supposed medium—the "ether" referred to on page 178—to be as rigid as steel, yet so tenuous that it would not impede noticeably the motions of the planets. You will learn in Chap. 18 that the transverse disturbance involved in light waves is not the mechanical shearing of some material medium but consists of periodically changing electromagnetic forces.

The fact that in an ordinary source of light countless individual and independent events contribute to the total effect has already been mentioned. These events take place in random directions so that the state of the vibrations in an ordinary beam of light must be somewhat as sketched in Fig. 14·17. Each plane represents, say, every millionth wave front in a beam of light advancing in the direction AB. Since the waves are transverse, the vibrations lie *in* the

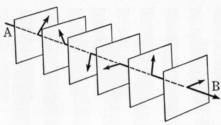

FIG. 14·17 Randomness of phase and direction of vibration in ordinary light.

wave fronts, as represented by the vectors. But for the reasons given above, these vectors are likely to be in different directions from one moment to the next, as the figure indicates. Figure 14·18a represents what would be seen by viewing Fig. 14·17 in a direction along the ray. The regular spacing of the vectors depicts the random orientation of the vibrations in a beam of ordinary light.

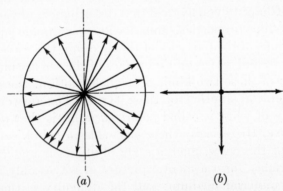

(a)   (b)

FIG. 14·18 End-on view of beam of ordinary light and its resolution into average components.

Finally it is convenient to resolve all the vibrations into components in two directions at right angles. The average effect is then as shown in Fig. 14·18b.

A mechanical analogue of the situation depicted in Fig. 14·17 is obtained by shaking one end of a stretched rope while changing the direction of shaking arbitrarily from one moment to the next. If the rope passes through a slotted box such as P in Fig. 14·19, only that part of the random motion of the rope which is in the direction of the slots will pass through. The transmitted vibrations are thus confined to a single plane and are said to be *plane-polarized*. This plane, which also contains the ray, is called the "plane of vibration." The polarized wave will be transmitted by a second slotted box A if the slots of the two boxes are parallel; it will not be transmitted if A is turned through a right angle so that its slots are

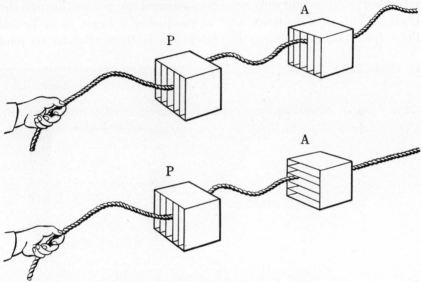

FIG. 14·19   Mechanical model of light polarization.

crosswise to those of P. Polarization is characteristic only of *transverse* waves. If the rope were replaced by a spiral spring, *longitudinal* waves in it would of course pass through the boxes regardless of their relative orientation.

It is precisely the fact that experiments corresponding to the above can be performed with light that proves the transversality of light waves. With sound waves such experiments are not possible.

14·17   Polarization by Double Refraction

If a natural crystal of the mineral calcite is placed on a printed page, two distinct refracted images of the print are seen (Fig. 14·20), whereas in ordinary transparent materials such as glass there is but one refracted ray. This phenomenon, *double refrac-*

tion, was discovered in the middle of the seventeenth century. Later, it was shown that the two rays coming through the crystal were *polarized in two directions at right angles,* as indicated in Fig. 14·21. The existence of two refracted rays can be explained with the aid of Huygens' principle on the basis of the fact that in a crystal such as calcite the speed of light has different values in different directions.

It is possible to absorb or otherwise get rid of one of the two refracted rays, so that only a single polarized ray passes through the crystal. This is a common way of producing a beam of polarized light from ordinary light. If this beam is then allowed to pass

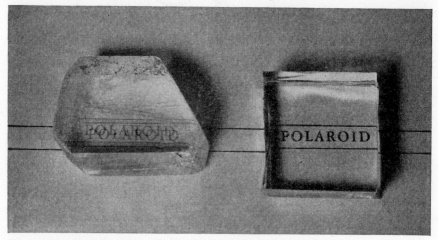

Fig. 14·20   Double refraction in calcite and ordinary single refraction in glass. (*Courtesy of Polaroid Corporation.*)

through a second crystal that is *similarly oriented,* it passes through with little weakening. To the eye it looks no different from ordinary light, but if the second crystal is now rotated around the incident ray, the transmitted light diminishes and is cut off completely after a rotation of 90 deg. A further turn through a right angle gradually restores full brightness, and bright and dark continue to alternate at positions 90 deg apart.

This state of affairs corresponds exactly to the situation in Fig. 14·19 and suggests, therefore, the transverse nature of light vibrations as first advanced by Young and Fresnel. Obviously the crystals possess some property analogous to "grain" or to the slots in the boxes in the figure. Large crystals of natural calcite are rare and expensive, but a manufactured polarizing material in the form of large sheets is now available,[1] and this has led to a number of new practical applications.

There is more that could be said regarding polarized light, for it forms an exceptionally rich (and complicated) branch of optics. Our main interest in it here, however, is the way it contributes to an understanding of the nature of light. If you are interested in further details about polarized light, including its applications to

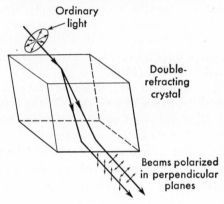

FIG. 14·21   Polarization of doubly refracted rays.

the elimination of glare, the study of stresses in structures, and the projection of three-dimensional motion pictures, look up Ref. 2 at the end of the chapter.

14·18 Conclusion

You have seen in the last four chapters how the discovery and interpretation of various optical phenomena led to the idea of light as a transverse wave motion. Diffraction and interference in particular demand a wave explanation, as does ordinary refraction. But the fact that the waves are transverse is brought out only by a study of polarization.

As long as intellectual curiosity exists in the world, the final chapter of the story of science will remain unwritten. While the wave theory explains perfectly the observed facts about light when in transit, it was later found necessary to modify and extend the wave theory in discussing what happens when light originates in a source or when it is absorbed in matter. This line of thought,

---

[1] The American trade name for this material is Polaroid.

which you will come to know as the quantum theory, will be introduced in a later chapter.

SUMMARY

Diffraction is the sidewise spreading of waves after passing the edge of an obstacle or after going through a narrow opening.

Diffraction imposes a limit on the ability to distinguish the images, in an optical instrument, of two points that are close together. This ability is termed the *resolving power* of the instrument.

Diffraction grating: In effect, a series of equally spaced narrow slits. Waves passing through combine to produce wave fronts moving in a number of definite directions, which depend on the wavelength. Thus the grating produces dispersion. The wavelength of a given radiation may be computed from Eq. (14·1).

Interference results when two sets of waves traverse the same space. The momentary disturbance at any point is the resultant of the two individual ones. Observable interference can be obtained only if the two sets of waves originate in the same source.

Plane-polarized light has its vibrations confined to a single plane. The phenomena of polarized light can be interpreted on the basis that light waves are *transverse*.

READING REFERENCES

1. Bragg, W. H.: "The Universe of Light," Macmillan, New York, 1930. The topics of the present chapter are treated in very clear fashion. See especially Chaps. IV–VI.
2. Taylor, Lloyd W.: "Physics, the Pioneer Science," Houghton Mifflin, Boston, 1941. The contrasting descriptions of interference by Newton and by Young are presented on pp. 504–515. Polarized light and its applications are treated in Chap. 38.
3. Cajori, F.: "A History of Physics," Macmillan, New York, 1929. Read pp. 96–97 and 148–156.
4. Michelson, A. A.: "Studies in Optics," University of Chicago Press, Chicago, 1927. While more technical than the other references given, Michelson's own account of many of his original researches will prove interesting.
5. Ingalls, A. G.: Ruling Engines, *Sci. American*, June, 1952, pp. 45–55.

FILM

"Light Waves and Their Uses," Encyclopaedia Britannica Films. 16 mm, sound, 1 reel.

EXERCISES

1. Explain why the low-pitched rumble of a train can be heard even when buildings intervene but the hiss of steam becomes audible only when the locomotive comes into unobstructed view.

2. An amateur astronomer, finding that the two components of a certain double star are not quite resolved in his telescope, changes the eyepiece to one of higher magnifying power. Is this likely to help?

3. Measure the positions of the "spectrum lines" in the upper part of Fig. 14·9, using a millimeter rule, and draw a *dispersion curve* for this prism by plotting wavelength against distance along the film. Make the graph full page size. Using the same set of axes, draw the dispersion curve for the grating spectrum. Compare the two.

4. By computing the image positions of two radiations of wavelength 5000 and 6000A formed by the grating arrangement described in the example on page 248, find the separation of the images in the first, second, and third orders, and show that the separation is proportional to the order.

5. A grating having 5000 lines per centimeter is used in conjunction with a lens of focal length 100 cm. How long a piece of photographic film is needed to record the entire visible spectrum (4000 to 7000A) in the first order?

6. In the preceding exercise, the image of a certain spectrum line is found to fall at a point on the film that is 4.5 cm from the red end of the spectrum. What is the wavelength of this line?

7. The iridescent coloration of mother-of-pearl or opal or of a phonograph record by sunlight reflected from it almost edgewise is not due to pigmentation of the material. How, then, do you explain it?

8. Describe the appearance of the screen in Young's experiment when white light is used. What is the color of the central bright band? Of the others?

9. In using light of a certain wavelength in a Michelson interferometer, it is found that 2500 complete interference bands pass across the field of view when the movable mirror is advanced a distance of 0.080 cm. Find the wavelength of the light used.

10. Ordinary light becomes polarized to some extent when it is reflected obliquely from a smooth surface. Suppose you are looking at the glare of a wet pavement through a disk of polarizing material. What would you expect to see if you were to rotate the disk slowly in front of your eye?

Chapter 15

ELECTROSTATICS

Few branches of science have had applications with such far-reaching consequences as those of electricity. The ways in which electrical devices have influenced the development of modern life need hardly be enumerated. The advent of electrotechnics is well within the memory of persons living today, who will be able to tell you of the difference between life before and after the initiation of the great changes in transportation, communication, lighting, etc., accompanying the development of technical electricity.

In examining the subject of electricity in this book we shall be more concerned, as in our study of previous topics, with matters of principle than with applications or accessories. You will learn something of what is known about the nature and behavior of electricity and how this fundamental knowledge enriched science as well as technology.

15·1 Early Discoveries

The original observations that gave rise to the science of electricity suggest nothing of familiar present-day electrical devices such as motors, radio, fluorescent lamps, or television receivers. Historians are not able to say precisely when electrical phenomena were first observed and recorded, but the original discoveries undoubtedly were made in ancient Greece. The philosopher Thales, who lived about 600 B.C., is said to have observed the ability of a piece of amber, after being rubbed, to attract and pick up small bits of straw, wood, or feathers. Apart from this fact, little of importance was discovered until 22 centuries later, the time of Shakespeare, when Gilbert[1] investigated the matter more thor-

---

[1] William Gilbert, court physician to Queen Elizabeth, philosopher, and experimenter. As a devoted practitioner and advocate of the experimental method he ranks with Galileo as a founder of modern physical science.

oughly and found that many other materials besides amber possess this power. He introduced the term **electrification** for the phenomenon, a name derived from the Greek word for amber.

It is known now that any two substances, when rubbed together, acquire **a charge of electricity,** as we say. You have probably noticed that a plastic or hard rubber comb becomes charged and often makes crackling noises when run through your hair or that a sheet of paper on which you have been writing will cling to the desk, particularly in dry weather. For reasons that will appear later, all electrical experiments of this nature are found to work best when everything is perfectly dry.

15·2   Dual Nature of Charge

A convenient detector of electric charge—one form of **electro-scope**—consists of a small ball of some light material such as pith or balsa wood covered with tin foil and hung from a silk thread. If any previously charged body, such as a stick of hard rubber or

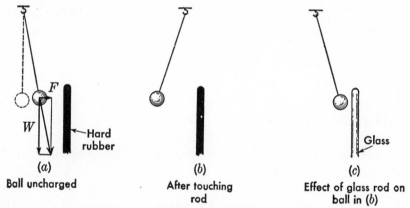

(a)   (b)   (c)
Ball uncharged   After touching   Effect of glass rod on
                              rod   ball in (b)

FIG. 15·1   Dual nature of electric charge.

sealing wax that has been rubbed with a piece of fur or flannel, is brought within an inch or two of the hanging ball, the ball will move toward the charged object, taking up a displaced position such that the thread lies along the resultant of the attracting force and the weight of the ball (Fig. 15·1a). This displacement is a measure of the force of attraction.

If, intentionally or otherwise, the ball should make contact with the charged rod, the force will almost immediately change to one of repulsion (sketch *b* of the figure), the ball bounding away to the opposite side. Now, with the ball still in this condition, if a rod of glass that has been rubbed with silk is brought near, the ball will be strongly attracted (sketch *c*). Similarly the uncharged ball is found to be attracted by a rubbed glass rod, then violently repelled after contact, and subsequently shows attraction for a hard rubber rod. Experiments of this nature show that *electric charges are of two kinds* and that *unlike* kinds *attract* each other; *like* kinds *repel* each other. Note that when the ball is uncharged it is attracted by a rubbed body of any sort. The reason for this will be explained below (page 273).

This dual nature of electricity was first brought to light by the experiments of Gray in England and of Du Fay in France in the early years of the eighteenth century. In our own country, Benjamin Franklin soon became interested in electrical phenomena.[1] He was the first to give the distinguishing names "positive" and "negative" to the two varieties of electric charge. This terminology is consistent with the fact that two opposite charges tend to cancel each other when put into contact.

The type of charge found on a *glass rod* after rubbing it with silk was arbitrarily termed *positive* (+), while the kind present on a *hard rubber rod* after rubbing it with fur was called *negative* (−).

15·3   Electricity a Constituent of Atoms

It is now known that the source of the electrification of a body is to be found in the atoms of the matter composing it. The general structure of any atom is such that it consists of a relatively compact and massive central *nucleus* carrying a positive electric charge. Distributed around this nucleus are a number of much less massive negatively charged particles called *electrons*. The nucleus contains certain entities called *protons*. All protons are alike; all carry the same amount of *positive* charge. All electrons are alike, and each bears a negative charge equal in amount (but opposite in kind) to that of a proton.[2]

---

[1] In addition to his well-known talents in politics and in business, Franklin had unusual abilities as an amateur scientist. Among his scientific and technological achievements are such inventions as the lightning rod, bifocal eyeglasses, and watertight compartments for ships.

[2] These statements will be augmented and their observational background will be given in the later chapters of this book.

In its normal state an atom is electrically **neutral**—that is, the number of electrons distributed about the nucleus is equal to the number of protons in the nucleus itself. However, certain atoms or aggregates of atoms seem to be able to seize more than their normal complement of electrons, and this electron-grasping ability varies greatly from one kind of matter to another. Thus, when two dissimilar materials are placed in good contact, some electrons may be given up by one and taken over by the other. This is what happens when electric charges are "produced" by rubbing. Glass, for example, parts with electrons when rubbed with silk and then has a deficiency of electrons, or a positive charge. The silk, having accepted these electrons, then has a negative charge.

It is wrong to say that charges are "produced" or "generated" by rubbing. What occurs is merely a reapportioning of the mixture of equal amounts of positive and negative charge that already exists. When a charge of either kind is given to any object, an equal and opposite one must appear elsewhere. This constitutes a fact of experience, known long before the discovery of electrons and protons.

The body that acquires extra electrons becomes negatively charged; the body that gives up electrons is left positively charged. The only purpose of rubbing is the promotion of good contact between considerable surface areas of the two dissimilar substances. Pressure alone will result in some transfer of charge between them.

In spite of the fact that modern theory has been able to localize electric charge and relate it to certain aspects of the behavior of the fundamental particles of matter, serious conceptual difficulties remain. Bertrand Russell[1] expresses the situation as follows:

Some readers may expect me at this stage to tell them what electricity "really is." The fact is that I have already said what it is. It is not a thing like St. Paul's Cathedral; *it is a way in which things behave.* When we have told how things behave when they are electrified, and under what circumstances they are electrified, we have told all there is to tell. When I say that an electron has a certain amount of negative electricity, I mean merely that it behaves in a certain way. Electricity is not like red paint, a substance which can be put on to the electron and taken off again, it is merely a convenient name for certain physical laws.

[1] "The ABC of Atoms," Dutton, New York, 1923.

15·4   Conduction by Solids

If a metal-covered ball hanging from a silk thread, as in Fig. 15·1, is given a charge of either sign, it will acquire the ability to attract light objects. If a similar uncharged ball is touched to it, the charge on the first ball will be shared by the two. Both balls will now have the power of picking up light objects, although to a lesser degree than the first ball originally. If a charged ball is touched by the hand or by a wire connected to the earth, it loses its charge completely and no longer exerts attraction.

It soon becomes evident that substances such as metals permit electric charges to move readily along them, while other materials such as silk or glass do not. The two classes of substances are called *conductors* and *insulators,* respectively, a distinction first drawn by Gray. The difference is one of degree only. The best conductors are common metals, carbon, and certain minerals; the best insulators are glass, mica, amber, porcelain, etc. Intermediate in this property are *semiconductors*—for example, the metals germanium and silicon, now finding increasing application in devices such as the transistor.

A charge applied at any point to a metal object will spread over the entire surface. If the object is not supported on some insulating material, the charge will flow off to the earth. On the other hand, a charge applied to or produced on an insulator remains localized at the point of application; it is a truly "static" charge (compare with the title of this chapter). Thus a charge produced by rubbing one end of a glass rod remains on the rod even if the other end is held in the experimenter's hand. Further, a charge can be generated by rubbing a metal ball, provided that it is held by a glass handle. If held directly in the hand, the ball cannot be given a charge.

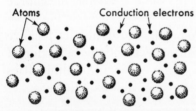

Atoms   Conduction electrons

Fig. 15·2   Conduction in a metal.

The conduction of electricity by solids is explained by the fact that in such objects there are always certain *free electrons,* or electrons temporarily detached from atoms, and that their number and mobility determine the ability of the material to conduct electricity. Always, in metallic conductors, it is the negative charges (free electrons) that move. The positive charges (atomic nuclei) remain fixed in the metal. A concerted movement of large numbers of free electrons in a conductor constitutes an ordinary **electric current** such as that flowing in a lamp or toaster. The behavior of such currents is discussed in the following chapters.

When a charged body is "grounded," or connected by a conductor to the earth, it loses its charge. If it was negative to begin with, grounding permits the excess electrons to flow from it to the earth through the medium of the free electrons in the connecting wire; if originally positive, electrons will be attracted to it from the earth in sufficient number to neutralize its charge. The earth acts merely as a tremendous receiver or contributor of electrons, its own electrical condition being virtually unaffected by such transfer.

15·5   The Leaf Electroscope

The hanging ball mentioned above will serve as one form of electroscope, or detector and measurer of electric charge, but a more sensitive instrument is the leaf electroscope, shown schematically in Fig. 15·3. With the help of this device a number of facts about electric charges can be demonstrated. A strip of gold leaf or other light metal foil hangs in contact with the flat plate of metal, which is connected to a rod having a metal ball at its upper end. The entire system is supported by an insulating ring and a case, which encloses the lower part of the device and protects the delicate leaf from disturbance by air currents.

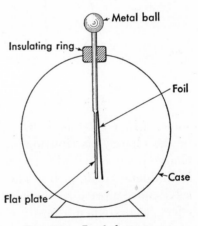

FIG. 15·3   Leaf electroscope.

If an electrified rod bearing either kind of charge is brought near the knob of the electroscope, the leaf rises; if the rod is then withdrawn without having touched the knob, the leaf falls back. However, if the rod is allowed to touch the knob, the leaf remains permanently deflected even after the rod is taken away. In this case a charge was actually transferred to the instrument, spreading over the whole insulated system including the flat plate and the foil.[1] Since their charges are of the same kind, plate and foil repel each other, making the foil stand out at an angle whose size depends on how much charge was given to the system.

15·6   Electrostatic Induction

How do you explain the temporary deflection produced when a charged rod approaches the knob of an uncharged electroscope? Suppose that a negatively charged rod is brought near. Then, since some of the electrons of the metallic electroscope system are free to move, they are repelled and shifted toward the far end. These excess electrons on both plate and leaf cause a repulsion, which moves the leaf. Meanwhile, the knob end, having been deprived of

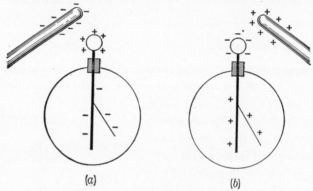

(a)   (b)

Fig. 15·4   Charges induced on an electroscope.

some of its electrons, is left with positive charge. Some indication of the charge distribution is given by Fig. 15·4a. As soon as the charged rod is withdrawn, the separation of charge produced by its influence disappears. The displaced electrons distribute themselves once more over the whole system, and the leaf falls. A similar effect occurs when a positively charged rod is brought near. Some of the free electrons are shifted toward the knob, leaving both plate and leaf positively charged and thus in a condition where they repel each other (Fig. 15·4b). In either instance the distribution of

---

[1] The transfer of a charge from the rubbed rod to the electroscope occurs literally only when the rod is negatively electrified. If positive, contact with the originally uncharged electroscope allows a number of free electrons from the electroscope to move over to the positive charges on the rod, leaving the instrument positively charged. The net effect, however, is the same as if an equivalent amount of positive electricity had been given directly to the electroscope.

charge on the electroscope is said to have been **induced** by the charge on the rod.

The process of induction makes possible the identification and approximate measurement of a charge without transferring or disturbing it in any way. Suppose that the instrument has been given, say, a negative charge to begin with. If a body bearing a negative charge is now brought near the knob, the deflection of the leaf will **increase,** more electrons being driven to the leaf and plate by the presence of the negatively charged body. But if a positively charged body is brought near the same instrument, some of the electrons in leaf and plate will be attracted toward the knob and the deflection will **decrease** somewhat. A similar sequence of events takes place

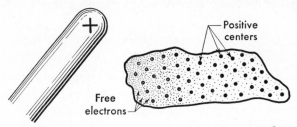

Fig. 15·5   A charged body always attracts a neutral one.

with a positively charged electroscope; in general, if the deflection of the leaf **increases** when a charged body is brought near the knob, the charged body has the **same** kind of electrification as the electroscope; if the deflection **decreases,** the **opposite** kind.

Electrostatic induction explains the fact that an electrified body, bearing either a positive or a negative charge, invariably **attracts** an uncharged object. By induction the near end of the latter acquires an excess of charge of opposite kind to that of the inducing body, while the far end obtains one of the same kind (Fig. 15·5). Since the charges of opposite kind are on the average closer to the inducing body and since it is a fact of experience that the force between two charges decreases if the distance of separation increases, it follows that the force of attraction will always predominate.

15·7   Law of Force between Charges

The quantitative relation behind the obvious fact that the electrostatic force between two charges must decrease in some way with their separation was carefully investigated by the French physicist and engineer Charles Coulomb in the latter part of the eighteenth century. Using a sensitive balance similar in principle to that with which Cavendish measured gravitational forces (page 90), he found that *the force between two small charged bodies varies inversely as the square of the distance between them*—the same dependence on distance that Newton deduced for the gravitational force between particles.[1]

Further, the amount of charge on each body under test could be altered in a known way by touching it with one or more uncharged balls of the same size. In this way the conclusion was also reached (by others than Coulomb) that the electrostatic *force varies directly as the product of the two quantities of charge.* Thus it became possible to state, in a form similar to the gravitational law, what has since become known as *Coulomb's law* of electrostatic force,

$$ f = \frac{Q_1 Q_2}{kd^2} \tag{15·1} $$

Here Q_1 and Q_2 are the two quantities of charge, d is their distance apart, f is the mutual force (which acts in the line joining the two charges), and k is a constant of which the value depends on the medium in which the two charges are located. This force acts, of course, equally on both charges.

The dependence of f on the intervening medium is one way in which electrostatic forces differ from gravitation; in the gravitational law of force the factor corresponding to k is a *universal* constant independent of surrounding materials (see page 90).

Experiment shows that for any insulating medium the value of k is greater than for a vacuum. This fact was discovered by Cavendish. By Eq. (15·1) this means that the force between two given charges a given distance apart is *less* when they are placed in, say, oil than when they are in a vacuum. The quantity k is called the *dielectric coefficient* of an insulating material, and its value is arbitrarily taken to be unity for a vacuum. Values for the most commonly used dielectrics (insulating substances) such as glass, mica, sulfur, and oils range up to about 10. Air has a value of about 1.0006—so near to unity that for almost all purposes one can set $k = 1$ in Eq. (15·1) for experiments carried out in air. A practical use of substances of high dielectric coefficient is in connection with capacitors (page 283).

---

[1] It should be remembered that both laws are valid, strictly speaking, only for small objects.

15·8   Units of Quantity of Charge

Coulomb's law cannot be used for computation until we have specified a unit for measuring quantity of charge. In many similar situations in physics the procedure is to substitute unity for each of the remaining quantities in the defining equation in order to arrive at a unit for the measurement of the quantity in question. Recall that, when it was necessary to define a new unit of force for use in connection with Newton's second law, the required unit was obtained by putting $m = 1$ and $a = 1$ in the equation $f = ma$ (page 81). Similarly, a unit for the measurement of quantity of electric charge may be defined by setting $k = 1$, $d = 1$, and $f = 1$ in Coulomb's law and decreeing then that Q_1 and Q_2 shall each be equal to 1. That is, a unit of charge is chosen to be of such size that, when placed 1 cm from an equal charge in a vacuum, the mutual force between charges is equal to 1 dyne.

The unit so specified is called *one electrostatic unit of charge,* abbreviated *esu.*[1] It was later found that, in terms of electrons, 1 esu is equal to an excess or a deficiency of about 2.1×10^9 electrons. Presently, in connection with electric currents, we shall use another and larger unit of quantity of charge called *one coulomb.* One coulomb is equal to 3×10^9 esu, or 6.3×10^{18} electron charges.[2]

15·9   The Electrostatic Field

The space in the neighborhood of charges, where electrostatic forces are detectable, is said to be occupied by an electrostatic *field.* This concept of a field of force is equally useful in talking of gravitation and, as will appear later, magnetic forces. In any instance where we deal with "action at a distance"—that is, with mutual forces exerted between bodies not in contact—we find an essential difficulty in understanding how the force can be transmitted across the intervening space. A "law of force" such as the gravitational equation or Coulomb's law does not explain the nature of this type of action—it merely gives the amount of the effect. However, the idea of considering the interaction to reside in some way in the space surrounding the bodies in question has shown itself to be an exceedingly useful one. As first developed by

---

[1] To be read "ee-ess-you."

[2] Make no effort to memorize these numbers; they are quoted here only to give you an idea of relative magnitudes.

Faraday[1] for the electrical case, it proved to be an extremely vivid and intuitive concept.

The **strength of the electric field** at any point is defined as **the force, in dynes, exerted on a charge of +1 esu placed there.** It follows that field strength is a vector quantity, since it has a given direction and magnitude. At each point in the field a definite field-strength vector can be drawn, as indicated in Fig. 15·6.

It is understood that the act of bringing the test charge of +1 esu to the point in question must not in itself appreciably change either the direction or strength of the field already existing at that place, for obviously a measurement is of no value if the mere act of making the determination alters what is being measured. If necessary, a field-strength determination could be made by measuring the force on a very small test charge of, say, +0.001 esu, then multiplying

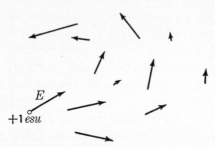

FIG. 15·6 A field vector can be drawn at each point.

the result by 1000 to get the magnitude of the field strength. In general, if the magnitude of the field strength at any point is denoted by E, then the force in dynes experienced by a charge of Q esu placed at that point will be

$$f = QE \qquad (15\cdot2)$$

The quantity E has the dimensions of **dynes per esu**.

15·10 Lines of Force

Faraday found it convenient to imagine an electric field mapped out by drawing so-called **lines of force** through such a space. A line of force may be traced by putting a small positive charge at any point and moving it always in the direction of the force exerted on it by the field. The resulting pictures for a few simple cases are

[1] Michael Faraday, English chemist and physicist, probably the greatest experimenter of the nineteenth century. In spite of extremely humble birth he succeeded in educating himself in science and became director of the laboratory of the Royal Institution in London at the age of thirty-four, a post he held for nearly half a century. His contributions to the science of electricity are among the most fundamental and far-reaching in the entire subject.

shown in Fig. 15·7. Sketch *a* represents a plane section of the field about a single positive "point charge" (or charged conducting sphere) located far from all other objects. Since a *positive* test charge placed anywhere in this field would be urged radially *outward*, the line of force at any point has this direction assigned to it. In *b* the reverse case is shown. The lines of force in the vicinity of a negative charge are directed radially inward.

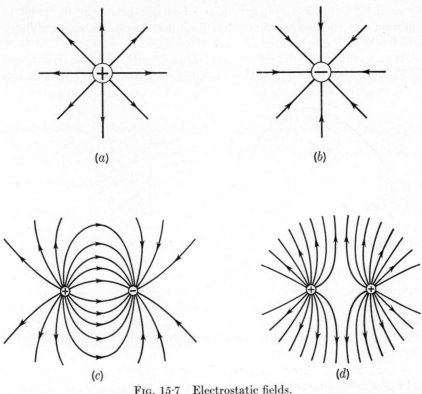

(a)   (b)

(c)   (d)

Fig. 15·7   Electrostatic fields.

In general, lines of force may be thought of as originating on positive charges and ending on negative charges. Sketch *c*, showing a plane section of the combined field of a positive and a negative charge some distance apart, illustrates the last statement. Each line of force represents the path that would be followed by a small, massless,[1] positively charged object that is set down near the fixed positive charge and allowed to move under the influence of the field. At any point, the field strength vector E is tangent to the

[1] Why?

line of force passing through that point. In *d* the field of two charges of the **same** kind is shown. In this instance the lines of force do not go across from one charge to the other but go off to a great distance or to objects in the vicinity.

If the charges that give rise to a field are all point charges, it is relatively simple to calculate the strength of the field at any place. It is only necessary to use Coulomb's law [Eq. (15·1)] to compute the force exerted by each field-producing charge on a +1 charge placed at the point in question and then to combine all of these forces into a single resultant, which will be the field-strength vector.

As an example, let the field be that caused by the two charges Q_1 and Q_2 in Fig. 15·8, and suppose that the field strength at P is required. If a

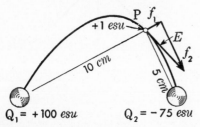

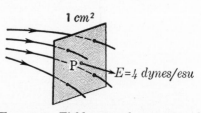

FIG. 15·8 Finding the field due to a set of point charges.

FIG. 15·9 Field strength represented by means of lines of force.

+1 charge is imagined placed at P, then by Coulomb's law Q_1 will repel it with a force given by $f_1 = (100 \times 1)/10^2 = 1$ dyne and at the same time Q_2 will attract it with a force of $f_2 = (75 \times 1)/5^2 = 3$ dynes. The resultant of f_1 and f_2, determined by making a scale drawing, is E, and this is the field vector at P. This vector is tangent to the line of force that passes through P.

A similar procedure would be followed if there were more than two field-producing charges.

From what has so far been said, it would seem that an unlimited number of lines of force might legitimately be drawn in any field. However, by agreeing to limit their number the lines may be used to give a measure of the **strength** of the field at any point, as well as its direction. **The number of lines drawn through each square centimeter of a surface placed perpendicular to the field is used to represent the field strength at that point.** Thus in Fig. 15·9 a field strength of 4 dynes/esu at the point P is represented by drawing just four lines of force through the 1-cm² area.

15·11 Further Properties of the Lines

A field whose lines of force are everywhere parallel and equally spaced is called a *uniform field*. Except near the edges, the field between two parallel flat metal plates carrying equal and opposite charges is uniform (Fig. 15·10a). If an insulated *conducting* body— say, a sphere—is introduced, the field is no longer uniform in the neighborhood of the sphere (Fig. 15·10b); for now charges are induced on the surface of the sphere as shown, and some of the lines of force originating on the top plate now end on the negative charges induced on the sphere, while other lines, terminating on the bottom plate, arise on the positive induced charges. Drawing c of the same figure shows the effect of placing a sphere of *insulating* material between the plates. Here the applied field brings about a

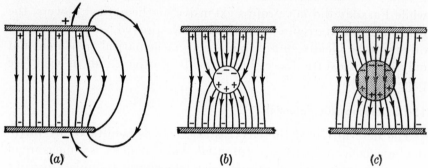

Fig. 15·10   Effect of bringing uncharged bodies into a uniform field.

slight separation of charge, or *polarization,* throughout the dielectric, and, in effect, small charges appear on the upper and lower surfaces of the body. Inside the dielectric, the effect of the field of these charges is to partially nullify the externally applied field. As a result, there are fewer lines in this region than there would be if the dielectric were absent.

Faraday imagined the lines of force to behave like *stretchable filaments* that at the same time tend to *repel each other in a sidewise direction.* These assumed qualities are in harmony with the observed features of electric fields. Tension in the lines of force running across from a positive to a negative charge, as in Fig. 15·7c, would account for the tendency of the two opposite charges to be drawn together. At the same time, the lines do not go straight across from one charge to the other but are bowed out, as they would be if they pushed each other aside. Similarly, the repulsion existing between the like charges in d of the figure is indicated by this second property of the lines. In connection with b and c of Fig. 15·10 the assumed properties of the lines of force together with the symmetry of their pattern explain the observed fact that there is no net force on either body in a uniform field.

Are lines of electric force *real?* Of course, we no more believe that the field is actually traversed by a set of stretched rubber bands than we endow with objective reality the lines of equal pressure or temperature on a weather map or the meridians and parallels on a geographical map. But in any such case the curves in question constitute a convenient representation of certain information. If we choose to follow Faraday in our way of thinking about lines of force, no harm can result as long as the analogies invoked are not carried too far. It is interesting to notice that, while Faraday did not profess extensive mathematical powers, the field idea and its representation by lines proved, in the hands of others, to be ideally suited to a strict mathematical treatment not only of electrostatic forces but of fields of other kinds as well (see page xii of Ref. 3).

15·12   Electrostatic Potential

The description of the electrostatic field is facilitated by introducing a concept called the *potential.* This quantity is a measure of

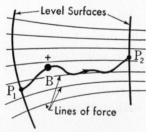

FIG. 15·11   Motion of a charge between two points in a field.

the tendency of a charge to move from one place to another in a field. Suppose, for example, that a small, positively charged body B (Fig. 15·11) is released at any place P_1 in an electrostatic field and allowed to move without acceleration. Any other point such as P_2 to which it may move as a result of the presence of the field is said to be at a *lower* potential than P_1. In particular, P_1 and P_2 may be two points of a wire or other conductor, in which case the *difference of potential* between them may be looked upon as the cause of the flow of current.[1]

There is a close correspondence between electrostatic potential

---

[1] Here again it must be remembered that in a metal the particles that actually move are the electrons; they go in a direction opposite to the conventional flow of current.

and the gravitational potential energy of a raised weight (page 99). If a body of small mass, say, a stone, is released in the neighborhood of any large body, such as the earth, the earth's gravitational field causes the stone to fall. In doing so the stone moves from a position where it had greater potential energy to one where it has less. The difference in PE of the stone in the two positions measures the work done by the agency that separates earth and stone by an amount equal to the distance between these two places.

Further, all points at the same distance from the center of the earth—that is, at the same level—are at the same potential. The work done in raising a weight from one of these level surfaces to any other depends only on the location of the two surfaces with respect to the center of the earth and not at all on the particular point in the lower surface from which one starts or the particular place in the upper surface where the path ends. Thus the work is given by PE $= mgh$, and besides depending on the values of m and g this is determined solely by the *vertical* distance between the level surfaces in which the initial and final locations lie.

In most problems involving either electric or gravitational potential, absolute values are not of interest and only a knowledge of the *difference* of potential between two positions is needed. Sea level forms a convenient level surface from which to measure gravitational PE. In electricity, whenever a reference level is required, the earth may be conveniently taken to have zero potential. A body is at a *positive* electrostatic potential if, when it is grounded, electrons flow up to it from the earth; its potential is *negative* if electrons flow from it to the earth when the ground connection is made.

15·13 Measurement of Potential; Units

In the gravitational situation the difference of potential of two level surfaces might be measured by the work done in moving a unit mass between them. In exactly the same way the measure of the electrostatic potential difference (PD) between two points (or between the level surfaces to which they belong) is the work done on unit charge when it is moved from one to the other. That is, using the symbol V for electrostatic potential,

$$\Delta V = \frac{\Delta W}{Q} \qquad (15 \cdot 3)$$

the Δ's representing, as always, changes in the quantities before which they appear. If the work is measured in ergs and the charge in esu, the potential difference is measured in *ergs per esu.* This unit proves somewhat large for most purposes connected with electric currents, and hence a smaller unit, called one *volt,* is used in practice. By definition,

$$1 \text{ volt} = \tfrac{1}{300} \text{ erg/esu} \qquad (15\cdot4)$$

For example, the potential difference maintained between the two wires of the ordinary house lighting circuit is about 115 volts. This means that for every esu of charge that flows through an appliance from one side of such a circuit to the other the electric company must deliver $\tfrac{115}{300} = 0.383$ erg of energy.

One coulomb was defined as 3×10^9 esu. Hence, to make 1 coulomb of charge pass between two points whose PD is 1 volt would require, according to Eq. (15·3), the expenditure of $(3 \times 10^9)/300 = 10^7$ ergs, or 1 joule of energy. In terms of practical units, then,

$$W_{\text{joules}} = Q_{\text{coulombs}} \cdot V_{\text{volts}} \qquad (15\cdot5)$$

The leaf electroscope described in the preceding pages is primarily a device for measuring *potential* rather than charge. This fact will be illustrated by considering the way in which such an instrument may be given a permanent charge by induction. As shown in Fig. 15·4 the leaf maintains a deflected position while a charged body is near the knob. The *net charge* on the electroscope system is *zero,* since no transfer to or from it has taken place. However, the *potential* of the system is *not zero.* Assuming the inducing body to be positive, the situation is represented in Fig. 15·12a. If the knob is now grounded as in *b,* electrons will come onto the system from the earth, attracted by the positive charge of the inducing rod. This action shows (page 281) that the electroscope was at a positive potential in *a.* Redistribution of the acquired electrons neutralizes the charge on leaf and plate, and the leaf hangs straight down. At the same time we know that the instrument is at zero potential because it is joined to the earth (whose potential is zero) by a conductor.

If the ground connection is now broken (sketch *c*), the system is still at zero potential but has a net negative charge, which was held on the knob throughout steps *b* and *c* by the presence of the inducing charge. When the latter is taken away, the extra electrons on the knob distribute themselves over the whole system, giving plate and leaf some additional negative charge, which causes the leaf to rise, as in *d.* The electroscope is then left with a net negative charge; also, it is at a negative potential.

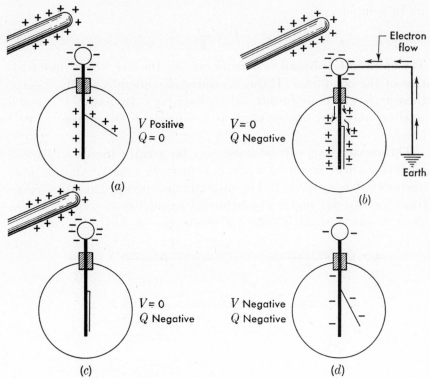

FIG. 15·12 Charging an electroscope by induction.

15·14 Capacity; Capacitors

How much electric charge can be put on a conductor? In principle there is no limit as long as the conductor is properly insulated
from its surroundings. A conductor does not behave toward electrification as a tank does toward water, for in the latter case there
is a definite limit to the capacity of the tank. Rather, the electrical
case is analogous to air confined under pressure in a tank. Pumping
more air into a tank raises the pressure within and makes it in-
creasingly difficult to pump in still more air.

In order to make a meaningful statement about the capacity
of the tank for air, the *pressure* at which it is confined must also
be given. In a similar way, the *electrical capacity*[1] of a conductor
is the constant **ratio of the quantity of charge on it** at any time
to the potential to which the application of this charge has raised

[1] More correctly but less frequently called "capacitance" when speaking of a
specific capacitor.

it. In symbols,

$$C = \frac{Q}{V} \tag{15·6}$$

The value of C is found to depend only on the size, shape, and location of the conductor. If Q is measured in coulombs and V in volts, then C is given in *farads* (after Faraday). In practice a much smaller unit, the *microfarad,* is required: 1 microfarad $= 10^{-6}$ farad.

The capacity of a conductor may be greatly increased by the inductive effect resulting when it is brought near to another conductor that is grounded. The usual arrangement, consisting effectively of two flat metal plates placed parallel to each other and a short distance apart, is called a condenser, or, better, a *capacitor*

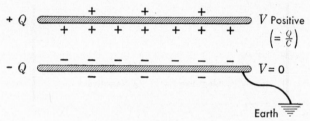

FIG. 15·13   A charged capacitor.

(Fig. 15·13). As mentioned, one of the pair is grounded. The two plates are separated by a layer of air or of some other dielectric material. Suppose the insulated plate is given a quantity Q of positive electrification. Electrons from the earth then flow to the other plate, giving it a total charge of $-Q$. The capacitor is said to be charged. The potentials of the two plates are as labeled in the figure.[1] If, after charging a capacitor, the two plates are joined by a wire, the excess electrons on one plate will flow over to the other, neutralizing its charge. The capacitor is said to have been discharged.

In Franklin's celebrated kite experiment he succeeded in charging a capacitor (Leyden jar) by connecting the kite string to the insulated coating, conclusively identifying lightning as an electrical phenomenon. In harmony with Eq. (15·6) the capacity is taken to be the amount of charge on *either* plate of a capacitor divided by the PD between the plates. In terms of its dimensions and the

[1] Why? What signs do the charge and potential have if the top plate was originally given a negative charge?

kind of insulating material used the capacity of a parallel-plate capacitor is given by

$$C_{\text{mfd}} = \frac{kA \times 10^{-5}}{36\pi d} \qquad (15 \cdot 7)$$

where A is the area of either plate (in square centimeters), d their distance apart (in centimeters), and k the dielectric coefficient (p. 274) of the material between the plates. Capacitors of various kinds are indispensable units in telephones, radio apparatus, and many other electrical devices.

SUMMARY

Electric charges are of two kinds, positive and negative. Like kinds repel, unlike kinds attract each other.

Electrostatic induction: The separation of charge on a conductor due to the influence of a nearby charged body. In a solid conductor, the charges that move are the (negative) electrons.

Coulomb's law: The force between two point charges is given by

$$f = \frac{Q_1 Q_2}{kd^2}$$

One *esu* of charge is that charge which exerts 1 dyne of force on an equal charge placed 1 cm from it in a vacuum. One *coulomb* = 3 × 10^9 esu.

Electrostatic field: Any region where a charged body experiences a force. The *field strength* is a vector whose magnitude is given by the force (in dynes) acting on 1 esu. Its direction is that of the force on a *positive* charge.

Potential: The difference in electrostatic potential (PD) between two points in a field is measured by the work done when 1 esu moves between these points. One *volt* = ⅟₃₀₀ erg/esu. A positive charge will of itself move from a point of higher to one of lower potential.

Capacitance: Ratio of quantity of charge on a conductor to its potential. In practical units

$$C_{\text{farads}} = \frac{Q_{\text{coulombs}}}{V_{\text{volts}}}$$

Capacitor: Essentially a pair of conducting plates separated by a layer of insulating material. One of the plates is usually grounded.

READING REFERENCES

1. Bragg, W. L.: "Electricity," Macmillan, New York, 1936. A refreshing and original treatment of the subject in terms easy to understand. Read Chap. I at this point.

2. Taylor, Lloyd W.: "Physics, the Pioneer Science," Houghton Mifflin, Boston, 1946. Electrostatics is admirably treated in Chap. 40.
3. Moulton, F. R., and J. J. Schifferes: "The Autobiography of Science," Doubleday, New York, 1945. For Franklin's account of the kite experiment, see pp. 234–236.
4. Magie, W. F.: "A Source Book in Physics," McGraw-Hill, New York, 1935. Coulomb's experiments on the force between charged bodies are described on p. 408.
5. Freeman, Ira M.: "Invitation to Experiment," Dutton, New York, 1940. Suggestions for performing many of the experiments of the present chapter with homemade equipment are given in Chap. 15.

FILM

"Electrostatics," Encyclopaedia Britannica Films. 16 mm, sound, 1 reel.

EXERCISES

1. What is the strength and direction of the electric field at a place 10 cm due north of a small spherical object carrying a charge of 300 esu? What force would act on a single electron (charge 4.8×10^{-10} esu) placed there?

2. Two equal, small conducting spheres carrying charges of $+100$ and -240 esu are brought into contact and then placed 3.5 cm apart. With what force do they then act on each other? Is the force one of attraction or repulsion?

3. Four identical conducting spheres, A, B, C, and D are suspended by silk threads. Ball A is touched by a rubbed glass rod, and then each of the other three is brought into contact with A and removed again, one after the other. When A and B are then placed with their centers 5 cm apart, they are found to repel each other with a force of 16 dynes. How much charge did the rod originally deliver to A?

4. Two small charged bodies, carrying $+10$ and $+40$ esu, respectively, are placed 6 cm apart. Find the location of a point between them where the electric-field strength is zero.

5. An experimenter rubs a fountain pen on his coat sleeve and then touches the pen to an insulated metal ball. If a charge of -0.010 esu is thereby given to the ball, about how many electrons were transferred from the pen to the ball?

6. In Fig. 15·5, why do not *all* the free electrons in the body move to the end closest to the charged rod?

7. Is the earth's gravitational field at a locality near sea level a uniform field? Which drawing of Fig. 15·7 would represent this field? What can be said of a *limited* portion of the earth's gravitational field?

8. Compute the force of attraction between the electron and the

proton in a hydrogen atom. The two particles are 5.3×10^{-9} cm apart, and their charges are each of magnitude 4.8×10^{-10} esu.

9. Read the description of the van de Graaff generator on pages 34 to 36 of Ref. 1.

10. In order to move a certain small charged body between two points in an electric field of PD 360 ergs/esu, 45 ergs of work must be done. What is the amount of charge on the body?

11. How much additional charge must be put on a conductor of capacitance 40 mfd in order to raise its potential by 50 volts?

12. A compact form of capacitor used in communications work consists of two long strips of tin foil separated by an insulating strip of treated paper. The assembly is rolled up into the form of a small cylinder. If each foil is 6 cm wide and 30 m long and the paper separator is 0.010 cm thick and of dielectric coefficient 2.2, what is the capacitance of the unit?

Chapter 16

ELECTRIC CURRENTS

16·1 Nature of a Current

The concept of an electric current as a state of motion of electric charges was introduced in Chap. 15. In a solid conductor such as a wire the current consists of a movement of electrons only. In certain solutions and in gases, however, currents are carried by means of positively and negatively charged atoms.[1] Furthermore, a beam of electrons or charged atoms may be made to traverse a vacuum without being confined to a conductor at all; yet such a beam constitutes an electric current in the true sense of the term. In fact, currents of the kind just mentioned are used in some of the most important experiments and applications of modern physics, several of which will be discussed later.

There is a close analogy between an electric current and the flow of a fluid. Restricting attention for the moment to conduction in a wire, the passage of electrons along the wire is comparable with the passage of water through a system of pipes. The rate at which the liquid flows past any point in the pipe line might be measured in such units as gallons per second or cubic feet per hour—that is, as quantity of liquid per unit time. In the electrical case the *intensity of the current* (sometimes called "current strength," or simply "current") is likewise measured by the quantity of charge passing during each unit of time. The practical unit of electric current is the *ampere,*[2] defined as a rate of flow of *one coulomb* of charge *per second,* or, using the conventional symbol I for current strength,

$$I_{\text{amp}} = \frac{Q_{\text{coulomb}}}{t_{\text{sec}}} \tag{16·1}$$

[1] These phenomena will be described below.

[2] After A. M. Ampère, brilliant French mathematician and physicist, whose important scientific work was done in the early part of the nineteenth century. His major contributions were connected with the relationship between electric currents and magnetism to be discussed later.

The current flowing in an ordinary 60-watt lamp amounts to about half an ampere.

To anyone who has not thought about the matter, the current in a wire would seem to be something that moves with lightninglike speed. This is far from true; the electrons in a metal are so numerous that, despite the very small charge carried by each, only a very slow *drift* of electrons is needed to maintain a sizable current. In an ordinary appliance the rate of electron drift may be only a fraction of a millimeter per second. This is superposed on the extremely swift *random* heat motion of the conduction electrons, which amounts on the average to about 500 kilometers per second.[1]

In a piece of copper wire carrying no current, the electrons passing through any cross section of the wire in either direction constitute a current of about a hundred billion amperes! The feeble currents used in telephone circuits amount to a one-way drift of perhaps one ten-millionth ampere, or a condition in which the natural electron motions are put off balance by the incredibly small amount of about 1 part in 10^{18}.

16·2   Potential Difference and Its Role in a Circuit

When a charged rod is touched to an insulated conductor or when the two plates of a charged capacitor are joined by a wire, there is a brief flow of charge, which soon stops when equilibrium is reached. To maintain a continuing current, two things are necessary: (1) there must be a *closed circuit,* or continuous path, for the charge; (2) a *difference of potential* must be maintained between two points of this circuit. In the examples just mentioned there is initially a difference of potential, but it soon vanishes as the charge redistributes itself. The discharge of a capacitor is analogous to what happens when two tanks containing water at different levels are joined by a pipe. The liquid flows until, in the final state, all the water has come to the same level (potential), and no further flow takes place.

The hydraulic analogue of a simple electric circuit is a system of pipes joined to a circulating pump (Fig. 16·1). As soon as the pump is started, water flows in all parts of the piping; as soon as the battery is connected into a complete circuit, electrons begin to drift through the conductors. Because of the intense Coulomb repulsion

[1] In the same way, the molecules of water whose organized motion constitutes the moderate flow of water in a pipe are at the same time moving individually in random directions with speeds a hundred thousand or more times the speed of the water as a whole.

between electrons when they are close together, the electron cloud in a metal behaves like a perfectly incompressible liquid. The moment that current is established anywhere in a simple circuit, current exists in all parts of the circuit. It is the attainment of this condition, not the movement of individual electrons, that occurs almost at once when the circuit is closed.

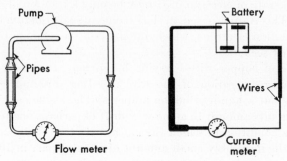

Fig. 16·1   Analogous liquid and electric circuits.

The battery does not "produce electricity" any more than the water pump manufactures water; it serves only to set in motion charges already present in the system. Its function is correctly described as maintaining a difference of potential (PD) between its terminals, and it is this PD which is responsible for and necessary to the existence of the current in the circuit.

Besides batteries, whose action depends on chemical effects to be described presently, there are several other practical sources of potential difference. *Generators* (dynamos), used wherever large currents are needed commercially, convert mechanical into electrical energy; the principle of their operation will be dealt with in Chap. 17. The *photoelectric effect* involves the release of electrons from matter by means of light, and the resulting current may

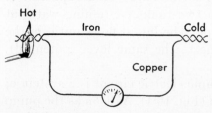

Fig. 16·2   The thermoelectric effect.

be used to measure the intensity of illumination. Because of its great theoretical importance, photoelectricity will be discussed further in Chap. 20.

Heating one of the two junctions in a circuit made up of two different metals (Fig. 16·2) gives rise to a PD producing a measurable current by means of the so-called *thermoelectric effect*. The strength of the resulting current may be used as a measure of the temperature difference between the junctions (thermoelectric thermometer). When a slight pressure is applied to certain crystals, detectable potential differences arise between metal plates in contact with crystal. This *piezoelectric effect* is used in some microphones and phonograph pickups.

16·3   Volta's Experiments

Shortly before the end of the eighteenth century the Italian physician and biologist Galvani discovered the effect upon which the action of chemical batteries depends. In experiments involving the dissection of a frog he found that the frog's leg twitched vigorously whenever it came into contact with two different metals, such as brass and iron. Galvani chose to believe that the contractions were due to some kind of "animal electricity," and a great series of discussions and heated arguments began to rage between prominent scientists of that day.

The true explanation was finally given by a countryman of Galvani's, the physicist Alessandro Volta, who ascribed the phenomenon to an effect of the moist contact between dissimilar metals. He tested this notion by eliminating the animal tissue altogether and built what came to be known as a voltaic pile—a stack of alternate zinc and copper disks separated by pieces of leather or paper soaked in salt water or lye. From this device he was able to obtain effects similar to those from generators of static charges or from charged capacitors, with the new feature that the operations could be repeated many times without replenishing any part of the system. After a long proc-

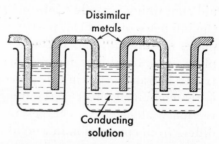

Dissimilar metals

Conducting solution

Fig. 16·3   Volta's "crown of cups."

ess of development there became available reliable and readily controlled sources of electricity operating on this principle. These chemical sources dominated the field of current electricity until the evolution of the generator about a century after Volta's experiments.

In addition to the electric pile Volta had constructed a "crown of cups" consisting of a series of vessels containing brine or lye and joined by alternate strips of two kinds of metal (Fig. 16·3). Each unit of the chain, consisting of a plate of each metal immersed in the solution, is called a *voltaic cell*. The whole series of several cells is called a *battery*. The dry cells now widely used in flashlights, portable radios, etc., use zinc and carbon as the two elements and a moist chemical paste in place of the liquid.

16·4   Ions in Liquids; Electrolysis

The key to an explanation of the voltaic cell was not realized until the latter part of the nineteenth century, principally through the work of the physical chemists Arrhenius in Sweden and Nernst in Germany. Most liquids, such as oils, organic compounds, and even water when extremely pure, do not conduct electricity to any great extent; however, the substances classed chemically as acids, bases, or salts, when in solution or melted, are good conductors. In all such cases it is found that a certain proportion of the molecules of the active substance split apart (*dissociate*) into individual atoms or groups of atoms at the time when the material is dissolved or melted. These entities differ from ordinary atoms in that they carry electric charges—positive if they are atoms of a metal, negative if atoms of a nonmetal. They are called *ions*. *An ion,* then, *is an atom or group of atoms bearing a resultant electric charge.*

In the process called *electrolysis* a difference of potential is applied to two plates (*electrodes*) immersed in an *electrolyte,* or liquid containing ions. The ions drift slowly through the liquid under the influence of the field, positive ions moving toward the negative plate, or *cathode,* and negative ions moving toward the positive plate, or *anode.*[1] The net result is that not only matter but electricity is transported in this process. The current in the electrolyte is the combined effect of the motion of positive charges in one direction and negative charges in the opposite direction. Thus it differs from conduction in a solid metal, where the current consists entirely of the motion of electrons in one direction.

The ions drift with speeds of the order of 0.001 cm/sec. When an ion reaches the electrode to which it has been attracted, it gives up its charge, becoming an ordinary atom of the element in question. If this is a metal, the atoms may adhere to the electrode (the cathode in this instance) in the form of a coating, in which case the process is the familiar one of *electroplating.* In other instances the neutralized ions may react chemically to form other products, or they may form bubbles of gas, which escape from the liquid. Quantitative aspects of the process of electrolysis will be discussed below

[1] The terms appearing here were introduced by Faraday.

(Sec. 16·7). We return now to a brief consideration of what happens in a voltaic cell.

16·5 Action of a Voltaic Cell

In electrolysis the application of a potential difference produces chemical changes within the cell; in the voltaic cell the reverse occurs, chemical effects serving to produce a usable potential difference. Figure 16·4a is a schematic representation of a solution of

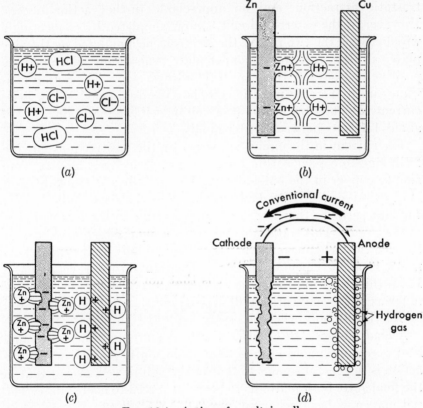

FIG. 16·4 Action of a voltaic cell.

hydrochloric acid (HCl) in water. Most of the hydrochloric acid molecules have dissociated into hydrogen ions (positive) and chloride ions (negative). In b, zinc (Zn) and copper (Cu) plates have been inserted. The zinc atoms have a strong tendency to detach themselves from the plate (dissolve), coming off as zinc ions, which carry a positive charge, and leaving behind electrons on the plate. Thus a PD is set up between the solution and the zinc plate.

The accumulating zinc ions drive some of the hydrogen ions toward the copper plate. In the meantime, some atoms of the copper plate have dissolved, but these are very few compared with the number of zinc atoms that have gone into solution. In sketch c, hydrogen ions have given up their positive charge to the copper plate. The neutral hydrogen atoms thus produced will form bubbles of hydrogen gas, which escapes from the solution. But the zinc ions are held to the neighborhood of the zinc plate by electrostatic attraction, and no appreciable further action occurs. However, if the external circuit is now completed by connecting a wire between the two plates, the electrons accumulated on the zinc plate can flow over to the copper plate, where they neutralize the positive charges left there by the hydrogen ions. The action continues until the zinc plate is completely eaten away. When little current is being drawn from it, a voltaic cell can maintain a PD of about 1.5 volts between its terminals.

The current in the circuit is carried by the positive ions moving from zinc to copper within the cell and by electrons moving from zinc to copper in the outside wire. The net effect is the same as if only positive electricity had circulated in the sense indicated by the large arrow—that is, from copper to zinc in the external part of the circuit. This is taken as the *conventional direction* of current by electrical engineers, although what actually takes place in a metal is a movement of negative electrons in the reverse sense. From this point on, the sense of a current will always be specified in terms of the conventional direction, and the electron motion will be referred to only when necessary.

A *lead storage cell* consists of a lead plate and one containing lead peroxide immersed in a dilute solution of sulfuric acid. The action is in general similar to that of the voltaic cell, except that in the final state both plates have been converted to lead sulfate. The cell may now be "recharged" by passing a current through it in the direction opposite to that which it previously furnished. This restores the plates to their original state, and the cell may be used repeatedly. A battery consisting of three such cells (total "voltage" about 6) is the source of current used in an automobile. The storage battery does not "store electricity"; the energy of the charging current is localized in the battery in the form of chemical energy, which is again converted into electrical energy when the battery is in use.

16·6 Chemical Equivalents

The chemical discoveries made by Dalton at the beginning of the nineteenth century (page 114n.) conclusively established the atomic nature of matter. Further evidence was soon to be provided by Faraday's quantitative experiments on electrolysis.

In chemistry we determine the so-called *atomic weights* of the elements. These are numbers that are proportional to the weights of single atoms of the elements, and the set of numbers is arbitrarily based on a value of 16.000 for oxygen. An amount of any element equal to its atomic weight in grams actually contains

Table 16·1 Chemical Equivalents

	Substance	Symbol	Atomic weight	Valence	Chemical equivalent $= \dfrac{atomic\ weight}{valence}$
Group 1: Metals	Hydrogen	H	1.008	1	1.008
	Silver	Ag	107.9	1	107.9
	Copper	Cu	63.57	2	31.79
				1	63.57
	Lead	Pb	207.2	4	51.80
				2	103.6
	Aluminum	Al	26.97	3	8.990
Group 2: Non-metals	Oxygen	O	16.00	2	8.000
	Chlorine	Cl	35.46	1	35.46
	Sulfate group	SO$_4$	96.06*	2	48.03
	Nitrate group	NO$_3$	62.01*	1	62.01

* Sum of atomic weights of constituents.

6.02×10^{23} atoms (page 130). Dalton and others established the fact that when given elements combine to form a specified compound, they do so in a definite proportion by weight. Table 16·1 gives the fundamental combining weights of a number of common elements, including two clusters of atoms that behave as single entities in their usual chemical reactions but that do not lead an independent existence and so cannot be isolated. Metals or units that behave like metals are listed in the first group; nonmetals or combinations like them are in the second group.

The simplest and most common chemical compounds are formed when an element in Group 1 combines with one from Group 2, and when such unions take place the weights involved are proportional to the combining weights listed. For example, if a chemist sets out to prepare the compound aluminum chloride and chooses to use 8.990 gm of aluminum, he finds that exactly 35.46 gm of chlorine will be required. Any excess of chlorine present will be rejected and will be left uncombined after the reaction is over; if less than this amount of chlorine is available, some of the aluminum will be left in the free state. For some entries in the table more than one possibility exists, as indicated by the multiple listings for copper and lead.

The number given as the *valence* is the chemist's measure of the combining power of an atom of given kind in the sense of the number of other atoms it can hold in combination. Valence may be referred to picturesquely as the number of "hooks" by which an atom seizes other suitable atoms in order to form a molecule of a compound.[1] The valence of a given element (or group) is equal to the number of times the equivalent weight is contained in the atomic weight (group weight).

16·7 Electrolysis and the Charge on an Ion

Faraday's measurements showed that *the mass of a given substance released* in an electrolytic cell *is proportional to the total quantity of electricity that has passed* through the cell. For example, if 1000 coulombs of electricity is sent through a silver plating cell, it is found that 1.118 gm of the metal plates out on the cathode (and the same weight dissolves from the anode). If 10,000 coulombs passes, 11.180 gm deposits, etc. This fact strongly suggests that each atom (ion) of a given element carries a definite amount of electricity through the solution. Faraday himself referred to the "atomicity of electric charge," anticipating the long sequence of corroborative discoveries and measurements that followed in related fields.

Since the quantity of electricity delivered in a given time by a steady current is, by Eq. (16·1), $Q = I \cdot t$, the result given above may be stated in the form

$$M = kIt \qquad\qquad (16·2)$$

where M is the mass of the element in question that deposits and k is a constant of proportionality. But the value of k differs from one element to another.

---

[1] More objectively, each "valence bond" is interpreted as the sharing of an electron between two combining atoms.

The fundamental relation between the values of k for different elements is disclosed by passing the same quantity of electricity through a number of cells, as illustrated in Fig. 16·5. Suppose that the apparatus is allowed to run until exactly 107.9 gm, or one equivalent weight, of silver has been deposited in the silver cell. Then it is found that equivalent weights of the various elements are liberated in the several other cells as well. The interpretation of this fact leads to important conclusions. A silver ion is formed by detaching a single electron from the normal silver atom. This leaves the ion with a positive charge equal in amount to the charge of an electron. The ion may be designated Ag^+. When 107.9 gm of silver is transported electrolytically, a total of $N = 6.02 \times 10^{23}$

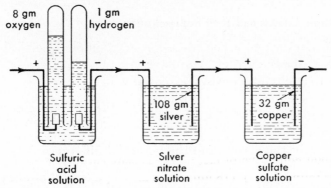

FIG. 16·5   A given quantity of electricity deposits equivalent weights.

electron charges are thus delivered, since this is the number of atoms in one atomic weight of any element.

In the case of copper, on the other hand, only 31.79 gm, or *half* the atomic weight, is found to be transported when the same total charge passes. This must mean that each copper ion carries twice as much charge as each silver ion, and the former is written Cu^{++}. Similarly, an ion of the element aluminum is Al^{+++}, and one of oxygen is O^{--}, etc. The modern interpretation of what chemists have been calling *valence is the number of electronic charges,* either positive or negative, *carried by an ion* of the element; and it is now known that atoms are held together in chemical combination by electrical forces.

Electrolysis experiments allow us to compute the quantity of charge carried by each ion. The amount of electricity required to liberate one chemical equivalent of any substance is called

one faraday; it is found experimentally to be about 96,500 coulombs. Now one equivalent weight of an element of unit valence
consists of $N = 6.02 \times 10^{23}$ atoms (page 130), so that the charge
carried by each ion of such an element will be

$$\frac{96,500}{6.02 \times 10^{23}} = 1.60 \times 10^{-19} \text{ coulomb}$$

This first determination of the **electron charge** was later verified
by other more direct methods (Chap. 18), one difficulty with the
above calculation being the fact that the value of N was not known
with sufficient accuracy. Nowadays the process is reversed, and the
value of N is computed from the more accurately determined figure for the electron charge.

16·8 Simple Circuits and Their Representation

We now return to a consideration of a simple electrical circuit
carrying a steady current. You have already seen (pages 288–290)
that such a circuit consists essentially of a source of potential
difference (such as a battery) whose terminals are joined by a conductor. A useful addition, in practice, is a simple switch for closing
and opening the circuit. If it is desired to know the magnitude of
the current in the circuit and the potential difference between any
two points, suitable measuring instruments called, respectively,
ammeters and **voltmeters** may be used. The principles and construction of such devices will be described in the next chapter.

Figure 16·6 is an electrician's diagram of such a simple circuit,
showing the conventional representation for each part. B is a battery consisting of three cells. The long stroke represents the positive terminal of each cell and the short, thick line the negative.
The zigzag line R is the conductor through which we wish to pass
the current, while the straight lines represent heavy connecting
wires. The ammeter A is connected **directly into the circuit,** while
the voltmeter V is in a **side circuit,** its terminals being connected
between the two points whose difference of potential is to be determined. When the switch K is closed, a steady current flows in
the circuit and the meters assume steady readings.

16·9 Ohm's Law

What features of the circuit determine the strength of the existing current? This question was answered early in the nineteenth

century by the careful experiments of a German science teacher, Georg Ohm. By inserting wires of different lengths, cross sections, and materials in place of R in a circuit like that of Fig. 16·6, he found that the current indicated by the meter A is directly proportional to the cross-section area of the wire and inversely proportional to its length, and depends in addition on the kind of metal of which the wire is made. The best conductors in this sense were found to be silver, copper, and gold.

Using a given wire, Ohm next tried the effect of changing the PD applied to its ends. This could be done, for example, by altering the number of cells in the battery B. It was found that the current in the circuit is strictly proportional to the applied PD. Expressed algebraically, this would be stated $I = kV$, where k is some characteristic of a given conductor, which may be called its **conductance**. It is more common, however, to look upon the wire as something that limits the strength of the current, and thus the reciprocal of k—the

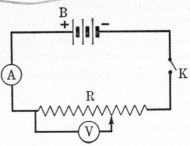

FIG. 16·6 Simple electric circuit.

resistance R of the wire—is the quantity usually specified. The resistance of an ordinary conductor is the same whether the current flows through it in one direction or the reverse. By using R, Ohm's result may be written

$$I = \frac{V}{R} \qquad\qquad (16\cdot3)$$

This is the celebrated **Ohm's law** of the electric circuit. In words, it states that *the current* in a simple circuit *is directly proportional to the applied potential difference and inversely proportional to the resistance* of the circuit.

In the customary fashion the fundamental equation is used to define a unit for the measurement of R. It is agreed that, if I is measured in amperes and V in volts, then R is specified in a unit called the **ohm**. Thus, a 1-ohm resistor is one that allows a current of 1 amp to flow when a PD of 1 volt is applied to its ends. For instance, the resistance of the filament in an ordinary 60-watt lamp is over 200 ohms, while the heating element of an electric iron may have a resistance of only around 20 ohms. It follows from Eq.

(16·3) that when both appliances are used with the same impressed voltage, the iron must carry about ten times as strong a current as the lamp.

There is an enormous range of resistance values among ordinary materials. A 1-cm cube of one of the best metallic conductors offers a resistance of only about 10^{-6} ohm to a current flowing between opposite faces of the cube. Semiconductors range from around 10^{-2} to 10^5 ohms, while the best insulators have resistances of the order of 10^{16} ohms.

The resistance of a given conductor is not an invariable quantity but changes to some extent with change in temperature, as originally observed by Ohm. For most conductors there is a slight increase in resistance as the temperature is raised. Once the rate of increase has been determined for a given kind of wire, the process may be turned around and temperatures determined by measuring the change in resistance of a coil of such wire (resistance thermometer). The most direct way to find the resistance of a conductor is to apply a given PD to its ends, measure the resulting current by means of an ammeter, and compute R by Ohm's law.

16·10 Potentials in a Series Circuit

As a modification of the simple circuit of Fig. 16·6 consider the one diagramed in Fig. 16·7, where a number of conductors are connected *in series,* or joined end to end. The current is the same in all these units, since any charge flowing into the first must next pass through the second, and so on—there being no side branches or other alternate paths.[1] Neither can there be any accumulation of charge at any point (page 290). It is therefore characteristic of a simple series circuit that the current is the same at all points. This means that, no matter at what place in the circuit the ammeter is inserted, its reading will be the same.

Suppose one terminal of the voltmeter to be connected at C and the other to some point D on the wire R_1. The point C is at the same potential as the positive terminal of the battery; for both the ammeter and the connecting wires have very low resistance, and this makes C in effect merely an extension of the battery terminal

[1] It is true that the voltmeter and its connectors constitute a bypass, but the resistance of such an instrument is ordinarily so high compared with that of the other units of the circuit that the voltmeter current is negligible compared with that in the main circuit.

itself. On the other hand, D will be at a lower potential than C, there being a steady fall of potential as we go to the right along R_1. This is analogous to the constant rate of decrease of pressure observed in going along a pipe carrying a steady current of fluid or the constant decline of temperature existing along a rod that is conducting heat from a hot body to a cold one.

At any time the voltmeter reads the difference in potential between C and D. If D is taken farther and farther to the right along R_1, the meter reading increases, since the potential of C remains

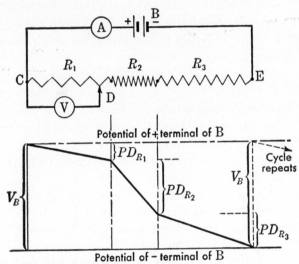

Fig. 16·7   Fall of potential in a series circuit.

fixed, but that of the other side of the voltmeter becomes progressively lower. The graph below the circuit represents the way in which the potential of the right-hand voltmeter terminal varies as D moves progressively to the right. All potentials are here arbitrarily referred to that of the negative terminal of the battery—the point in the circuit which has a lower potential than any other. If R_2 has a higher resistance per unit length than R_1, the graph line for the former will be steeper, as shown. For R_3, which has a smaller resistance per unit length, the line is less steep. The moving contact of the voltmeter has now arrived at E, which is at the same potential as the negative terminal of the battery. The battery itself may be looked upon as maintaining the sudden "lift" in potential, V_B, which brings conditions back to those at the positive terminal.

16·11   Equivalent Resistance of a Series Circuit

The fall in potential that exists across the ends of any one of the conductors (or across any portion of any one) when the current is flowing may be looked upon as the cause of the current. The magnitude of the current, the measured potential drop, and the resistance of the part of the conductor in question simultaneously satisfy Ohm's law—that is, *Ohm's law applies to any part of a circuit as well as to the circuit as a whole.* In considering *an entire circuit, V* represents the sum (with due attention to direction) of the driving potentials maintained by all the batteries or other sources of voltage in the circuit; in applying Ohm's law to any *part of a circuit, V* represents the fall of potential along the conductor caused by its resistance.

The fact that Ohm's law is applicable to all or to part of a circuit often makes it possible to reduce complicated groups of resistors effectively to a single unit whose resistance can be calculated from those of the separate parts. For example, suppose that a number of conductors are joined *in series,* as in Fig. 16·7. What is the combined resistance of this combination? We know from the diagram that the total potential drop across a number of conductors in series is the sum of the separate PD's, so that if V_1, V_2, V_3, etc., are the separate values the total drop will be

$$V = V_1 + V_2 + V_3 + \cdots \qquad (16\cdot4)$$

where the dots indicate any further V's that may be present in the set.

If R represents the equivalent resistance of the whole set, then Ohm's law applied to the entire circuit is, by Eq. (16·3), $V = IR$. Similarly, applied to each conductor separately, $V_1 = IR_1$; $V_2 = IR_2$; $V_3 = IR_3$, etc. Note that the current I is the same for all. Substituting these values into (16·4),

$$IR = IR_1 + IR_2 + IR_3 + \cdots$$

or

$$R = R_1 + R_2 + R_3 + \cdots \qquad (16\cdot5)$$

This states that *the equivalent resistance of a number of conductors in series is the sum of the individual resistances.*

Example 1: Two conductors of resistance 2 ohms and 3 ohms are connected in a simple series circuit with a 10-volt battery. What current does the battery deliver, and what is the PD across each conductor?

The equivalent resistance of both conductors in series is

$$2 + 3 = 5 \text{ ohms}$$

Upon applying Ohm's law to the entire circuit, the current is then

$$I = \frac{V}{R} = \frac{10}{5} = 2 \text{ amp}$$

The PD across the 2-ohm conductor is given by applying Ohm's law to this part of the circuit: $V_1 = IR_1 = 2 \times 2 = 4$ volts. Similarly, the PD across the 3-ohm element is $V_2 = IR_2 = 2 \times 3 = 6$ volts. The sum of the two PD's is 10, the voltage of the battery, as it must be.

Example 2: The solution and contacts within a battery possess a small but not always negligible resistance called the *internal resistance.* Suppose that in a signaling installation 10 dry cells, each having a terminal PD under no load of 1.5 volts and an internal resistance of 0.05 ohm, are joined in series with a coil of resistance 2 ohms. What current exists in the circuit, and what is the reading of a voltmeter connected across the battery when the current is flowing?

The total resistance of the circuit will be

$$2.0 + (10 \times 0.05) = 2.5 \text{ ohms}$$

The driving potential of the entire battery will be $10 \times 1.5 = 15$ volts. Ohm's law for the circuit as a whole then gives $I = 15/2.5 = 6$ amp. The reading of the voltmeter will be *less than* 15 volts, for there is a potential drop of amount $V = IR_i$ (R_i = total internal resistance) *in the battery itself.* This internal fall of potential amounts to

$$6 \times 10 \times 0.05 = 3 \text{ volts}$$

hence the voltmeter reads only $15 - 3 = 12$ volts. This result also follows from the fact that the voltmeter, while connected across the battery, is at the same time connected across the coil. The PD between the ends of the coil is $V = IR = 6 \times 2 = 12$ volts, as above.

The outcome of the computation clarifies the distinction between the driving potential of a battery and the PD between its terminals during operation. The former exists only as long as the load is negligible; but as soon as the battery is required to drive appreciable current in the circuit, it is no longer able to maintain this value of the PD between its terminals unless the internal resistance—and so the internal fall of potential—is inappreciable.

16·12 Equivalent Resistance of a Branched Circuit

If it is desired to interrupt the current in any one of a set of conductors connected in series, then the current must be stopped in all of them. On the other hand, electrical household appliances should be independently operable; for this reason they are connected *in parallel* as shown schematically in Fig. 16·8. It is not difficult to compute the combined resistance in this case. We note that the current in the main circuit divides at A among the several branches and that the separate currents reunite at B. Thus we have

$$I = I_1 + I_2 + I_3 + \cdots \tag{16·6}$$

Since all individual conductors have the points A and B in common, the PD must be the same for each of them and this is the

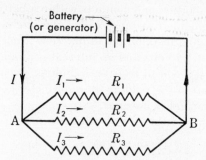

FIG. 16·8   Conductors in parallel.

total drop in the circuit. Ohm's law applied to the entire circuit yields $I = V/R$; for the several elements, $I_1 = V/R_1$, $I_2 = V/R_2$, etc. Substituting in Eq. (16·6) gives

$$\frac{V}{R} = \frac{V}{R_1} + \frac{V}{R_2} + \frac{V}{R_3} + \cdots$$

or

$$\frac{1}{R} = \frac{1}{R_1} + \frac{1}{R_2} + \frac{1}{R_3} + \cdots \tag{16·7}$$

The reciprocal of the equivalent resistance of a number of conductors in parallel is equal to the sum of the reciprocals of the several values.[1]

Example: Three conductors of resistance 4, 6, and 12 ohms are connected in parallel, and a 3-volt battery is connected across their common

[1] You should avoid making the mistake of inverting both sides of the equation *term by term*. All the fractions on the right must first be brought over a common denominator. In fact, this is the best way to reduce a numerical problem in order to avoid inaccuracies caused by rounding off decimal values. After inversion, the terms of the fraction may be divided out and a decimal result obtained.

terminals (circuit similar to Fig. 16·8). What current does the battery deliver, and what is the current in each branch?

The equivalent resistance R of the set is given by

$$\frac{1}{R} = \frac{1}{4} + \frac{1}{6} + \frac{1}{12} = \frac{6}{12} \quad \text{or} \quad R = 2 \text{ ohms}$$

Note that the value of R is less than that of any of the separate resistances. This is understandable since every time an additional branch is connected in a parallel circuit another path is provided for the passage of current: the conductance $(1/R)$ of the circuit is thus increased.

The current in the main circuit is $I = V/R = \frac{3}{2} = 1.5$ amp. The current in the 4-ohm resistor is $I_1 = V/R_1 = \frac{3}{4} = 0.75$ amp. Similarly, the current in the 6-ohm branch is $\frac{3}{6} = 0.50$ amp, and that in the 12-ohm branch is $\frac{3}{12} = 0.25$ amp. The sum is, of course, 1.50 amp, as required.

It should be noted that the main current divides among the several branches in such a way that greater amounts flow in the branches of smaller resistance. The often-heard statement that "the current takes the path of least resistance" really should be "*most of the current* takes the path of least resistance." But there is always some current in the other branches, too.

16·13   Importance and Limitations of Ohm's Law

While series and parallel connections constitute two very common arrangements of conductors, other more complicated hookups are often met with in practice. It is possible, by using generalizations of Ohm's law, to solve such "network" problems and even to handle examples where the current strength varies with time. These more complex situations will not be dealt with here.

It should be mentioned also that, while Ohm's law is valid for the electron currents in solid conductors, it does **not** hold for the ion currents in electrolytes. Neither is it applicable to the conduction of electricity in gases or to electron currents in a vacuum, to be described in later chapters.

In closing the present discussion it may be pointed out that Ohm's law, together with its extensions, succeeded in placing the whole subject of current electricity on a firm, exact basis and opened the way for the remarkable electrotechnical developments of modern times.

16·14   Power Expended in a Circuit

Equation (15·5) on page 282 gave the amount of energy W (in joules) expended in moving a quantity Q (in coulombs) of charge between two points whose potential difference is V (in volts) as $W = QV$. If both sides of this relation are divided by the time t (in seconds) taken to transfer the charge, the result is

$$\frac{W}{t} = \frac{Q}{t} V$$

But W/t is merely the rate of doing work (in joules per second), or the *power* that is expended (in watts) and Q/t is, by Eq. (16·1), the strength of the current I (in amperes) that flows. Then the above equation becomes simply

$$P_{\text{watts}} = I_{\text{amp}} V_{\text{volts}} \tag{16·8}$$

This means that *the rate of expenditure of energy* in any element of a circuit *is equal to the product of the current flowing and the PD between the terminals* of this element. For example, if a certain appliance draws a current of 4 amp when connected to a 120-volt circuit, it is taking energy from the source at the rate of 480 watts. If the current is variable in strength, the equation still gives the *instantaneous* value of the power.

What becomes of the energy used to maintain a current in a circuit? The answer depends on the nature of the items that make up the circuit. If there is a motor connected into the circuit, this transforms some of the expended electrical energy into mechanical work; if a storage battery is being charged, some electrical energy is converted into chemical energy. Other units that may be present, such as capacitors or coils, may change some of the energy of the current into that of electric fields or of radiated electric waves. But always the fate of at least part of the energy put into a circuit by the battery or generator is *heat.*

Whenever a current flows in any material conductor, some of the energy goes into the form of random motion of the molecules by a process analogous to friction. This happens in the connecting wires of a circuit, in the windings of a motor, even in the electrolyte of a battery that is being charged. And there are certain appliances where the heating effect is exactly what is wanted—electric toasters, heating pads, filament lamps, etc. If it is desired to know the rate of dissipation of energy in such an element directly in heat units, this can be obtained at once from Eq. (16·8). Since 4.18 joules of mechanical energy is equivalent to 1 cal (page 132), it follows that 1 watt—which is 1 joule/sec—is equivalent to

$1/4.18 = 0.239$ cal/sec. Then the power equation (16·8) becomes

$$H_{cal/sec} = 0.239 I_{amp} \cdot V_{volts} \qquad (16·9)$$

Alternative forms of this relation may be obtained by substituting for either I or V, using Ohm's law. For instance, in terms of the resistance of the conductor and the potential applied, this becomes $H = 0.239 V^2/R$; in terms of resistance and current, $H = 0.239 I^2 R$. Inasmuch as the resistance of a conductor varies with its temperature, the heating produced by the current will alter the value of R, and care must be taken to use the value appropriate to the temperature attained in any particular experiment.

Example: A lamp whose resistance is 210 ohms is connected to a 100-volt generator by means of two long wires, each of resistance 20 ohms. Find (a) the current in the lamp, (b) the PD across it, and (c) the amount of heat developed in the lamp in 5.0 min.

(a) The total resistance of the (series) circuit is $20 + 210 + 20 = 250$ ohms. Hence, by Ohm's law, the current in the circuit amounts to $I = {}^{100}\!/_{250} = 0.40$ amp.

(b) The PD across the lamp is found by applying Ohm's law to the lamp alone. We have $V = IR$, or $V = 0.40 \times 210 = 84$ volts, the required PD. Notice that there is a "line drop" of $100 - 84 = 16$ volts occasioned by appreciable resistance in the line itself.

(c) According to Eq. (16·9), $H = 0.239 \times 0.40 \times 84 = 8.03$ cal/sec. In 5.0 min, or 300 sec, the quantity of heat produced will be $Q = 8.03 \times 300 = 2410$ cal.

SUMMARY

Intensity of a current is the rate of flow of charge. One *ampere* is a rate of movement of charge of 1 coulomb/sec.

To initiate or maintain a current, a potential difference must be applied between two points in a complete conducting circuit.

Voltaic cell: A device for maintaining a PD by means of chemical action. Consists of two dissimilar substances placed in a liquid containing *ions* (electrified atoms or atom groups).

Electrolysis: Production of chemical changes in an ionized liquid by passage of a current through it. Faraday found that a given total charge liberated *chemically equivalent* amounts of various materials and concluded that each ion carries a definite amount of charge for each of its valences.

Ohm's law: Under constant conditions the current in any metallic conductor is directly proportional to the PD applied to its ends:

$I_{\text{amp}} = V_{\text{volts}}/R_{\text{ohms}}$. R is the **resistance** of the conductor. Ohm's law may be applied to all or part of any steady-current metallic circuit.

Power expended in a circuit element: $P_{\text{watts}} = I_{\text{amp}} \cdot V_{\text{volts}}$. If the energy is converted entirely into heat, $H_{\text{cal/sec}} = 0.239 I_{\text{amp}} \cdot V_{\text{volts}}$.

READING REFERENCES

1. Taylor, Lloyd W.: "Physics, the Pioneer Science," Houghton Mifflin, Boston, 1946. Read Chap. 43.
2. Bragg, W. L.: "Electricity," Macmillan, New York, 1936. Read pp. 44–79.
3. Cajori, F.: "A History of Physics," Macmillan, New York, 1929. Pages 137–142, 223–230, and 235–240 are of interest.
4. Watson, E. C.: The First Electric Battery, *Am. Jour. Phys.*, Vol. 13, pp. 397–406, 1945. Volta's own description of his battery, together with reproductions of original plates and photographs. Very interesting.
5. Magie, W. F.: "A Source Book in Physics," McGraw-Hill, New York, 1935. Faraday's work on electrolysis, pp. 492–498.

EXERCISES

1. Criticize the following expressions sometimes heard in reference to electric currents:

(a) "The battery furnishes electricity."

(b) "The electric iron uses up five amperes of current."

(c) "Electricity is stored in a storage battery."

(d) "The wire contains two amperes of electricity."

2. If you were given a silver electrolytic cell, a stop watch, and a chemical balance, could you devise an experiment for measuring the strength of the current flowing in the cell?

3. How long will it take a steady current of 0.020 amp, flowing through a copper electrolytic cell, to deposit 127 gm of this metal?

4. In order to check the readings of an ammeter, the instrument is connected in series with a silver electrolytic cell. During a certain run, the ammeter reads 0.0500 amp, and 0.0322 gm silver deposits in 10.0 min. What is the error of the ammeter at this point of its range?

5. In a certain electrolytic cell using dilute sulfuric acid as an electrolyte, 6.75×10^{17} SO_4^{--} ions and 13.5×10^{17} H^+ ions pass through a cross section of the cell each second. Find the strength of the current being supplied to the cell.

6. Passage of current through the human body may be dangerous, for the electrolysis of body fluids may cause irreparable damage to the cells. The resistance of the human body is of the order of a few thousand ohms for steady current, and currents approaching 0.1 amp are usually fatal. Is it safe to switch on a light while standing on a wet floor?

7. Three coils of resistance 3, 4, and 6 ohms are joined in series with a 6-volt battery. What is the resulting current in the circuit? What is the PD across the largest resistor? If this resistor is mistakenly replaced in the circuit by a voltmeter drawing negligible current, what will be the reading of the voltmeter?

8. Solve Exercise 7 when the three resistors are joined in parallel.

9. The no-current voltage of an automobile battery is 6.0 volts, and its internal resistance is 0.05 ohm. There are two headlights, each of resistance 2.0 ohms, and two taillights, each of resistance 3.0 ohms, all connected in parallel. Find the battery terminal voltage when all these lamps are on.

10. In the automobile electrical system described in Exercise 9 there is also a starting motor of effective resistance 0.2 ohm. If, with the lights all on, the starter is operated, find the battery terminal voltage under these conditions and also the total current flowing through the lamps. Does the result explain the dimming of the lamps when the starter is used?

11. Does the rate of development of heat in a wire carrying a given current depend on the direction of the current? In arriving at an answer, notice that the rate of heating depends only on I^2R (page 307) and that reversing the current (that is, changing I to $-I$) leaves I^2 unchanged.

12. A lamp whose nominal power rating is 50 watts is connected into a circuit where the PD across the filament is measured as 103 volts and the current through it as 0.500 amp. What is the true power consumption under these conditions?

13. In Exercise 12 find the resistance of the filament under operating conditions.

14. Your monthly electric bill is for the total electrical energy used, and the company charges a certain price for each kilowatt-hour (= power × time = energy) delivered. If the rate is 6 cents per kilowatt-hour, what is the amount of the bill during a month when ten 60-watt lamps are run simultaneously for 120 hr, a 550-watt toaster for 5 hr, a 200-watt washing machine for 4 hr, and a 40-watt radio for 80 hr?

15. An average office worker has a food requirement of about 2500 kg-cal (see footnote, page 131) per day. At the rate that is charged in your locality, how much would the equivalent amount of electrical energy cost? Compare with your estimate of the cost of the corresponding amount of food.

Chapter 17

ELECTROMAGNETISM

17·1   Magnetic Effect of a Current; Oersted's Discovery

If two straight wires, each carrying a current, are placed parallel to each other, it is found that they exert a mutual force in their common plane and in a direction at right angles to their length (Fig. 17·1). The force is one of attraction if the two currents are in the same direction, repulsion if in opposite directions. The magnitude of the force is found to be proportional to the product of the two current strengths.

This force is not an electrostatic one, for the wires themselves have no resultant *charge* even when the currents are flowing—electrons entering each wire at one end are leaving in equal number at the other end. Rather, the force exerted by one wire on the other must be ascribed to some kind of interaction resulting from the *motion* of electrons in the two wires. Similar interactions are observed between free streams of charged particles in a vacuum. There is no explanation for this phenomenon—it must be accepted as an empirical fact. However, further experimentation brings out many details that make this effect one of the most useful of all of the applications of electricity.

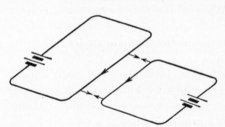

FIG. 17·1   Two currents exert forces on each other.

The crucial observation that opened up the whole field of experiment and practical technique was the discovery by the Danish scientist H. C. Oersted, in 1820, that a compass needle placed just below a wire carrying a current takes a position nearly perpendicular to the wire while the current is flowing. If the current is sent through the wire in the reverse sense, the needle again swings toward a plane perpendicular to the wire but with its ends **reversed** (Fig. 17·2). The effect lasts only while the current flows.

The action on the compass—which is a *magnet*—implies that the *existence of a current of electricity* in a wire in some way *produces magnetic effects.* The entire subject has developed from the point of view that a current gives rise to magnetic effects; and even

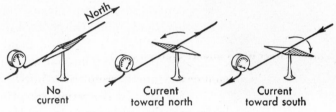

No current   Current toward north   Current toward south

FIG. 17·2   Oersted's discovery.

in the case of one current reacting on another, where no actual magnets are involved, the observations are customarily described in terms of the interaction of the magnetic effects produced by the two currents.

17·2   Material Magnets; Law of Force

The existence of natural magnetism had been known for nearly 25 centuries before Oersted's experiment. The ancient Greeks found that a certain kind of rock had the ability to attract pieces of iron. The early Chinese discovered that a splinter of this rock suspended from a thread would set itself always in a north-south direction, and they were probably the first to use the device as a compass. It was not until the beginning of the seventeenth century that Gilbert (see footnote, page 266) gathered the known data on the behavior of magnets and published them together with his own careful findings.

The basic facts about magnets are worth attention at this point. You will find that there are far-reaching similarities between magnetic and electrostatic forces; at the same time there exist differences that deserve notice.

In addition to natural magnets a permanent magnet can be made from a bar of steel by stroking it always in one direction with one end of a natural magnet or—better—by placing it inside a coil through which a strong electric current is passed. Besides iron and steel only a very few other substances can be magnetized—the elements nickel, cobalt and gadolinium, and certain alloys. Compare this with the fact that an electrostatic charge can be placed on *any* insulated object, regardless of its composition.

If a magnetized bar or a splinter of magnetic ore is dipped into a heap of iron filings, heavy tufts of filings cling to the bar near each end but hardly any attach themselves at the middle (Fig. 17·3).

Fig. 17·3   Iron filings cling to a bar magnet near its poles. (*Courtesy of Prof. W. B. Anderson.*)

The outside effects seem to be concentrated at two places, one near each end, called the *poles* of the magnet. When the bar is suspended as a compass, the pole that turns toward the north is called a north-seeking (or simply *N*) pole; the other is a south-seeking (or *S*) pole. If one pole of a bar magnet is brought first near one end and then near the other end of a suspended magnet (compass needle), it is found that *like poles repel* each other and *unlike poles attract*—exactly the type of rule you already know to hold for the forces between electric charges.

Quantitatively, too, the correspondence is close, for Coulomb (page 273) found that the same type of force law which holds in electrostatics is valid for magnet poles. Symbolically, the force between two magnet poles is given by

$$f = \frac{p_1 p_2}{\mu d^2} \tag{17·1}$$

where p_1 and p_2 represent the **strengths** of the two poles and d is their distance apart. The constant of proportionality μ is called the **permeability** of the medium, and its value is arbitrarily taken to be unity for a vacuum (for air it is practically 1, also). Similar to what was done in the electrical case, the force law is used to define an absolute unit of pole strength. *A unit pole is such that in a vacuum it acts on an equal pole one centimeter away with a force of one dyne.*

17·3   Magnetic Fields

The field concept is fully as valuable in magnetism as in electrostatics. A *magnetic field* is any region in the neighborhood of permanent magnets or of electric currents where a magnet pole or a current-carrying conductor experiences a force. The *field strength* at any point is defined as the *vector representing the force, in dynes, acting on a unit N pole placed at that point.* The symbol for magnetic-field strength is H, and the unit for measuring it is called one *oersted*. Thus "oersted" is merely a single word for "dynes per unit pole." The earth's magnetic field, which causes a compass needle to take up a north-south position, has a strength

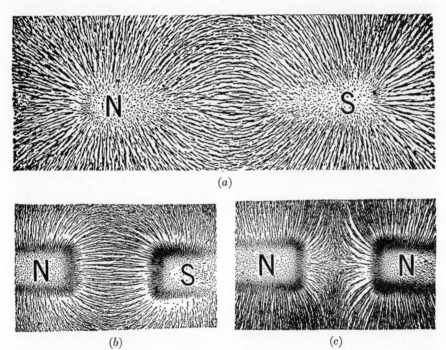

(a)

(b)   (c)

FIG. 17·4   Magnetic fields mapped by means of iron filings. (*From Weber, White, and Manning, "College Technical Physics."*)

of about 0.5 oersted, while electrically produced fields of the order of 100,000 oersteds are used in the large cyclotrons (page 437).

As in his discussion of electrostatic fields, Faraday found the concept of lines of force a useful one for magnetic fields. A magnetic line of force may be traced by moving a small compass needle always in the direction indicated by its N pole. The lines in a cross-section of a field may be made evident by scattering iron filings on a card placed over a magnet or magnets. Each filing becomes, temporarily, a small magnet by magnetic induction (see below) and alines itself in the field.

Figure 17·4 shows the pattern of filings produced (*a*) by a bar magnet, (*b*) between unlike poles of two bars placed opposite each other, and (*c*) between like poles of the two. The qualities with which Faraday endowed the lines of force in the electrostatic case are also evident here. In *b* the lines, acting like stretched filaments, tend to draw the two magnets together, while in *c* the sidewise repulsion of the lines would operate to push the two magnets apart. The lines of magnetic force are always assumed to be *closed curves.* In the case of a bar magnet they are imagined to go through the bar itself and to be directed from *N* to *S* outside the magnet.

The strength of the field at any point is depicted by the number of lines drawn through a 1-cm² area held normal to the field at that point, just as in electrostatics (see page 278 and Fig. 15·9 there).

17·4 Theory of Material Magnets

If a piece of soft iron is placed in a magnetic field, it acquires poles and exhibits all the properties of a natural magnet, but only as

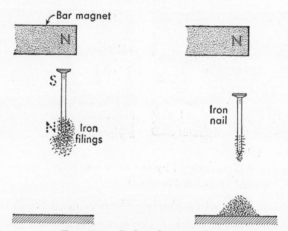

Fig. 17·5   Induced magnetism.

long as it remains in the stronger parts of the field (Fig. 17·5). The bar is said to be magnetized by induction.[1] This behavior is explained by the assumption that a piece of iron or other magnetic material consists of elementary magnets. These are not individual atoms or molecules, as was once believed, but little atom groups called *domains.* Each one may contain millions of atoms.

[1] Compare the phenomenon of electrostatic induction described on pp. 272, 273.

In an unmagnetized piece of iron or steel these domains are oriented in random directions, as represented schematically in Fig. 17·6a. When an external field is applied, these units line up in the general direction of the field (sketch b).[1] When so alined, the adjoining N and S poles of the elementary magnets cancel as regards their outside influence, and only the free poles at the ends operate to produce the effect of two poles for the entire bar. This explains why breaking a magnet gives rise to a pair of new poles, with opposite kinds on the two sides of the break. It is impossible to produce a magnet having but one pole.

When a bar of soft iron that has been magnetized by induction is removed from the field, the domains return readily to their random orientations and the bar is a magnet no longer; but when a piece of hard steel is removed from a magnetizing field, it retains

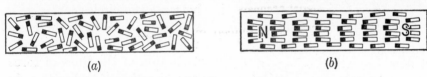

(a)   (b)

FIG. 17·6   Magnetizing a bar lines up the elementary magnets.

a great part of its magnetism. This must mean that the elementary magnets turn more freely in soft iron than in hard steel, where they tend to preserve their alinement for a long time.

Following Oersted's discovery, Ampère made a significant contribution to the subject of magnetism by suggesting that the elementary magnets themselves owe their existence to the circulation of electric charge in the molecules of the material. This view met with great opposition, for there was no evidence at that time for such submolecular movement of charge. More than half a century later, Rowland showed experimentally that isolated charges in motion affect a compass needle in the same way as does a current in a conductor. Moreover, modern theory fully vindicates Ampère's idea by accounting for the magnetic properties of substances in terms of the circulation of charge within the atoms composing them. The greater part of the magnetic effect seems to be due to the spinning motion of electrons (page 399).

[1] The domain boundaries and their changes can actually be observed by coating a specimen with magnetic powders.

17·5   Field of a Straight Current

Ampère examined the consequences of Oersted's experiment both experimentally and mathematically and succeeded in describing the magnetic fields of currents in conductors having various forms. Similar to the method used for mapping the field of a permanent magnet, the lines of force associated with a current in a straight wire may be traced experimentally by moving a small compass needle from place to place near the wire or by scattering iron filings on a card through which a vertical wire passes. Whichever method is used, the lines are found to be circles lying in such a plane, with their common center at the wire (Fig. 17·7). The strength of the field at any point is found to decrease with the distance from the wire, as shown in the figure by the increasing spacing between the circles.

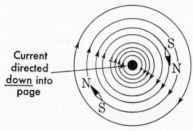

Current directed down into page

FIG. 17·7   Magnetic field of the current in a straight wire.

As already mentioned, there is a definite relation between the sense of circulation of the lines of force and the direction of the current in the wire. But how can these be correlated? The very fact that the magnetic force at a given point is not *in* the line joining this point and the wire but is in the *perpendicular* direction was extremely puzzling to the pioneers in this field, for the forces of interaction commonly met with in physics—gravitation, electrostatics, etc.—lie along the line connecting the two objects. Here we are faced with a different kind of directional relation. One way to describe it is by using the celebrated *right-hand rule*:

Imagine the wire to be grasped with the right hand, with the thumb extended in the direction of (conventional) flow of the current; then the fingers will encircle the wire in the direction of the lines of magnetic force.

Notice that this is merely an empirical rule for keeping directions straight; it says nothing about any *reason* for this particular relation.

The direction of the mutual force between two parallel currents, referred to on page 310, can be predicted by means of the ideas just mentioned. Figure 17·8a shows the fields of currents flowing in the same direction in two parallel wires. At any point there can be but a *single* field vector, which is the resultant of the two separate ones. The two fields, each consisting of concentric circular lines, combine in this way to give the single field represented in sketch *b*. Since the lines may be thought of as stretched filaments, their effect would be to draw the two wires together, which is what is observed

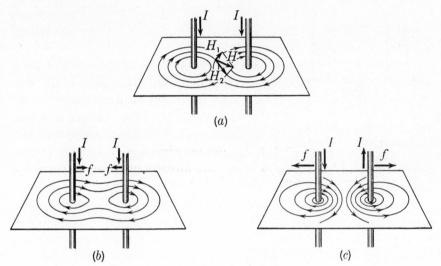

(a)

(b)   (c)

FIG. 17·8   Magnetic field of two parallel currents.

to happen (page 310). On the other hand, if the two currents are in *opposite* directions, the composite field is as shown in sketch *c*. Here the transverse action of the lines of force crowded together between the wires would operate to push the latter apart, which is what occurs.

17·6 Straight Current in an External Field

Instead of placing a current-carrying wire in the magnetic field due to another single wire, we may put it into a *uniform field*. As in electrostatics, such a field is one whose lines of force are everywhere parallel and equally spaced. A limited portion of the earth's field or the field between large, flat, parallel pole faces of an electromagnet (Fig. 17·9) is very nearly of this nature. If a current-carrying wire is placed between the pole pieces, it is found to be acted upon by a force whose direction is perpendicular to both the direction of the field and that of the wire. That is, the three vectors *current, field, and mechanical force are mutually per-pendicular,* like the three edges of a cube that meet at one corner. In the event that the wire is not placed perpendicular to the field, only the field's component in a direction normal to the wire is effective.

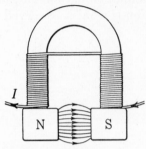

The magnitude of the force is found to be given by

$$f = \frac{HIl}{10} \qquad (17 \cdot 2)$$

where f is the force in dynes, H the field strength in oersteds, I the current in amperes, and l the length of the wire in the field, in centimeters. The direction of the resulting force is found to reverse if *either* the direction of the current or that of the magnetic field is reversed; it remains unchanged when *both* are reversed.

FIG. 17·9   Horseshoe electromagnet.

There are thumb rules for predicting the directional relations, but you will not wish to burden your memory with them, for it is easy to figure out the directions from what you already know. For instance, Fig. 17·10a shows a current-carrying wire located

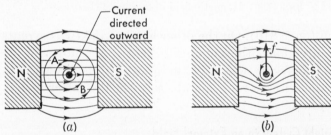

FIG. 17·10   Current-carrying wire in a magnetic field.

in the uniform magnetic field produced by an electromagnet. Any mechanical effect on the wire can be attributed to the interaction of the two magnetic fields—that of the current in the wire and that of the magnet. The lines of force of both fields are shown in sketch *a*. At a point above the wire, such as *A*, the two fields are in opposite directions and so at least partly annul each other; at *B* the two are in the same direction, and the resultant field is strengthened. The composite field is shown in *b*. The effect of the tensed lines of force would be to move the wire in the direction shown.

It must be mentioned again that this procedure is merely one for keeping directions straight; it is not an "explanation" of the effects observed.

The transverse force just discussed for the current in a wire is observed also for a stream of free charged particles such as electrons or ions. For such a situation, Eq. (17·2) can be modified. If each particle carries a charge Q esu and moves with a speed v cm/sec, then the relation becomes

$$f = \frac{HQv}{3 \times 10^{10}} \tag{17·3}$$

This equation will prove useful in later work.

17·7 Loops, Coils, and Electromagnets

One way of increasing the magnetic effect of a current is to bend the wire into the form of a circular loop. Each small segment of the wire is surrounded by circular lines of force of the kind described above. The right-hand rule shows that all these lines go through

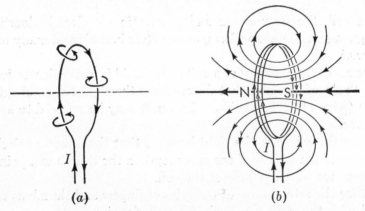

(a)   (b)

FIG. 17·11   Field of a single loop and of a flat coil.

the coil in one sense, entering at one face and leaving from the other (Fig. 17·11a). The magnetic field is increased by using a *flat, circular coil* consisting of a number of identical loops through which the current passes always in the same sense. Such a coil acts like a bar magnet of relatively large cross section and small length, with north polarity near one face and south polarity near the other (Fig. 17·11b).

Another form of coil, even more widely used, is the **solenoid,** made by winding many turns of wire on a cylinder. Here again the effects of the several turns add up to produce a field exactly like that of a bar magnet. The strength of such a solenoid may be increased hundreds and even thousands of times by placing a soft-iron core inside the coil (Fig. 17·12). This is the device usually called an **electromagnet.** It is superior to a permanent magnet in that it can be made much stronger; and its strength can be controlled and its polarity reversed by suitably changing the current

Fɪɢ. 17·12   Air-cored and iron-cored solenoids.

in the coil. Electromagnets find application in electric doorbells, lifting magnets, loud-speakers, motors (see below), and many other devices.[1]

The magnetic polarity of a coil or solenoid is conveniently found by a "rule of thumb" that differs from the right-hand rule given above (page 316). To avoid confusion, it may be referred to as the *coil rule.*

Grasp the coil with the right hand so that the fingers encircle it in the direction of flow of the current; then the thumb will point in the direction of the *N* pole of the coil.

Notice the interchange of the roles of fingers and thumb as compared with the right-hand rule for a single wire.

17·8 Current Meters

The commonest forms of ammeters and voltmeters (page 298) operate on the basis of the force exerted on a current-carrying conductor in a magnetic field. According to Eq. (17·2) the force is related in a definite way to the strength of the current, so that, with a fixed setup, f may be used as a measure of I.

[1] For a particularly spectacular application, see p. 440.

It is interesting to note that, as a matter of fact, nearly all fundamental electrical and magnetic determinations are based on the measurement of *mechanical* quantities. Thus pole strengths and quantities of charge are determined by measuring *force,* through the use of Coulomb's law; field strength is specified as the *force* acting on a unit charge or unit pole; potential difference is measured by the *work* done on unit charge; a quantity of electricity is most accurately measured by passing it through an electrolytic cell and *weighing* (a mechanical process) the deposit produced. Many other examples can be given.

The usual form of current-measuring instrument is of the moving-coil type, in which the torque (turning effect) on a pivoted coil placed in the field of a strong permanent magnet is used as a measure of the current sent through the coil. Figure 17·13 is a schematic drawing of the arrangement. When a steady current exists in the coil, which is usually wound in rectangular form as shown, one face of the coil acquires north polarity, the other south. There is

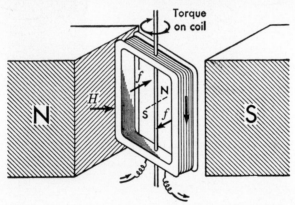

FIG. 17·13   Moving-coil galvanometer (schematic).

then a tendency for the coil to rotate as indicated, each of its poles trying to get nearer to the pole of the permanent magnet that is of opposite kind.

If the coil were free to turn, it would rotate until it arrived at a position perpendicular to the field and would then stop. Instead of allowing this to happen, a spring is provided that opposes the turning of the coil, so that with any given current flowing it rotates only to the point where the opposing elastic torque of the spring becomes equal to the electromagnetic torque. A light pointer attached to the coil moves over a scale to indicate the strength of the current flowing in the coil. In order to read the current direct in amperes, this scale must be calibrated by comparison with a standard instrument or in some other way.

A further refinement in a practical instrument consists in placing a stationary cylindrical piece of iron inside the coil and shaping the pole pieces of the permanent magnet so that the field is everywhere normal to the direction of motion of the vertical wires. This permits the instrument to have a scale with *uniform* graduations, a great convenience in practice. The sketch of Fig. 17·14 corresponds more closely to the actual construction of such a meter. The

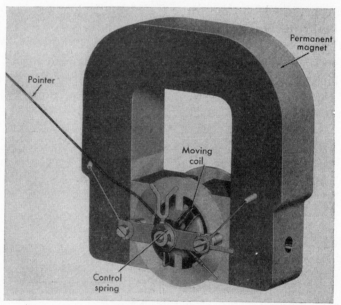

FIG. 17·14   Internal construction of an actual moving-coil meter. (*Courtesy of Weston Electrical Instrument Corporation.*)

most sensitive current-measuring instruments of the moving-coil type can respond to currents as small as 10^{-11} amp.

By the simple expedient of putting a high-resistance coil in series with the moving coil, an instrument of the above kind can be made into a voltmeter. The resistance coil is built into the case of the meter. The deflection of the moving coil is proportional to the current through the meter, which in turn—by Ohm's law—is proportional to the PD applied to the instrument. Therefore, once the scale has been properly calibrated, the instrument may be used to read PD direct in volts. As already explained (page 298), the meter must be connected across the two points in the circuit whose PD is required. Also, the combined resistance of both fixed and movable coils must be large enough to ensure that the current taken from the main circuit will be small.

17·9 Electric Motors

When a current-bearing coil turns in a magnetic field, it acquires kinetic energy. If this turning is allowed to continue instead of being arrested (as by the control springs in a meter), a continuous conversion of electromagnetic into mechanical energy takes place. A device for doing this is an *electric motor*. The principle of operation of a motor that uses steady currents is shown by Fig. 17·15. As in the meters described above, there is a loop of wire pivoted to rotate in a magnetic field. Since continuous rotation is desired, the

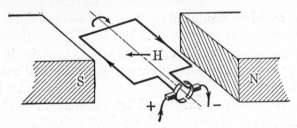

FIG. 17·15   Principle of the electric motor.

current can no longer be led into and out of the loop by fixed wires; instead, this is done through a split ring (commutator) on which sliding contacts (brushes) bear. When the current is sent through as shown, the loop turns in the indicated direction until its plane is vertical. At that moment, however, the current through the loop is automatically reversed by the switching around of connections as the commutator gaps pass the brushes. This reversal of the current enables the coil to make another half turn, when reversal occurs again, and so on. The result is continuous rotation in one direction.

A practical motor, such as the "starter" of an automobile, differs from the sketch of Fig. 17·15 in several ways. The single loop is replaced by a set of separate loops wound into recesses in a soft-iron core at various angles, and the commutator consists of many segments. Opposite ones are connected to the ends of each loop. The field magnet is not a permanent magnet but an electromagnet energized by passing all or part of the current through its windings (see Fig. 17·16).

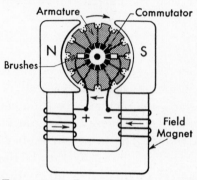

FIG. 17·16 Design of an actual motor.

While there are many variants in electric-motor design, the principle of all is the same—the conversion of electrical into mechanical energy by means of the interaction of current-carrying conductors on each other through the agency of their magnetic fields.

17·10 Discovery of Electromagnetic Induction

In the years immediately following Oersted's discovery that magnetism could be produced by means of electric currents, many experimenters sought an answer to the natural question of whether the reciprocal effect might exist—whether, that is, it might be possible to produce an electric current by means of magnets. An affirmative answer was given almost simultaneously by the experiments performed by Henry[1] and by Faraday in 1831. Each of these investigators observed independently that a galvanometer connected to a coil showed a momentary current when a current was started or interrupted in a separate nearby circuit.

In essence, the setup is represented by Fig. 17·17a. When the switch S is closed, allowing the battery to establish a current in coil C_1, a momentary "kick" of current is registered by the galvanometer G in the adjoining but completely detached circuit containing the coil C_2. Now, with a steady current flowing in circuit 1, nothing further happens in the second; but when the switch is opened, a momentary current impulse, opposite in direction to the previous one, is noted in circuit 2.

Faraday also observed such transient currents when, with the current in the first circuit flowing, the distance apart of the two coils was suddenly changed. It was found that the effects were

---

[1] Joseph Henry, versatile and distinguished American physicist, who became first head of the Smithsonian Institution in Washington. He made several basic discoveries, not only in electricity but in other branches of physics as well. He was one of the first to promote the world-wide exchange of scientific publications.

greatly increased if the two coils were provided with iron cores. Further, transient current flow was observed in a single circuit like that in Fig. 17·17b when one pole of a magnet was thrust toward the coil, with a reverse current noted while the magnet was being withdrawn. The current in each instance was found to increase with the speed of motion of the magnet. The use of an S pole produced in each case a current opposite to that obtained with an N pole. In all these examples the current is said to be

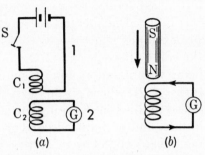

FIG. 17·17   Arrangements for inducing currents.

produced by induction. Since this word has already been used elsewhere for entirely different effects (pages 272 and 314), the present application is usually referred to as *electromagnetic induction.* Fundamentally the operations carried out above may be looked upon as inducing a "driving potential" that propels charge forward at all points of the circuit. This voltage is not localized as it is when a battery is used to maintain a current in a circuit.

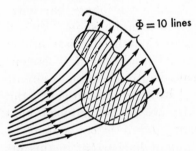

FIG. 17·18   Flux through an area.

17·11   Magnetic Flux

Faraday was able to find one simple description that embraced all the results detailed above. To see how this was accomplished, consider what is meant by *magnetic flux.* This is simply a name for the total number of lines of magnetic force that thread their way through any specified closed curve in a field (Fig. 17·18).

You are already familiar with the idea of representing the field strength at any point by the number of lines of force drawn through each square centimeter of an area that is normal to the direction of the field. Consider only the simple case where the field strength is constant over the entire area in question. The total flux Φ will be the product of the area A and the number of lines per unit area, which is given by H. Thus

$$\Phi = AH \qquad\qquad (17\cdot4)$$

Review the circumstances of each of Faraday's tests described in the last section and you find that in every case where a current was induced in the coil there was a *change* in the flux through it. For example, when the switch is closed in the circuit of Fig. 17·17a, the coil C_1 becomes an electromagnet and lines of force spring into being within and around it. Some of these lines thread through the turns of C_2, where no flux existed before, and thus a current is induced in this coil. Keeping the current constant produces no change in flux, and no induced current flows after the first instant. Opening the switch in circuit 1, however, causes the field of C_1 to vanish, the flux through C_2 decreases to zero, and a transient current again exists. In sketch *b*, moving the magnet toward or away from the coil changes the number of lines of force passing through the coil, and this again constitutes a change of flux.

In some arrangements for inducing current, it is more direct to think only of a single conductor rather than of a complete circuit.

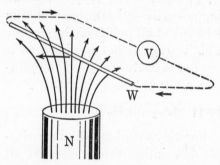

FIG. 17·19 Driving voltage induced in a straight wire.

When the wire W in Fig. 17·19 is moved crosswise above the pole of a stationary bar magnet, it can be shown that a driving potential exists in the wire. If and only if W is connected into a complete circuit will it be possible to verify the existence of an induced *current*, and it is convenient to think of the current in this instance as being due to the "cutting of lines of force" by the wire. However, this way of looking at the origin of the current is really equivalent to the idea of change of flux; for whatever the shape of a circuit of which W is a part, the flux through it must change when W cuts lines of force.

17·12   Direction and Magnitude of Induced Voltage

In the description of Faraday's experiments in Sec. 17·10 it was pointed out that there is always a definite relation between the direction of the causative action and that of the induced current. A law first formulated by the Russian physicist **H. F. E. Lenz** tells the direction of the effect in any instance: *The induced current is always in such a direction that its magnetic effect opposes the action which gives rise to the current.* To illustrate this: In Fig. 17·17b the current induced in the coil must be in the sense shown, for with this direction of the current the coil rule says that the *approach* of the *N* pole of the bar magnet would be opposed by the presence of an *N* pole at the upper end of the coil. Similarly, upon removal of the bar the current would have to be in the reverse sense, producing an *S* pole at the top end of the coil to oppose the withdrawal of the bar.

Lenz's law will be recognized as merely a special case of the conservation of energy; for if the magnetic effect of an induced current were to act in a direction to *reinforce* its cause, the action would increase of its own accord beyond all bounds and infinite currents would be generated without payment in the form of work done. This does not happen, as we know, and therefore the magnetic effect must *hinder* the action that causes it.

In an experiment like the one shown in Fig. 17·17b it is observed that the driving potential in the coil increases when the bar magnet is moved more rapidly. It can be shown that the induced current (or the induced driving potential, which is more fundamental) is directly proportional to the *rate* at which the flux changes. Explicitly, it is found that

$$V_{\text{volts}} = 10^{-8}\frac{\Delta\Phi}{\Delta t} \qquad (17\cdot5)$$

where V is the induced driving potential and $\Delta\Phi$ is the change in flux taking place in a time interval Δt sec. If a coil of several turns is used, $\Delta\Phi$ must be the sum of the flux changes in all the turns; the individual turns act like battery cells in series, and their contributions to the total driving potential must be added.

17·13 Generators

The induced currents obtained in the experiments of Henry and Faraday were feeble, short-lived, and seemingly of little importance outside the laboratory; yet the development of continuously operating generators based on these very principles has given us the only adequate source of the tremendous quantities of electrical energy used today. As in the electric motor, the essential parts of a generator are a coil, a magnetic field in which the coil may rotate, and some means for connecting the coil to an external circuit. In fact the same machine may be used for either purpose. When a current is passed into the coil, it rotates and acts as a motor; when the coil is mechanically turned, an induced current results and the machine becomes a generator.

Lenz's law, applied to Fig. 17·20, reveals the nature of the voltage induced in the coil as it is turned. Starting with the plane of the coil normal to the field (sketch *a*), rotation in the indicated direction must make the right-hand face of the coil an *N* pole and the other an *S* pole, so that the forces between the poles of the coil

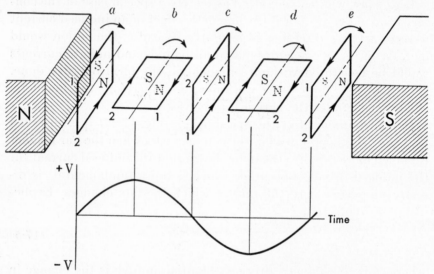

Fig. 17·20   Operation of a simple generator.

and those of the field magnet act to hinder the turning. By the coil rule this means that the current—or the voltage—in the coil is in the direction shown by the arrows. By the time the coil has turned 90 deg (sketch *b*), the voltage has increased to its maximum value because the *rate of change* of flux through the coil has gradually increased during this operation. As the coil now approaches the position of sketch *c*, the voltage falls again to small values, and when it passes this place, the voltage actually *reverses*. (Notice that the arrow along wire 1 is now directed inward, where before it was outward; similarly the direction of the voltage in wire 2 has reversed.) In the ensuing 90 deg of turning the voltage assumes greater and greater *negative* values and in the last quarter turn lapses back to zero, after which the whole sequence of events repeats itself. The voltage curve is shown below the coil diagrams. It makes clear the fact that the voltage is *alternating*—that is, first in one sense, then in the other.

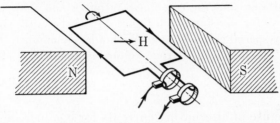

FIG. 17·21   Slip-ring connections of a simple generator.

If, now, the coil is connected to an outside circuit by means of slip rings and brushes as in Fig. 17·21, the current in this circuit will be an *alternating current* and the frequency of its complete alternations will be the same as the number of rotations per second of the coil. Thus an alternating current is the kind that is naturally

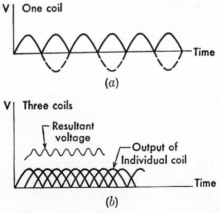

FIG. 17·22   Commutated output of a generator.

induced by turning a coil in a magnetic field. For some uses a *direct current*—one that flows always in one direction—may be required. In this event the slip rings must be replaced by a commutator, which acts to switch over the outside connection each time the coil reaches a position perpendicular to the field. This has the effect of reversing alternate loops of the output curve (Fig. 17·22a).

The current in the outside circuit, while now always in one direction, is still not a **steady** current and for some uses may be quite inacceptable. A more constant current would result if, instead of a single coil, there were several coils set at various angles with each other. The output curve of each coil would then reach its maximum when the others were at intermediate positions, and the combined output would show less variation than the curve for any single coil. Figure 17·22b shows the situation when three equally spaced coils are used. With a larger number of coils hardly any "ripple" remains—the output voltage is practically constant.

17·14   The Transformer

The wide use of alternating currents for commercial purposes is made possible by a device called the **transformer**. In essence, it is merely the combination of two coils illustrated in Fig. 17·17a. Any **variation** of current in one coil induces a corresponding voltage in the other. With an alternating current flowing in the primary coil C_1, there is a continual variation of magnetic flux through the secondary coil C_2. As a result, an alternating current is induced in C_2, and this current has the same frequency as the current in C_1. Simple air-cored transformers are used in radio and television apparatus, but in power circuits the two coils are wound on a closed ring made of an alloy of high permeability, which acts to increase and concentrate the magnetic flux. Such a closed-core transformer is shown schematically in Fig. 17·23. With this arrangement the flux at any given time is the same for all turns, with the result that *the voltages in the two coils are in the same ratio as the numbers of turns.* That is, if the primary voltage is 100 and if the secondary coil has 1000 times as many turns as the primary, then the voltage of the current induced in the secondary will be 100,000. The energy losses in a well-designed transformer are small—perhaps less than 3 per cent on the average—and hence the *power* developed by the secondary current is essentially equal to that of the primary. But the power in either circuit, as in the case of direct currents, turns out to be proportional to the product of current and voltage; there-

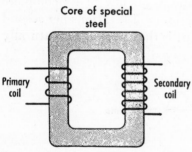

Core of special steel

Primary coil

Secondary coil

Fig. 17·23   A transformer (schematic).

fore the currents in the two coils must be inversely proportional to the numbers of turns. In the above example the secondary current would be 0.001 of that in the primary. Transformers may be used either way around—to step up the voltage, with consequent lowering of current, or to step down the voltage, the current increasing in the same ratio.

Whenever electric power is to be used at a great distance from the generator, it is transmitted in the form of a high-voltage alternating current, for the use of high voltage makes possible the reduction of the current, which in turn means smaller power loss in the transmission line. The generator voltage may be not more than 10,000, and the current may be led to a step-up transformer, which puts it into the cross-country transmission line at a voltage of perhaps 230,000. At the edge of a city where the energy is to be used, step-down transformers may reduce the voltage to about 2300, and additional transformers farther along the line then reduce the voltage to a safe value of around 115 for use in individual houses.

17·15   The Telephone

In principle the telephone consists of a **transmitter** for converting sound vibrations of the voice into corresponding variations of an electric current and a **receiver** for changing these varying currents back into audible sounds at the far end of the line. The most

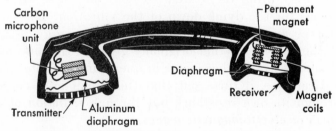

FIG. 17·24   The telephone handset (simplified).

commonly used type of transmitter utilizes the fact that the resistance of loosely packed carbon granules changes when pressure is applied. Sound waves from the voice, impinging on a thin metal diaphragm (Fig. 17·24), alter the resistance of the capsule of carbon granules and produce corresponding changes in the current sent through it by a battery (Fig. 17·25). These variations in current are impressed on the transformer, sent over the line to another transformer at the distant end, and duplicated in coils wound on the poles of the permanent magnet of the receiver. The corresponding variations in the strength of these poles make the metal diaphragm vibrate to reproduce with fair fidelity the sound waves that originally activated the transmitter. On a long line, repeating

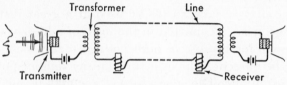

FIG. 17·25   Simple telephone circuit.

devices transfer the vibrations from one section of line to the next, boosting their energy in the process. The equipment required for modern telephony is extremely complex.

17·16 Electromagnetic Waves

If a charged capacitor is "short-circuited" by joining the plates with a wire or with a coil, the ensuing current generally is not a mere lapse back to the uncharged state but may be *oscillatory*. An electric circuit of the kind described is the counterpart of an elastic vibrating system in mechanics—for example, a tuning fork. In the mechanical case, air resistance and internal friction in the fork ultimately bring the system to rest, but these are not the only reasons for the dying down of the vibration. The fact that sound waves are sent out means that their energy, too, must come at the expense of that originally given to the fork, and this drain of energy is a further factor in quenching the vibrations. In the electrical case, it turns out that the circuit loses energy not only through its own resistance but through *radiation of energy* in the form of *electromagnetic waves*.

This process of radiation was predicted in 1865 by the brilliant mathematical theory developed by Maxwell,[1] which showed light and other forms of electromagnetic waves to be of the same essential nature (see page 236). In 1888, several years after Maxwell's death, the German experimenter Hertz was able to produce these

[1] James Clerk Maxwell, brilliant theoretical physicist, was born in Scotland the same year that Faraday and Henry discovered electromagnetic induction. His outstanding contributions were in the fields of heat and electromagnetism although he did important original work in several other branches of physics.

waves and show that they have the properties of reflection, refraction, and interference possessed by light waves. Later their speed in free space was found to be identical with that of light. Through the developments in technique attributable to Marconi and to other pioneers, transmission of electromagnetic waves over long distances and their use in communication ultimately became the realities that we take for granted today. Radiotelephony, that is, transmission of sounds of music and speech, is made possible by oscillating circuits capable of radiating large amounts of power in the form of electromagnetic waves. The frequencies ordinarily used in broadcasting are of the order of a million cycles, or vibrations, per second. These waves are *modulated* by impressing on them the waves of the sounds to be transmitted (frequencies of the order of a hundred or a thousand). This is done either by changing the amplitude of the radio waves in the tempo of the sound waves (amplitude modulation) or by altering the frequency according to this pattern (frequency modulation). A receiving circuit whose electrical components, such as coils and condensers, are properly adjusted (tuned) will respond by resonance to the incoming radio waves and reject those of other frequencies. The operation of modern radio and other electronic circuits is made possible only by the use of electron tubes to be described in the next chapter.

SUMMARY

A current in a wire *is accompanied by a magnetic field* whose lines of force are circles surrounding the wire. The direction of the field is given by the right-hand rule (page 316).

The magnetic-field vector at any point is the force acting on a unit *N* pole. It is measured in *oersteds* (dynes per unit pole).

A straight current-carrying wire held normal to a magnetic field is acted upon by a force which is normal to both current and field and the magnitude of which is given by $f = HIl/10$.

Electric motor: Through the mechanical interaction of their magnetic fields, two sets of current-carrying conductors are able to exert forces on each other. In a motor, this results in the transformation of electrical into mechanical energy.

Induced voltage arises in a circuit when the *magnetic flux*—the number of lines of force threading through the circuit—*is changing* or when any portion of the circuit is cutting such lines. Direction of induced voltage is such that its effects oppose its cause (*Lenz's law*). Magnitude is given by $V = 10^{-8} \Delta\Phi/\Delta t$.

Generator: A device for continuous production of induced currents, thus changing mechanical into electrical energy.

Transformer: A pair of coils, usually wound on a core of magnetic material. A varying voltage (current) in one induces a varying voltage (current) in the other. The effective voltages of the two currents are proportional to the respective numbers of turns in the two coils.

Electromagnetic waves: Emitted into surrounding space by a circuit carrying an oscillating current. May be received by another circuit adjusted to respond to their frequency by *resonance.*

READING REFERENCES

1. Taylor, Lloyd W.: "Physics, the Pioneer Science," Houghton Mifflin, Boston, 1946. Read Chaps. 42, 45, and 46.
2. Moulton, F. R., and J. J. Schifferes: "The Autobiography of Science," Doubleday, New York, 1945. Excerpts from the writings of Faraday and of Henry, pp. 288–292.
3. Bragg, W. L.: "Electricity," Macmillan, New York, 1936. Read Chaps. III–V.
4. Cajori, F.: "A History of Physics," Macmillan, New York, 1929. The work of Oersted and of Ampère is discussed on pp. 231–234.
5. Bozorth, R. M.: Magnetic Materials, *Sci. American*, Vol. 192, No. 1, pp. 68–73, 1955. A clear description of the domain theory and the experimental evidence relating to it.

FILM

"Electrodynamics," Encyclopaedia Britannica Films. 16 mm, sound, 1 reel.

EXERCISES

1. Look up the connection between magnetism and the story of "Snow White and the Seven Dwarfs" in Ref 1.

2. List the ways in which magnetic phenomena are similar to those of electrostatics, considering such points as existence of attraction or repulsion, dependence of force on distance, effect of the medium, and substances involved.

3. Using the idea of magnetic induction, explain why a piece of ordinary iron will be attracted by *either* pole of a bar magnet.

4. The device of replacing an actual magnet in effect by two localized poles makes possible the determination of the field vector at any point, as in the electrostatic example on page 278. Compute the strength of the magnetic field at a point that is 10 cm from each pole of a bar magnet whose poles, each of 400 units, are 10 cm apart. What is the direction of the field at this point? Does this agree with *a* and *b* of Fig. 17·4?

5. The two poles of a straight bar magnet are 5.0 cm apart and each is of strength 60 units. The N pole of a long bar magnet of pole strength 20 units is placed at a point located 4.0 cm from the N pole and 3.0 cm from the S pole of the first bar. The S pole of the second magnet is far away. Compute the magnitude of the force exerted on the 20-unit N pole by the first bar. Indicate the approximate direction of this force on a diagram.

6. Draw a diagram, similar to Fig. 17·10, but with **both** the direction of the current and that of the external field **reversed**. Sketch the composite field, and show that the direction of the force acting on the wire is the same as before.

7. When no current is being drawn from a generator, the only work needed to keep it turning is the amount required to overcome friction; but as soon as the outside circuit is closed, the generator becomes very hard to turn and acts as if it were immersed in molasses. Explain.

8. Read the interesting account of the evolution of motors and generators in Chap. 46 of Ref. 1.

9. A horizontal wire 10 cm long is suspended from one arm of a balance, and a current of 10 amp is sent through it. If the wire is in a horizontal magnetic field of 196 oersteds whose lines of force are perpendicular to the wire, how much weight must be added to one side of the balance in order to restore equilibrium?

10. Over a small area, the earth's magnetic field may be considered uniform. At a certain station in the tropics, the strength of the field is 0.35 oersted, and the lines dip downward at an angle of 30 deg below the horizontal. Find the magnetic flux through a closed plane loop of wire of area 150 cm^2 lying on a table.

11. An iron rod 1 m long oriented in the east-west direction is falling in a horizontal position. Neglecting air resistance, what will be the PD between its ends after dropping a distance of 100 m from rest at a place where the strength of the horizontal component of the earth's magnetic field is 0.20 oersted?

12. A circular coil of 100 turns, of effective radius 4 cm, is in a magnetic field of 100 oersteds, the plane of the coil being perpendicular to the field. If the coil is jerked out of the field in 0.01 sec, what driving potential is induced in it? If the coil is connected into a circuit whose total resistance, including that of the coil itself, is 48 ohms, what average current flows during the process?

Chapter 18

ELECTRONS

The nineteenth century was a period in which the great theories underlying the major divisions of what is called "classical physics" were brought to a high state of perfection. The kinetic theory of matter not only had placed the atomic concept on a firm basis but had brought the entire subject of heat within the domain of mechanics. The principle of the conservation of energy came into its own as the basic unifying idea of the whole subject. Phenomena that were apparently distinct and unrelated were brought together under the head of electromagnetism, with momentous developments resulting on the practical side. And perhaps most outstanding of all was Maxwell's electromagnetic theory of radiation, which showed that all of wave optics is a branch of electromagnetism. It is not surprising that several prominent scientists expressed the opinion that all the major fundamental laws of physics had already been discovered and that these were not likely to be supplanted in the future.

But just before the end of the nineteenth century there came in rapid succession a series of remarkable discoveries concerned with phenomena entirely unknown to earlier science. These discoveries and the theoretical structures erected to account for them touched off a "chain reaction" of scientific activity that has made the last half century a period of tremendously increased rate of acquisition of scientific information. But even more significant is the revolutionary nature of some of the new phenomena and their impact on the life and future of the entire human race. The newer physics is usually referred to as "modern physics." The remaining chapters of this book will attempt to give some account of the main discoveries and trends of thought of this period and to assess their importance to civilization.

The beginnings of modern physics are connected with the investigation of the passage of electricity through gases at reduced pressure—a line of inquiry that contributed to an understanding of the structure of the atom and led to the discovery of the electron.

18·1 Discharge of Electricity through a Gas

Air or any other gas at normal atmospheric pressure is a very poor conductor of electricity, and usually the potential difference between two nearby conductors must be raised to several thousand volts before any appreciable current will pass between them. When this occurs, it is in the form of a sudden spark, as in a lightning flash. The process is in reality a very complicated one, and it was not until experiments were made with gases at reduced pressure that the phenomenon began to be understood. As early as 1853

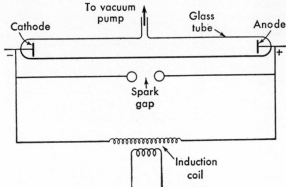

FIG. 18·1   Tube for studying electrical discharge through gases.

the French experimenter Masson found that when a source of high voltage was connected to wires sealed into the ends of a partly pumped out glass tube the sudden spark observed in air at normal pressure gave way to a soft glow which filled the tube. With the improvement of vacuum pumps other workers, notably Goldstein in Germany and Crookes in England, made such discharge tubes and studied their operation.

Suppose a long tube like that shown in Fig. 18·1 is connected to a vacuum pump. Sealed into each end of the tube is a disklike metal electrode, the two being connected to the secondary of an *induction coil,* which is a type of transformer producing a high-voltage current flowing almost entirely in one direction. The negative electrode (cathode) is at the left. An external *spark gap,* consisting of two metal balls separated a few millimeters, is connected as shown.

The appearance of the glow in the tube changes markedly with changes in the pressure of the contained gas. If, starting with the air in the tube at normal atmospheric pressure, the coil is switched on, a spark passes at the gap but nothing happens inside the tube. The pump is now started; and when the pressure in the tube has dropped to nearly $\frac{1}{100}$ atm, thin, wavering bluish streamers begin to play between the electrodes (Fig. 18·2a). At the same time the spark at the gap ceases; it is now easier for the discharge to pass through the long column of air at low pressure than across the much shorter gap at normal pressure. When the pressure has fallen to roughly $\frac{1}{200}$ atm, the color of the glow changes to salmon pink and fills the whole cross section of the tube (sketch b). This

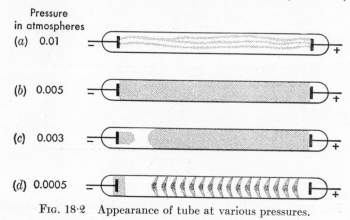

Pressure
in atmospheres
(a) 0.01

(b) 0.005

(c) 0.003

(d) 0.0005

Fig. 18·2   Appearance of tube at various pressures.

stage of the discharge is used for examining the spectra of gases and vapors in tubes of this kind. It is also the condition maintained in tube-type signs used commercially.

Further pumping makes the glow divide into two parts—a short bluish tuft at the cathode and a long pink column extending up to the anode, with a dark space between them, as in c. At still lower pressure, corresponding to that existing about 30 miles up in the atmosphere, the long pink column of light breaks up into rather evenly spaced crosswise layers (sketch d). As pumping continues, this column fades in color and retreats toward the anode. At a pressure of around 10^{-5} atm a new effect appears. The **glass** of the tube itself glows with a greenish light, while the contained gas loses its luminosity almost entirely.[1]

---

[1] The color changes described here refer to a tube of ordinary colorless glass initially filled with air. If other types of glass or contained gases are used, the colors

The main features of the complex phenomena of discharge at reduced pressure are explained on the basis of ions, which are always present to some extent in ordinary gases.[1] These ions are accelerated when the potential is applied to the electrodes. Positive ions striking the cathode knock out electrons, which in turn acquire kinetic energy until, when they collide with neutral atoms of the gas, they ionize these in turn by knocking electrons loose. The process builds up rapidly, since the newly formed ions as well as the electrons detached in the operation are then accelerated in the electric field. Also, because of the low density of the gas, they can acquire high speed before experiencing their next collision. Part of the energy acquired by the atoms that are struck is sent out again in the form of radiation. This part of the process will be discussed more fully in a later chapter.

18·2   Cathode Rays

The glow emitted by the glass as described above is found to be a fluorescence (page 234) stimulated by something coming out of the cathode of the tube in straight lines. Goldstein introduced the term *cathode rays* for this emanation. An obstacle such as a piece of metal placed in the path of the rays will cast a sharp "shadow" on the side of the tube. Other experiments show that the rays carry energy and that they can produce the effects of mechanical impact and raise the temperature of a material surface on which they fall. Crookes concluded that the cathode rays consist of streams of particles. The fact that the rays come only from the cathode of the tube suggested that they might be negatively charged. Hertz tried to deviate the rays by applying an electric field and also attempted to detect a magnetic field near a cathode-ray beam but was unsuccessful. It remained for Perrin to collect the rays in a small metal cylinder placed inside the tube and to verify the fact that they carry a negative charge. He also showed that the rays could be deflected sidewise by placing the tube between the poles of a magnet, and the direction of deflection was in agreement with the idea that the rays carry a *negative* charge. But the definite proof that the rays consist of streams of identical, electrified particles and the

will, of course, be different, but the various stages of the process will be essentially the same. The last stage described above is not illustrated in the figure.

[1] Cosmic rays and radioactive materials in the earth's crust ordinarily ionize about 10 air molecules per cubic centimeter per second.

first quantitative measurements of their characteristics are to be credited to the famous experiments of **J. J. Thomson,**[1] performed in 1897. He was able to deflect cathode rays electrically and succeeded also in determining the speed and *the ratio of charge to mass* for the individual particles constituting these rays.

A diagram of the vacuum tube used by Thomson is shown in Fig. 18·3. Rays originating at the cathode are limited to a narrow beam by the small holes in the diaphragms. The anode is placed in a side tube, its position being of little importance. The beam next passes between two metal plates, between which an electric field may be created by a high-voltage battery. The pair of oppositely charged plates is in effect a capacitor. In this same portion

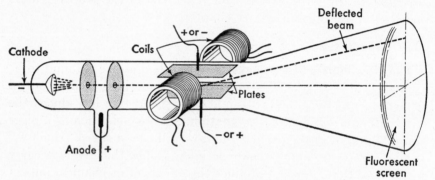

FIG. 18·3   Thomson's e/m apparatus.

of the tube the beam also passes through the magnetic field caused by a current in the two solenoidal coils. Finally the rays hit the end of the tube, which is coated with a material that fluoresces more brightly than glass when struck by the cathode beam.

18·3   Measurement of Cathode-ray Speeds

Depending upon its direction the electric field is capable of deflecting the beam either upward or downward in a vertical plane. Thus the path of the rays will be straight before they enter the capacitor, curved while between the plates, and again straight (but inclined to the axis of the tube) after leaving the space between

[1] Joseph John Thomson, gifted English experimental physicist, winner of a Nobel prize for his work in this field of investigation. He became the inspiring leader of a group of researchers who contributed importantly to the development of modern physics.

the plates (see Fig. 18·4). When the electric field is on, the bright spot produced by impact of the rays on the end of the tube no longer will be at the center but will be above or below this point.

The magnetic field is directed along the common axis of the two coils; and since the force exerted on the moving charges will be normal to both the field and the direction of motion of the charges, the magnetic deflection will be in the up-and-down direction, as was the electrical one. By applying the electric and magnetic fields in the proper directions and by adjusting their strengths, it is possible to make the deflection in the upward direction caused by one just large enough to cancel the downward deflection due to the other, so that the spot of light again falls at the exact center of the screen.

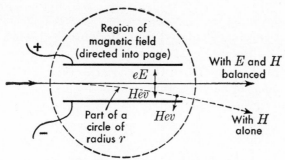

Fig. 18·4   Effect of fields on cathode-ray particles.

Suppose that each cathode-ray particle has a (negative) charge of e esu. Then an electric field of strength E dynes/esu will exert a force of eE dynes on such a particle (page 276), and the force will be in a direction **opposite** to that of the field, since the charge is **negative.** If the particles are moving with a speed v cm/sec, a magnetic field of strength H oersteds will exert on each one a force amounting to $Hev/(3 \times 10^{10})$ dynes (page 319). When the two effects are made to balance,

$$eE = \frac{Hev}{3 \times 10^{10}} \qquad \text{or} \qquad v = 3 \times 10^{10}\,\frac{E}{H} \qquad (18\cdot1)$$

The field strengths E and H are readily measured, so that the speed of the cathode-ray particles can be computed. It usually turns out to be of the order of one-tenth the speed of light or more, the exact value depending on the voltage applied to the tube.

18·4   Determination of e/m

Thomson was next concerned with finding the amount of charge carried by each particle, as well as its mass. Applying the magnetic field alone, he measured the resulting deflection of the spot on the screen. Now the particles are acted upon by a constant force of amount Hev all the time they are in the magnetic field, and the force is always at right angles to their direction of motion. This means that their path while in the field is a part of a circle, since this is the shape of path for which the centripetal force (page 142) furnished by the magnetic field would be constant in amount. Equating the general expression for centripetal force, mv^2/r, to the particular value that holds here, we have

$$\frac{mv^2}{r} = \frac{Hev}{3 \times 10^{10}} \qquad \text{or} \qquad \frac{e}{m} = 3 \times 10^{10} \frac{v}{Hr} \qquad (18\cdot2)$$

The radius r can be calculated from the observed deflection of the beam and the dimensions of the tube, H is measurable, and v can be found from Eq. (18·1), so that e/m, the ratio of the charge (in esu) to the mass of each particle, can be evaluated.

But neither e nor m **separately** can be found from these experiments. Nevertheless, the results so far described are of greatest importance. For one thing, when the magnetic field is applied, the trace of the cathode ray on the end of the tube does not spread out but remains a small spot. This shows that the particles constituting the beam are all **alike**—all have the same value of e/m. Moreover, no matter what the nature of the gas originally in the tube or the material of which the electrodes are made, the same value for e/m always results. The cathode-ray particles must be some sort of universal ingredient of all kinds of matter. They are, in fact, individual **electrons,** as will be made clear below.

The best numerical value of e/m is found to be

$$\frac{e}{m} = 5.28 \times 10^{17} \text{ esu/gm} = 1.76 \times 10^8 \text{ coulombs/gm}$$

The large size of these numbers impressed Thomson. In your study of electrolysis, you saw (page 297) how the charge on an ion could be determined. Dividing this charge by the mass of the ion yields its charge-to-mass ratio, and the largest numerical value is found to be that of the hydrogen ion. But the above value of e/m found for a cathode-ray particle is nearly 2000 times **larger** than even that of the hydrogen ion. Thomson saw that this must mean that e is very large for cathode particles, or that m is very small, or both. He inclined to the idea that the *smallness of m* was responsible— that cathode particles were in some way constituents of the atoms of matter. This view, then, represents the first experimentally supported conclusion that particles smaller than atoms exist, and this feature of Thomson's result is probably the most important of all.

18·5 Determination of e

Thomson and his coworkers carried out a series of experiments in which they succeeded in measuring the charge carried by a cloud of droplets of water condensed on ions in the air and thus obtained a value for the smallest charge on any one droplet, which was presumably that of a single electron. A more reliable method was developed by Millikan,[1] beginning about 1909. His method is depicted in Fig. 18·5. Droplets of oil from a sprayer are allowed to enter the space between the plates of a condenser, where they are strongly illuminated from one side and are observed through a low-powered microscope.

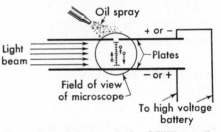

A drop of the kind used (perhaps 10^{-4} cm in diameter) reaches its terminal speed within a few thousandths of a second and continues to fall at a constant rate of the order of 1 mm/sec. The terminal speed

Fig. 18·5 Scheme of the Millikan oil-drop experiment.

is found by clocking the drop as it moves between reference marks located a given distance apart. There is a known relation between the terminal speed of a sphere falling in air and its mass, and thus in this indirect way the mass of the drop under observation can be determined.

If a high-voltage battery is now connected to the plates, the drop will, in general, change its speed abruptly; it may even start to rise. The reason is that, as in the process of rubbing, the act of spraying the oil usually gives a charge to each drop. Depending on

---

[1] Robert A. Millikan, late American physicist. Besides his work on the measurement of e and fundamental investigations of the photoelectric effect, for which he was awarded a Nobel prize, he was known for his studies in the field of cosmic rays.

the sign of this charge and the direction of the field between the plates, the drop will experience an electrostatic force, either up or down. A valuable feature of Millikan's method is the possibility of altering the charge on a drop by allowing it to pick up an occasional ion from the air. Abundant ions may be produced for this purpose by admitting a beam of X rays into the space between the plates. A given droplet, once its mass has been determined from the rate of fall in the absence of the electric field, can often be used for a whole series of observations.

Reduction of the observations makes it possible to compute the charge on the drop in each case, and the remarkable result is that *these charges are invariably integral multiples of a certain smallest value*—the so-called *charge on the electron.* This is found to be the same as the charge on each ion of an element of valence 1 in electrolysis (page 298). The best present value is

$$e = 4.80 \times 10^{-10} \text{ esu} = 1.60 \times 10^{-19} \text{ coulomb}$$

Along with the speed of light, the constant of gravitation, and one or two other quantities the charge on the electron seems to be one of the fundamental constants of nature. It enters into many basic relations in physics that at first sight are not directly concerned with electric charge.

What Millikan's experiment showed conclusively is that electric charge, like matter, possesses a kind of *atomicity*—electricity occurs only in discrete amounts, all of which are multiples of e. No smaller charge than e has ever been shown to exist.

18·6 The Mass of the Electron

With e/m known from experiments like those of Thomson and e determined by Millikan's work, the value of m, the mass of the electron, may be computed by simple division. Using the best present values for each of these quantities,

$$m = \frac{e}{e/m} = \frac{4.80 \times 10^{-10} \text{ esu}}{5.27 \times 10^{17} \text{ esu/gm}} = 9.11 \times 10^{-28} \text{ gm}$$

This mass is approximately 1840 times smaller than the mass of the lightest atom—that of hydrogen.

It was by means of experiments with electrons that another result of great general importance was obtained. When e/m was measured for electrons of greater and greater speed, it was found that the value of this ratio decreased markedly, especially for the very fast electrons ejected from radioactive atoms, where the speeds approach that of light. There is no reason to assume that the charge on an electron depends on how it moves, and hence this variation in e/m must mean that the mass of an electron increases as it moves faster. This conclusion is quite at odds with previous ideas as to the nature of mass, for classical mechanics assumed that the mass of a given object was invariable. But Thomson and others calculated, on the basis of electromagnetic theory, that the inertia of a charged body should increase in a certain way with its speed of motion, and the experiments agreed with this result.

Later, the theory of relativity led to the same result for **any** moving body, whether electrically charged or not. The mass m of a body moving with a speed v relative to the observer is given by the theory as

$$m = \frac{m_0}{\sqrt{1 - (v/c)^2}} \quad (18\cdot3)$$

where m_0 is the mass of the body at very low speeds (the "rest mass") and c is the speed of light.[1] According to this relation the mass of a moving body remains practically the same as its rest mass as long as the speed is small but increases rapidly at higher speeds, becoming infinitely large as the speed approaches that of light. A graph of Eq. (18·3) is shown in Fig. 18·6, from which these features are apparent.

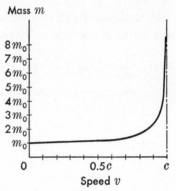

Fig. 18·6 Dependence of mass of a body on its speed.

The surprising result just described raises the interesting question of whether the entire mass of a body may not be ascribable to the electromagnetic inertia of its charged constituents, with no additional "material mass" whatever. This view would take away most of the apparent substantiality of material bodies, replacing what we crudely visualize as lumps of matter by *local concentrations of energy*. On this point the theory of relativity has something further to say (page 409).

[1] Notice the presence here of the ubiquitous c in a situation apparently having nothing whatever to do with optics. This quantity appears in a great many other formulas of the theory of relativity.

ELECTRONICS

The tremendous impact of the discovery of the electron on scientific thought has been matched in importance by the remarkable technical developments that followed. It is no overstatement to say that several of our major industries—including radio, motion pictures, television, and important branches of telephony and transportation—could not exist without the applications of electronic devices which have become familiar in recent years. It is, of course, impossible to give any reasonably full account of the various phases of electronics in the present book, but a few outstanding principles and their applications are worthy of mention. More comprehensive accounts are given in Refs. 3–6.

18·7 Thermionic Emission; The Diode

As you know, a metallic conductor contains large numbers of free electrons, which move about among the atoms of the metal. If the metal is placed in a vacuum and heated, some of the electrons attain speeds high enough to enable them to break away from the metal and form a cloud of detached electrons in the space around the wire. This process, which may be visualized as a sort of "evaporation" of electrons from the metal, is referred to as *thermionic emission.*

The discovery of the phenomenon may be traced to a chance observation of Edison's in 1883 in connection with work on his early filament lamps. He noticed that a small current could be made to pass between the hot filament and an additional electrode sealed into the side of the lamp whenever the extra electrode was given a positive polarity, but not when it was made negative. A few years later Fleming, in England, showed that the effect was due to electrons released from the heated filament and attracted to the nearby positive electrode, and the "Fleming valve" was soon used to *rectify* alternating currents. In this country the two-element tube (filament and plate) is usually called a *diode.* Its action in allowing a current to flow only in one direction will be evident from Fig. 18·7a. The filament is heated by passing a current through it by means of a battery, which is not shown in the sketch. If a source of alternating voltage is connected between the filament and the plate, a current will flow in the plate circuit during the half cycle when the plate is positive with respect to the filament, but not when the potential difference is the other way around. In the former case, electrons are attracted to the plate and continue around the circuit; in the latter, they are repelled, and no current can pass. Thus an alternating voltage impressed on the tube is changed to an **intermittent direct current** in a resistor ("load") located as shown in Fig. 18·7.

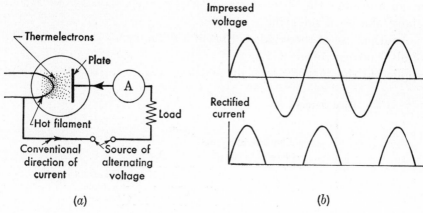

(a)   (b)

FIG. 18·7   The diode as a rectifier.

By using two diodes both loops of the alternating-current cycle can be utilized, and by passing the output current through a suitable circuit consisting of condensers and coils the pulsations can be smoothed out almost completely. In order to eliminate disturbing effects of residual gas, the pressure to which a vacuum tube must be reduced in manufacture is as low as one-billionth of an atmosphere.

18·8 The Triode; Amplification and Detection of Signals

The modification of Fleming's valve that universalized its use was the introduction of a third element by the American experimenter De Forest about fifty years ago. The new element is a wire mesh, or **grid,** inserted between filament and plate; the tube is then called a **triode.** Small changes in the potential applied to the grid now produce large changes in the electron current from filament to plate, so that the grid provides a sensitive control of this current. The curve of Fig. 18·8 shows the relation between the voltage applied to the grid and the current flowing to the plate in a typical three-element tube. The middle part of such a curve is quite straight; and if any form of voltage change is applied to the grid somewhere in this range, the corresponding voltage variation in the external circuit will be of exactly the same form but much increased because of the steepness of slope of the curve. The tube will *amplify* the impressed disturbance without appreciably distorting it. The consequent voltage changes may in turn be applied to the grid of another triode, resulting in a further increase, and in this way several stages of amplification may be used. In its role as an amplifier the three-element tube is an indispensable tool in many phases of scientific research.

Another use of the triode is that of a *detector,* or partial rectifier, of alternating voltages. For this purpose, the oscillating voltage is applied at the *curved* "toe" of the tube's characteristic graph (Fig.

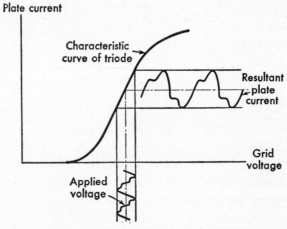

Fig. 18·8   The triode as an amplifier.

18·9). When small voltage variations are applied to the grid as shown, the varying slope at different parts of the curve will give rise to a plate current whose average value lies predominantly on *one* side of the zero line.

The original voltage oscillations may be those induced in the collecting wire (*antenna*) of a radio receiving set by electromagnetic waves coming from a broadcasting station. The oscillations used have frequencies of the order of a million per second. Applied directly to a telephone receiver or loud-speaker, they would be incapable of setting the diaphragm into vibration because of its inertia. But the primary electromagnetic wave, or *carrier wave,* is *modulated* prior to being broadcast, as explained on page 333. This means that the sound vibrations to be transmitted are superimposed on the carrier, giving the latter a variation whose frequency is, at most, several thousand vibrations per second. These pulses, after amplification, are able to actuate a receiver or speaker, making it reproduce the original sound.

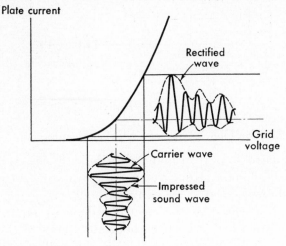

Fig. 18·9   The triode as a detector.

18·9 Oscillating Circuits

A third important function of the triode is that of an *oscillator*. By suitably connecting such a tube into a circuit, it can be made to regulate the feeding of energy into the circuit from a battery so that an oscillating current of considerable strength is maintained. The frequency of these oscillations, however, is determined solely by the electrical constants of the circuit itself. A microphone converts the wave form of the sounds to be broadcast into a corresponding voltage pattern as in telephony. This signal is amplified and then combined with the carrier wave to produce the modulated wave form described above. Through the aerial some of the energy of the circuit is radiated into surrounding space in the form of electromagnetic waves.

A very simple *receiving circuit* is diagramed in Fig. 18·10. By tuning the circuit it can be made to respond to waves of a selected frequency impinging on the areial. The corresponding variations in potential of the grid causes the triode, acting as a detector, to send a signal current through the telephone receiver or loudspeaker, which reproduces the sound.

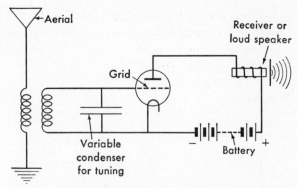

FIG. 18·10   Simple receiving circuit.

18·10   The Electron Gun; Energy of a Moving Electron

An indispensable part of many electronic devices is an arrangement for producing a strong yet narrow beam of fast electrons of constant known speed. The early cathode-ray experiments had shown that the speed of the electrons depends on the potential difference applied between the cathode and anode of the tube. The

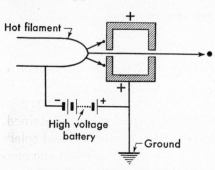

FIG. 18·11   Electron gun.

assembly called an *electron gun* consists of a heated filament as a source of electrons and an accelerating field through which they are allowed to fall to attain a desired speed. The essential construction is shown in Fig. 18·11. Electrons leaving the filament are attracted by the positively charged metal plates, and a narrow beam passes through the holes. The entire assembly is, of course, placed in a high vacuum and usually forms a part of some more elaborate device such as one of those described below.

An electron of charge e (in coulombs) that has fallen through a **PD** of V volts has had an amount of work done on it by the electric field equal to eV joules, according to Eq. (15·5), page 282. If the electron has lost no energy while falling through the field, it will then have kinetic energy of this amount. Its speed will be given by

$$eV = \frac{1}{2}\,mv^2 \qquad \text{or} \qquad v = \sqrt{2\,\frac{e}{m}\,V} \qquad (18·4)$$

Example: What is the speed of an electron that has fallen through a PD of 16,000 volts? In Eq. (18·4), e/m must be in esu per gram, and V must be divided by 300 in order to express the KE in ergs (see Eq. (15·4), page 282). Substituting the proper numerical values,

$$v = \sqrt{\frac{2(5.27 \times 10^{17})(16 \times 10^3)}{300}} = 7.5 \times 10^9 \text{ cm/sec}$$

which is about one-fourth the speed of light.

If, instead of an electron, a *doubly charged* ion had traversed the same PD, its energy would be *twice* as much as that acquired by the electron (see Exercise 5).

Since the high-speed electrons and ions used as projectiles in many physics experiments today are often accelerated electrically, their energy is conveniently specified in terms of their charge and the PD through which they have been made to fall. A particle is said to have one *electron volt* of KE if it has an energy equal to that of an electron which has fallen through a PD of one volt. In terms of the usual energy unit, the erg, one electron volt (abbreviated "ev") is equivalent to 1.60×10^{-12} erg. A unit 1,000,000 times as large is called one *mega-electron volt* (Mev), and modern nuclear experiments use particles whose energies are stated in billions of electron volts (Bev).

18·11 Cathode-ray Oscilloscope

One of the most useful of all electronic devices both in research and in practice, the *cathode-ray oscilloscope,* makes use of an electron gun. This instrument is an outgrowth of the Thomson apparatus. The electron beam is made to pass between two pairs of parallel plates (Fig. 18·12), one pair being at right angles to the other. Potentials applied to the plates are capable of deflecting the electron beam both horizontally and vertically.[1] Because of the high speed and negligible inertia of the electrons they can respond to changes in voltage that may be much too rapid to be traced by any other means. The path of the beam is marked by the luminous curve traced on the fluorescent coating at the end of the tube.

The form of a sound wave may be studied by picking the wave up by means of a microphone, which produces correspond-

[1] In some designs, the plates are replaced by two sets of coils, which serve the same purpose.

ing voltage variations in an attached amplifier circuit. The output is then applied to one pair of plates of the oscillograph, while a "sweep" voltage, which moves the beam across the screen periodically, is applied to the other pair. When the frequency of the sweep

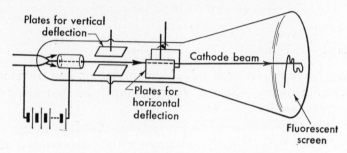

FIG. 18·12   Cathode-ray oscilloscope.

voltage is adjusted to agree with that of the disturbance to be analyzed, a stationary wave-form curve appears on the screen.

18·12   Television

The tube used to reproduce the picture in a television receiver is essentially a cathode-ray oscilloscope. One pair of plates or coils makes the beam move periodically *across* the screen while the other moves it suddenly *down* a short distance after each sweep so that the path of the light spot on the screen is like that followed

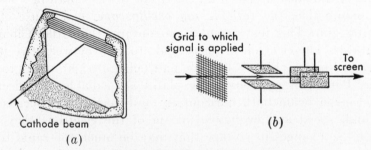

FIG. 18·13   Television receiving tube.

by the eye in reading a printed page (Fig. 18·13a). Thus a rectangular screen is completely "painted" with light, and all this must take place within about a thirtieth of a second so that the persistence of the impression on the eye may give the illusion of a stationary field of view. In order to convert this uniformly illuminated rectangle into a picture, it is necessary to vary the brightness of the spot from place to place as it traverses the screen. This is done by impressing the incoming signal on a grid mounted in the tube (see figure). The received signal is produced at the sending station by some means of optically "scanning" the scene and converting the variations in illumination into corresponding variations in voltage in the sending circuit. There are several ways of doing this, but the details are too technical for present discussion.

Other important uses of the oscilloscope are in connection with the various forms of radar apparatus (see Ref. 5).

18·13   The Electron Microscope

It has been known for many years that a stream of electrons coming from a point source can be brought to a focus at another point by either electric or magnetic means. An electrostatic system that acts toward cathode rays in much the same way as a lens does toward light rays is diagramed in Fig. 18·14. Rays from a small source are made to pass through a focal point by the electrostatic action of the charged plates.

A *magnetic* electron lens, on the other hand, consists of a coil of special form that produces a nonuniform magnetic field. An electron entering a magnetic field at an angle to the lines of force will follow a path that spirals around the lines of force, and the theory of the magnetic lens shows that electrons coming from a single point will be brought together again at another point, or focus.

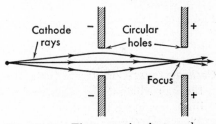

FIG. 18·14   Electrostatic electron lens.

A combination of electron lenses can be arranged to form an *electron microscope.* By means of a final image on a fluorescent screen or on a photographic plate, such an instrument can make visible the form and structure of objects placed in the path of the rays. Features of certain viruses, crystals, and even large molecules that are far beyond the resolving power of optical microscopes have been revealed by this instrument. The increased resolution is connected with the wavelike character of electrons, to be discussed later (Chap. 21). Magnifying powers of the order of 100,000— roughly twenty times the largest possible with optical microscopes—are attained. A form of electron microscope using magnetic lenses is shown diagrammatically in Fig. 18.15.

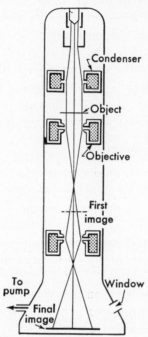

FIG. 18·15   Diagram of a magnetic electron microscope. (*After Prof. C. A. Culver.*)

SUMMARY

Cathode rays: Come from the cathode in a highly evacuated glass tube through which a high-voltage discharge passes. They travel in straight lines, possess KE, and can be deviated by electric or magnetic fields. They are *streams of fast electrons.*

Speed and charge-mass ratio of cathode-ray electrons first measured by Thomson by bending rays in applied fields. Regardless of their source, all cathode-ray electrons have same value of e/m. Large value of e/m suggested that electrons are much less massive than atoms.

Charge on the electron: Millikan's experiment shows it to be identical with charge on hydrogen ion. It is the smallest amount of charge that can exist independently.

Mass of electron: Computed from values of e and e/m; turns out to be about $\frac{1}{1840}$ of mass of a hydrogen atom. Inertia (mass) of electron found to increase with speed, in harmony with theory.

Thermionic emission: Profuse "evaporation" of electrons from a heated filament. Attracted to a nearby positively charged plate, the electrons carry a current across the space in one direction only (use of *diode* as a *rectifier*).

Triode: Relatively small PD's applied to a *grid* placed between filament and plate are able to control and modify electron current flowing to the plate. Such a triode may be used as a *detector* (partial rectifier) or as an *amplifier* of oscillating voltages. The tube may also serve to *control and maintain the oscillations* of a suitable circuit.

Electron volt (ev): The quantity of energy possessed by an electron or singly charged ion that has fallen unhindered through a PD of 1 volt.

Mega-electron volt: 1 Mev = 10^6 ev; *billion electron volts:* 1 Bev = 10^9 ev.

Cathode-ray oscilloscope: A device that traces the variation in time of an impressed voltage, using a beam of cathode rays as a "pointer."

Electron microscope: An *electron lens,* using either electric or magnetic fields, can be used to bring cathode rays to a focus. A combination of such lenses—an *electron miscoscope*—is capable of very high resolution of the details of an object placed in the path of the rays.

READING REFERENCES

1. Moulton, F. R., and J. J. Schifferes: "The Autobiography of Science," Doubleday, New York, 1948. J. J. Thomson describes his discovery of the electron, pp. 502–506.
2. Thomson, John J.: "Recollections and Reflections," Macmillan, New York, 1937. Personalized narrative of the author's work and that of some of his contemporaries. An interesting human document.
3. Cosslett, V. E.: "The Electron Microscope," Sigma Books, London, 1947. Development, construction, and uses of this instrument.
4. Pierce, J. R.: Electronics, *Sci. American,* Vol. 183, No. 4, pp. 30–39, 1950. A brief but informative survey of the field.
5. Upton, M.: "Electronics for Everyone," Devin-Adair, New York, 1954. An interesting nontechnical book on the history and applications of electronics.

FILMS

"Electrons," Encyclopaedia Britannica Films. 16 mm, sound, 1 reel.

"Electronics at Work," Westinghouse Electric Corp. 16 mm, sound, 2 reels (transportation costs only).

"The Triode," U.S. Office of Education. 16 mm, sound, 1 reel.

EXERCISES

1. Refer to page 288, and compare conduction in a solid with cathode rays, as regards direction of motion of the individual electrons, their speed, the number taking part, etc.

2. In a repetition of Millikan's experiment it was found that a certain oil drop carrying 3 electron charges could just be balanced against gravity when the field between the plates had a strength of 7.0 dynes/esu. What was the diameter of the drop? Assume the density (page 23) of the oil to have been 0.90 gm/cm^3.

3. If the drop in Exercise 2 suddenly picks up an additional electron, what will be its initial acceleration?

4. An electron coming from the heated filament of an electron gun falls through a PD of 800 volts. What is then its kinetic energy in electron volts? In ergs? How fast is it going?

5. If, in the example on page 351, a doubly charged calcium ion had fallen through the PD of 16,000 volts, instead of the electron, how would its energy compare with that of the electron? Its *speed?* (A calcium atom is about 73,000 times as massive as an electron.)

6. An electron going in a straight line at a speed of 5×10^7 cm/sec in a vacuum tube enters a region where its motion is opposed by a uniform electric field whose lines of force are parallel to the path of the electron. Through how much of a PD does the electron fall before coming to rest?

7. Compute the acceleration of an electron in a field of strength 2.0 dynes/esu inside a partly evacuated tube. If the electron can travel an average distance of 0.50 mm between collisions with gas atoms in the tube, how much energy (in electron volts) is it capable of giving up in such a collision?

8. A beam of cathode rays enters the space between the charged plates of a Thomson tube (Fig. 18·3). The electric field there succeeds in bending the rays into a circular arc of radius 20.0 cm. If the field has a strength of 5.0 dynes/esu, what was the speed of the entering beam?

9. The rectangular face of a television tube is 18 in. wide. The cathode beam traces 525 lines 30 times each second, covering alternate lines first, then going back and filling in (this reduces flicker). How fast does the spot move along the face of the tube? If your eye could scan the text of this book at this speed, how long would it take to read the entire volume, assuming that there are 500 pages, each having 30 lines of text, each line being 4½ in. long?

10. What is the diameter of the influenza virus if its image in an electron microscope adjusted to give a magnification of 60,000 is about the size of a pea (0.6 cm)?

Chapter 19

ISOTOPES, X RAYS, AND NATURAL RADIOACTIVITY

Looking back at the early pages of Chap. 7, you will recall that the working hypothesis that matter consists of molecules proved able to explain a great range of both chemical and physical phenomena. On this basis our belief in the "reality" of molecules is amply justified. However, ordinary large-scale chemical and physical experiments always involve great aggregates of molecules, never single ones, and it would be desirable to find ways of dealing with such particles individually. Experiments connected with the passage of electricity through gases were the first to provide this opportunity, as already illustrated for electrons in Chap. 18. The work to be described below continues the story and leads to important refinements and extensions of the knowledge previously obtained by chemical experimentation.

19·1 Positive Rays

When an electrical discharge takes place in a tube like that shown in Fig. 19·1, the main part of the glow is confined to the

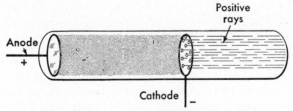

FIG. 19·1 Production of positive rays.

space to the left of the perforated cathode but faintly luminous beams are visible beyond the holes. These beams are due to rapidly moving positive ions, which shoot through the holes into the space beyond. They produce ionization by collision (page 339) and make

357

the gas in their path radiate light. By deflecting them in electric and magnetic fields, it can be shown that these so-called *positive rays* consist of atoms or molecules that have lost one or more electrons and thus have acquired a positive charge.

In 1907, Thomson undertook an investigation of positive rays, using an apparatus shown diagrammatically in Fig. 19·2. Positive ions of the residual gas or gases in the large bulb at the left are limited to a narrow beam by passing through the long, narrow hole in the cathode. They next pass into a space where electric and magnetic fields may be applied. Notice, however, that the arrangement of the two fields differs from that of Thomson's e/m apparatus (Fig. 18·3, page 340); there the two fields were *at right angles* to each other, while here they act *in the same line.* This means that the deflection due to the electric field will be *in* the plane of the

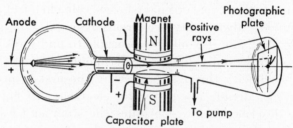

FIG. 19·2   Thomson's positive-ray apparatus.

page, while the magnetic deflection will be *perpendicular* to it. The theory of the instrument shows that, regardless of any difference in speed, all positive ions having a given ratio of charge to mass will strike a fluorescent or photographic plate placed at the end of the tube at points which lie on a given curve. From the known strengths of the two fields the charge-mass ratio can then be calculated for each type of ion present.

The identifications which Thomson made were always in agreement with the idea that in becoming an ion a given atom could be made to give up an amount of electric charge equal to an *integral multiple* but never a fractional part of what was later called the "charge on the electron."

Among the ions detected in these experiments were singly ionized hydrogen atoms (H^+), singly ionized oxygen atoms (O^+), doubly ionized oxygen atoms (O^{++}), singly ionized carbon monoxide molecules (CO^+), etc. The apparatus, in effect, makes possible the determination of the mass of *single* atoms and molecules. Since it sorts out a group of ions with respect to their individual masses in a way suggesting the analysis of a set of wavelengths by an optical spectrograph, any instrument of this type is called a *mass spectrograph.*

19·2 Periodic Table of the Elements

It has been found that all the great variety of substances known to chemistry—approaching a million diverse kinds of matter—are merely different combinations of about 100 fundamental substances, the chemical elements. Almost all these elements have been found on earth, and a majority have been identified spectroscopically in the sun and in the stars. The interpretation of compounds in terms of their constituent elements represents a tremendous simplification and unification of chemical knowledge, without which modern chemical science would be impossible.

Nearly a century ago the Russian chemist Mendeléeff (and independently the German chemist Lothar Meyer) discovered that when the chemical elements are arranged in the order of increasing atomic weight their valence and other chemical properties repeat themselves at regular intervals—that is, *periodically.* This empirical fact suggested that there was some feature of the nature of atoms differing from the simple, ultimate quality ascribed to them up to that time, but the solution of the problem was not to come for nearly half a century.

A tabulation of the elements, extended and revised according to present information, is reproduced below (Table 19·1). In each space is given the atomic number (the order of appearance of the element in the list), the chemical symbol and full name of the element, and (where known) its atomic weight based on the arbitrary value 16.000 for oxygen. Going down the list, elements having similar chemical behavior are encountered periodically; the arrangement is such that all elements in a given column have like chemical properties.

It is worth noticing that many of the atomic weights are quite close to whole numbers, particularly in the earlier part of the table. This fact is interesting in the light of the suggestion, made by the Scottish physician William Prout in 1818, that the atoms of all the elements are really aggregates of hydrogen atoms.

Table 19·1   Periodic

	I	II	III	IV	V
1	1 H Hydrogen 1.0080				
2	3 Li Lithium 6.940	4 Be Beryllium 9.02	5 B Boron 10.82	6 C Carbon 12.01	7 N Nitrogen 14.008
3	11 Na Sodium 22.997	12 Mg Magnesium 24.32	13 Al Aluminum 26.97	14 Si Silicon 28.06	15 P Phosphorus 30.98
4	19 K Potassium 39.096	20 Ca Calcium 40.08	21 Sc Scandium 45.10	22 Ti Titanium 47.90	23 V Vanadium 50.95
	29 Cu Copper 63.57	30 Zn Zinc 65.38	31 Ga Gallium 69.72	32 Ge Germanium 72.60	33 As Arsenic 74.91
5	37 Rb Rubidium 85.48	38 Sr Strontium 87.63	39 Y Yttrium 88.92	40 Zr Zirconium 91.22	41 Nb Niobium 92.91
	47 Ag Silver 107.880	48 Cd Cadmium 112.41	49 In Indium 114.76	50 Sn Tin 118.70	51 Sb Antimony 121.76
6	55 Cs Cesium 132.91	56 Ba Barium 137.36	57–71 *Lanthanide* *series***	72 Hf Hafnium 178.6	73 Ta Tantalum 180.88
	79 Au Gold 197.2	80 Hg Mercury 200.61	81 Tl Thallium 204.39	82 Pb Lead 207.21	83 Bi Bismuth 209.00
7	87 Fr Francium 223	88 Ra Radium 226.05	89–100 *Actinide* *series*†		

* LANTHANIDE SERIES:

57 La Lanthanum 138.92	58 Ce Cerium 140.13	59 Pr Praseodymium 140.92	60 Nd Neodymium 144.27	61 Pm Promethium 147
62 Sm Samarium 150.43	63 Eu Europium 152.0	64 Gd Gadolinium 156.9	65 Tb Terbium 159.2	66 Dy Dysprosium 162.46
67 Ho Holmium 164.94	68 Er Erbium 167.64	69 Tm Thulium 169.4	70 Yb Ytterbium 173.04	71 Lu Lutecium 174.99

Table of the Elements

VI	VII	VIII		
		2 He Helium 4.003		
8 O Oxygen 16.0000	9 F Fluorine 19.00	10 Ne Neon 20.183		
16 S Sulfur 32.06	17 Cl Chlorine 35.457	18 Ar Argon 39.944		
24 Cr Chromium 52.01	25 Mn Manganese 54.93	26 Fe Iron 55.85	27 Co Cobalt 58.94	28 Ni Nickel 58.69
34 Se Selenium 78.96	35 Br Bromine 79.916	36 Kr Krypton 83.7		
42 Mo Molybdenum 95.95	43 Tc Technetium 99	44 Ru Ruthenium 101.7	45 Rh Rhodium 102.91	46 Pd Palladium 106.7
52 Te Tellurium 127.61	53 I Iodine 126.92	54 Xe Xenon 131.3		
74 W Wolfram 183.92	75 Re Rhenium 186.31	76 Os Osmium 190.2	77 Ir Iridium 193.1	78 Pt Platinum 195.23
84 Po Polonium 210	85 At Astatine 211	86 Rn Radon 222		

† ACTINIDE SERIES:

89 Ac Actinium 227	90 Th Thorium 232.12	91 Pa Protactinium 231	92 U Uranium 238.07
93 Np Neptunium 237	94 Pu Plutonium 239	95 Am Americium 241	96 Cm Curium 242
97 Bk Berkelium 243	98 Cf Californium 244	99 Es Einsteinium —	100 Fm Fermium —

19·3   Isotopes

When Thomson sought to determine the mass of the atoms of neon (chemical atomic weight 20.183), he found no curve at the place on the plate corresponding to this atomic weight; instead, there was a well-defined curve due to particles of mass 20 and a fainter but definite one due to those of mass 22. Thomson's bold yet inevitable conclusion was that neon is composed of two kinds of atoms not separable chemically but occurring in nature in a ratio of lighter to heavier of about 9:1. The chemically determined atomic weight of 20.2 is merely the average value for the natural mixture of the two.

This situation made plausible the notion that many other elements might be mixtures of atoms having integral or very nearly integral weights, and subsequent experiments confirmed the idea fully. *Over three-quarters of all the known elements are found to be mixtures of from 2 to as many as 10 different kinds of atoms.* At the present time about 1300 ultimate varieties are known. All atom species of different weight belonging to the same chemical element are called *isotopes* of that element.

How is it possible to reconcile the existence of isotopes with Dalton's hypothesis, amply confirmed by the most diverse chemical observations, that all atoms of a given chemical element are identical? To answer this question, recall the basic features of the structure of atoms according to our present knowledge. Although the supporting evidence will have to wait until later, it may be mentioned here again that an atom consists of a relatively compact and massive central nucleus surrounded by a number of electrons. The nucleus carries a positive charge of electricity due to the presence in it of one or more protons. An atom in its normal state has just as many electrons disposed *about* the nucleus as there are protons *in* the nucleus, so that the whole structure is electrically neutral. The number of nuclear protons (or of external electrons) is the same as the *atomic number P* of the element—the number giving its position in the periodic table.

19·4   Properties Determined by Nucleus and by External Electrons

The chemical properties of an atom are determined exclusively by the group of external electrons. The nucleus is, in a sense, deeply embedded in the electron aggregate and so does not play a part in any chemical hookups into which the atom may enter. The several isotopes of an element all have the same external electron structure, only their nuclei being different. Hence from the strictly *chemical* point of view Dalton's hypothesis remains valid. For the two isotopes of neon discovered by Thomson the situation is as represented schematically in Fig. 19·3.[1] The nuclear charge of 10 electron charges is furnished in each case by 10 protons. The balance of the mass of each nucleus is made up by *neutrons*. Each has about the same mass as a proton but no electric charge. Protons and neutrons are known collectively as *nucleons.*

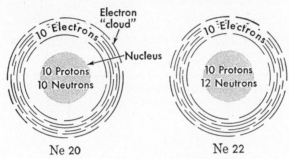

Ne 20   Ne 22

FIG. 19·3   Schematic composition of the atoms of Ne 20 and Ne 22.

It may be said that there are no differences between the several isotopes of a given element except the very slight ones that depend on atomic mass. Such differences may be used to bring about a partial separation of the isotopes. For instance, the lighter isotopes in a mixture will evaporate slightly more profusely from a liquid, or diffuse more rapidly through a porous wall, or be transported in greater number in an electrolytic cell. By passing the material repeatedly through such processes, greater and greater separation is attained, but the techniques are time-consuming and expensive. Another possibility, of course, is to use an electromagnetic means of separation, as in Thomson's mass spectrograph and others to be described presently. This method, too, has its great difficulties, but it and a diffusion process were the two schemes used to separate the isotopes of uranium for the atomic bomb (page 455).

19·5   Other Forms of Mass Spectrograph

An improvement on Thomson's mass spectrograph, which converted the device into a true precision instrument, was made by

---

[1] It is interesting to note that a third neon isotope of mass 21, present in natural neon to the extent of less than ⅛ per cent, was later discovered.

F. W. Aston, working in Thomson's laboratory. In this apparatus a narrow beam of positive ions passes first through an electric field and then through a magnetic field, which bends it in the opposite direction. When conditions are properly arranged, all ions of a given charge-mass ratio are brought to a sharp focus at a given point on a photographic plate. Each isotope of the substances present as positive ions will then reveal itself as an image on the plate, provided that it is present in sufficient quantity. In this way Aston found among other things that chlorine has two isotopes of masses 35 and 37, occurring in a ratio of about 3:1. For investigating elements that are not gases a special anode containing a compound of the element in question may be used.

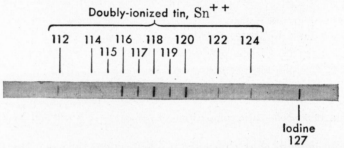

FIG. 19·4   A mass spectrum. (*From a plate by Prof. K. T. Bainbridge.*)

Improved mass spectrographs have been designed and used by several investigators since the pioneer work of Thomson and Aston. All use a combination of electric and magnetic fields for deflection and focusing. Figure 19·4 shows a typical photographic record of a mass analysis. Similar to the procedure in optical spectroscopy, the masses are determined by interpolating between the values for ions of known mass introduced into the apparatus, and the relative abundance is found either from the relative darkness of the images on the photographic plate or by an electrical method. The best instruments are able to detect a difference in mass of about 1 part in 100,000.

19·6 Atomic-mass Scale

As noted before, the standard for chemical atomic weights was established by taking the atomic weight of ordinary oxygen as 16.000. Discovery of the existence of isotopes of oxygen having masses of 17 and 18 (total abundance about $\frac{1}{4}$ per cent) has complicated the situation wherever highly accurate mass values are required. As a result, there is a slight discrepancy between the chemical scale, based on ordinary oxygen as 16, and the mass-spectrograph scale, which takes the mass of the most common isotope equal to 16 exactly. A value given on the mass-spectrograph scale is about 1 part in 4000 larger than the chemically determined figure.

One-sixteenth of the mass of the oxygen isotope 16 is defined as *one atomic-mass unit,* abbreviated amu.

$$1 \text{ amu} = 1.66 \times 10^{-24} \text{ gm} \tag{19·1}$$

The mass of an electron at rest is

$$m_0 = 0.00055 \text{ amu} \tag{19·2}$$

In view of the existence of isotopes it is necessary to attach to the chemical symbol for a given atom two numbers that specify exactly which atom variety is meant. For instance, in place of using merely the symbol Li for a lithium atom, it should be written either $_3\text{Li}^6$ or $_3\text{Li}^7$, depending on which isotope of this element is meant. The *subscript,* written to the left of the symbol, is the *atomic number P* of the element, while the *superscript,* written to the right, is the *mass number A* of the particular isotope—the nearest integer to the mass expressed in amu.[1] A complete symbol, written as described, stands either for the specified isotope as a substance or, more particularly, for a single atom or ion of this substance. Finally, if N represents the number of neutrons in a nucleus, then we have

$$A = P + N \tag{19·3}$$

X RAYS

19·7 Early History of the Rays

The chance discovery of X rays by Röntgen[2] in 1895 proved to be one of the most important events in modern science, not only

---

[1] The two lithium isotopes mentioned have atomic masses, as determined by mass spectra, of 6.01692 and 7.01816 amu, respectively. Existing departures from whole numbers shown by these and by most other atoms cannot be attributed to the presence of still other isotopes, since the figures are obtained from mass spectra. The cause of such "mass defects" will be discussed later.

[2] Wilhelm Röntgen, German experimental physicist and teacher. He received (1901) the first Nobel prize ever awarded in physics for "the exceptional services rendered by him in the discovery of the special rays which have been called after him."

because of the practical applications it has found but also for its role in the development of physical and biological science. One indication of the significance of this branch of physics is the circumstance that at least six Nobel prize awards have been made in this field. Like most "accidental discoveries," Röntgen's success was only the culmination of a careful series of experiments, and his cautious and thorough exploration of the results of the first findings constitutes a model of scientific enterprise.

Röntgen had been experimenting with cathode rays. While working with a tube pumped out to the stage where the glass showed fluorescence, he noticed that a bright fluorescent glow was also produced on a coated screen several feet away even when the discharge tube was covered with opaque paper. He reasoned that

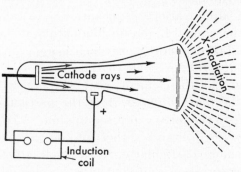

FIG. 19·5   Apparatus used by Röntgen when he discovered X rays.

some type of invisible but penetrating radiation was being given off. It turned out that these rays came from the walls of the tube and were strongest near the place where the cathode rays struck the glass (Fig. 19·5). It was Röntgen himself who first noted that these *X rays,* as he called them, could penetrate parts of the body and so reveal internal structure; within a few weeks of his first production of the rays they were already being used in medicine.

The original series of experiments revealed the following properties of the rays: They travel in straight lines and cast sharp shadows but are not deflected by a magnet; they are absorbed more by dense than by tenuous substances; they produce fluorescence in suitable materials, are capable of affecting a photographic plate, can discharge electrified bodies, and produce chemical changes. On the other hand, neither Röntgen nor the many other experimenters who then turned to explore this promising new field found any evidence that the rays could be reflected, refracted, or diffracted. The proof of the nature of the radiation was not disclosed for nearly two decades. Before considering such questions, it may be of interest to see how the method of generating X rays has evolved since the time of their discovery.

19·8 X-ray Tubes

Röntgen realized that the radiations were produced in some way by the impact of cathode rays on a solid object. He modified the original design so that instead of hitting the walls of the tube the electrons struck a metal *target* inside the tube. High-speed cathode rays are concentrated on the face of this target, and the X radiation is given off as shown (Fig. 19·6).

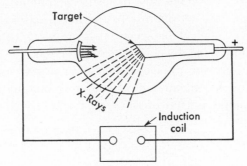

FIG. 19·6   Gas-filled X-ray tube.

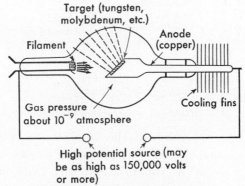

FIG. 19·7   Coolidge X-ray tube.

In this tube the cathode-ray electrons are supplied by ionization of the residual gas, and the fact that the quantity of gas present may change owing to absorption or emission by the glass makes the operation of such a tube unreliable. A great improvement was introduced by the American physicist W. D. Coolidge in 1913. This was the substitution of a heated filament as the source of electrons, the tube being pumped out to the highest possible vacuum. The X rays obtainable from a Coolidge tube are much more intense and are subject to better control than those from a gas-filled tube, and the former type has become the standard for use in medicine and in industry (see Fig. 19·7).

The efficiency of an X-ray tube is surprisingly low. Less than 1 per cent of the energy supplied in electrical form goes into radiation. The remainder appears mainly as heat in the target, which in many installations must be cooled by means of circulating water.

19·9   The Betatron

Although special tubes for X-ray therapy designed for operation at voltages up to 2,000,000 are in use, the difficulties of working with such potentials set a limit to further progress in this direction. A novel type of electron accelerator (or X-ray tube) was developed by the American physicist D. W. Kerst in 1941. In place of using high voltage, the device, called a *betatron,* supplies energy to the electrons by means of a changing magnetic field. The underlying principle is that of the transformer.

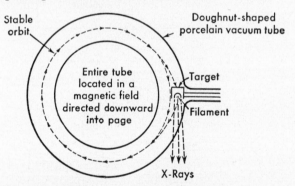

Fig. 19·8   Scheme of construction of the betatron.

In studying the operation of the transformer (page 330), you found that a driving voltage was produced in the secondary coil whenever the current in the primary was *changing.* Since the varying current in the primary is accompanied by a correspondingly changing magnetic field, this amounts to saying that the driving voltage produced in the secondary is due to the change of the magnetic flux which threads through its windings.

If the electrons that constitute the secondary current could travel in a vacuum instead of among the atoms of a wire, they would acquire greater and greater speed while the driving voltage acts. This is exactly what happens in the betatron. The secondary is a stream of free electrons, and the magnetic field serves a double purpose. It exerts a transverse force on the moving electrons, which confines them to a circular path, and at the same time accelerates them by means of its changing strength, as explained above.

The device is shown diagrammatically in Fig. 19·8. Electrons coming from the filament make several hundred thousand revolutions during the time the strength of the magnetic field is rising to its maximum, gaining energy with each turn. After they have been given the desired energy, the electrons are deflected out of their stable orbit and allowed to hit the target, producing X rays. An installation capable of giving electrons an energy of 100 Mev is now in operation, and the design of even more powerful betatrons is being considered.

19·10   Penetration and Absorption of the Rays

One of the properties of X rays most familiar to the average person is their ability to penetrate solid matter. The penetration of the rays increases with the voltage applied to the tube and decreases with the density of the material traversed. Radiation from a tube operating at a fairly low voltage is said to be *soft;* that produced at high voltages and having great penetration is called *hard.* The dependence on density is what makes possible the use of X rays in revealing the internal structure of the body. Because radiation of a given hardness is absorbed more strongly by dense materials such as bone and foreign metallic objects than by the tissues, these features show up in a photograph. An X-ray picture is, of course, not taken by means of a camera, since it is not possible to make a lens for use with these rays. Instead, the image is merely a shadow cast on the photographic plate.

The energy removed from a beam of X rays by absorption in matter is converted partly into heat and partly into a *secondary X radiation,* which is emitted in all directions, thus effectively weakening the original beam. The extent of the scattering depends on the number of electrons in the material through which the rays are passing, and it is possible to calculate a relation between the strength of scattered radiation and the number of electrons *in each atom* of the scatterer. When experimental values are substituted in the case of carbon, for example, the number of electrons per atom turns out to be 6, which is the same as the atomic number of this element.

The intensity of a parallel beam of X rays falls off very rapidly with the distance it goes in a given material, as shown graphically in Fig. 19·9. Elements of high atomic number are the best absorbers since they have more external electrons. For instance, a sheet of lead only 3 mm thick gives sufficient protection to persons working with tubes using voltage up to 50,000, while if aluminum were used as a shield it would have to be about 1 in. thick to have the same effectiveness. Using X rays produced in the 100-Mev betatron, metal castings nearly 2 ft thick may be inspected for hidden defects.

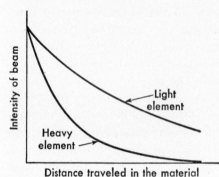

FIG. 19·9 Absorption of X rays in different materials.

The intensity of a beam of X rays is best measured either by its effect on a photographic plate or by its ability to *ionize* the atoms or molecules of a substance into which it passes. Figure 19·10 shows a diagram of a typical *ionization chamber*. Any ions formed are made to move to one or the other of the two electrodes by means

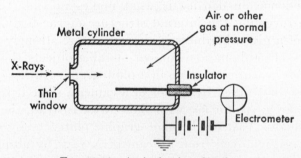

FIG. 19·10 An ionization chamber.

of the PD applied by the battery. Experience shows that the ionization current, measured by the electrometer, is proportional to the intensity of the X-ray beam.

The usefulness of X rays in the destruction of malignant tissue is probably due to their ability to ionize. Both normal and cancerous cells may be destroyed in this way, but the latter are less resistive so that with properly controlled dosage it is often possible to eradicate them.

19·11   Diffraction of X Rays; Laue's Experiment

For many years following their discovery the nature of X rays remained in doubt. Experiments designed to prove their wave

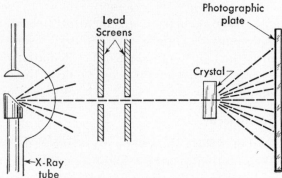

FIG. 19·11   The Laue experiment.

character or to reveal their possible particlelike attributes were equally unsuccessful. You will recall that the most convincing evidence for the wave nature of light is furnished by the fact that

light can be diffracted and that appreciable diffraction effects can be obtained with a grating, for example, only when the grating space is not too many times bigger than the wavelength to be examined.

It occurred to the German theoretical physicist Max von Laue, in 1912, that the regular arrangement of atoms in a crystalline solid constitutes a sort of three-dimensional grating whose spacing might be of the right order of magnitude to diffract X rays,

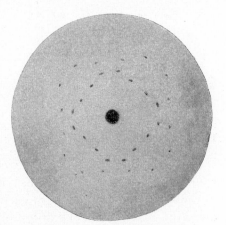

FIG. 19·12   A Laue-spot pattern.

provided that they are waves. This "hunch" proved correct. The experiment was carried out, and it was found that *rays sent through a crystal were thrown off in certain definite directions in space.* The apparatus is diagramed in Fig. 19·11. A narrow beam of X rays was allowed to strike a thin crystal of zinc sulfide, behind which was placed a photographic plate. Besides the heavy spot due to the direct beam the photograph showed a number of symmetrically arranged weaker spots (Fig. 19·12). The position of these spots agreed with Laue's theory of a three-dimensional grating.

The experiment not only demonstrated the wave character of X rays but also proved that the symmetry shown by natural crystals is traceable to the regular arrangement of their atoms—something that could only be inferred previously. Using crystals of known structure, the Laue method permits calculation of the wavelength of the X rays used. This turns out to be of the order of 10^{-8} cm, or 1A (compare page 236).

19·12   X-ray Spectroscopy

The geometry of a three-dimensional grating is not simple, and the direct interpretation of a Laue photograph is a complex procedure. A simplified way of looking at the matter was worked out by the English physicists W. H. Bragg and W. L. Bragg, father and son, about 1913. They realized that the production of the spots in such a picture could be ascribed to a kind of mirrorlike reflection of the X rays from various sets of planes of atoms in the crystal. Consider Fig. 19·13 to represent a section of a crystal of ordinary salt (NaCl). Through this network of regularly spaced atoms, various sets of parallel planes may be drawn. Each set is able to act as a reflector for the rays, giving rise to radiation coming off in definite directions only. Some of the planes are shown in the figure. The intensity of each spot will depend on the number and kind of atoms in the group of planes concerned.

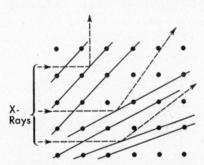

FIG. 19·13   Reflection of X rays by planes of atoms in a crystal.

The rays penetrate many layers, and the apparent reflection is to be ascribed to secondary waves started out from the individual atoms of these planes by the incident beam. There will be certain directions for which the secondary waves will be *in the same phase* and thus unite to form a "reflected" ray, whereas in other directions the phases will not agree and no such reinforcement will occur.

On the basis of this view of the process of reflection the Braggs constructed an *X-ray spectrometer* (Fig. 19·14). X rays from the target of a tube are limited to a narrow beam and allowed to strike the face of a crystal (rock salt, quartz, etc.) mounted on a table

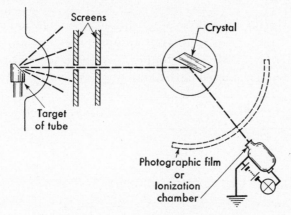

FIG. 19·14   An X-ray crystal spectrometer.

which can be rotated about an axis normal to the plane of the diagram, so that the rays can be made to strike the crystal at any desired angle. The reflected beam may be received on a photographic film, or its position and intensity may be recorded by means of an ionization chamber that can be turned independently about the

same axis as the crystal. The images on the film or the positions for which ionization currents were observed were found to agree with the Bragg relation mentioned above.

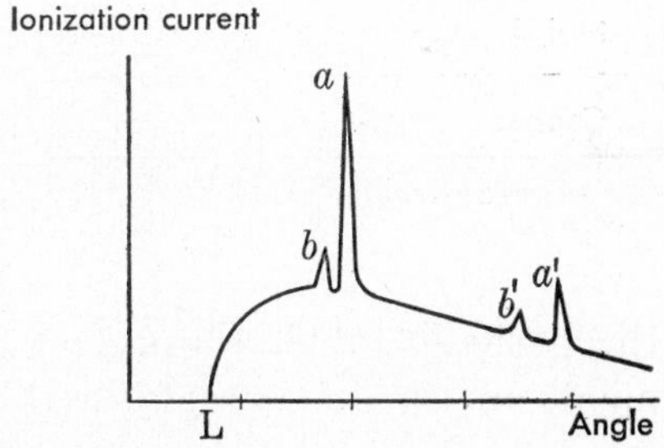

A typical ionization record, using X rays from a target made of a given element (say, platinum) is shown in Fig. 19·15. The curve shows that the radiation consists

FIG. 19·15   Characteristic X-ray spectrum of an element.

of a continuous background on which are superposed certain sharp peaks. These peaks correspond to *X-ray spectrum lines*—definite wavelengths radiated by the element in question and making up what is called its *characteristic radiation*. The continuous background will be referred to later.

In the figure the lines a' and b' occur at positions corresponding, respectively, to twice the wavelength of *a* and *b*. Both pairs are in fact merely *first- and second-order spectra* of the same two wavelengths.

19·13 Moseley's Law

In 1913, during the course of a brilliant investigation of the characteristic X radiations of a large number of elements, the English physicist H. G. J. Moseley found a systematic relation between the characteristic wavelengths and the position of the element in

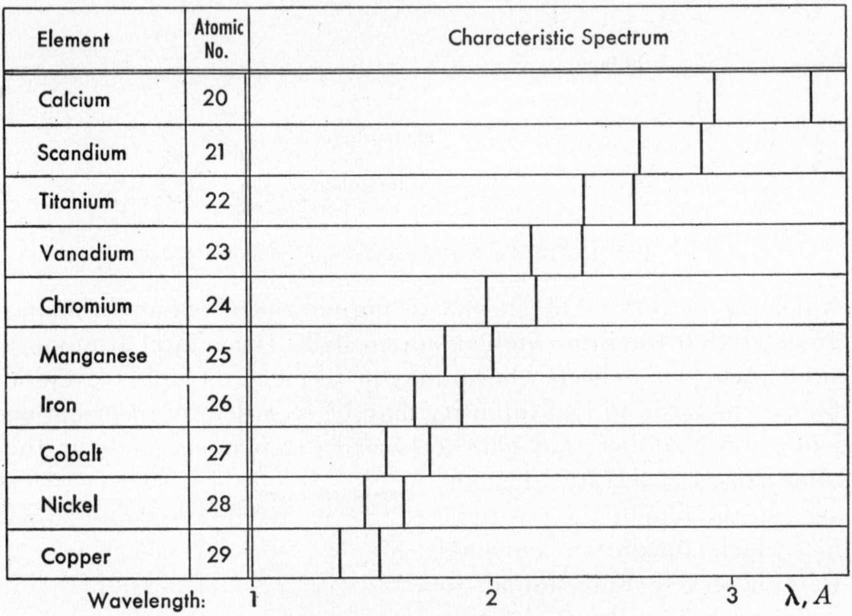

Element	Atomic No.	Characteristic Spectrum
Calcium	20	
Scandium	21	
Titanium	22	
Vanadium	23	
Chromium	24	
Manganese	25	
Iron	26	
Cobalt	27	
Nickel	28	
Copper	29	

Wavelength: 1   2   3 λ, A

FIG. 19·16   Moseley's law.

the periodic table. Employing almost all the available solid elements in turn as targets in the X-ray tube, he used the crystal spectrometer to determine the wavelengths radiated. It was found that there is a progressive shift toward shorter wavelengths as one moves down through the periodic table. Figure 19·16 is a drawing showing, one below the other, the spectra of one set of elements investigated. When the square root of the frequency of each member of the pair of characteristic lines is plotted against atomic number, a straight line results.

The investigation even led to the correct assignment of atomic numbers for cases like the pair of elements nickel and cobalt, which had to be put in reverse order of their atomic weights in order to fit the scheme. It also indicated the existence of elements which had not yet been discovered chemically up to that time and predicted their X-ray spectra.

Most important of all, the regularity found by Moseley showed conclusively the fundamental importance of atomic number and confirmed the view, suggested by mass spectra, that the atoms of the various elements are built up in some progressive way from more fundamental units. The application of the quantum theory finally showed how the pieces of evidence from various quarters could be fitted together into a comprehensive theory of atomic structure. This will be considered in a subsequent chapter.

NATURAL RADIOACTIVITY

19·14 Historical

The discovery of radioactivity is an excellent example of how wrong assumptions sometimes lead to results of value. When Röntgen's first experiments with X rays were reported in France in January, 1896, it occurred to A. H. Becquerel that penetrating radiations might invariably be connected with luminescent materials, since X rays were produced where the glass of a cathode-ray tube showed its strongest fluorescent glow. Becquerel began a series of tests of minerals known to show phosphorescence after exposure to light. Samples were placed in contact with a photographic plate wrapped in black paper, and the whole arrangement was placed in sunlight. Among the materials tested the only one that gave positive results was a compound of the element uranium, and the surprising fact that this mineral produced the effect even when not previously exposed to light convinced the experimenter that it could emit some kind of penetrating radiation quite independent of its ability to show phosphorescence.

An extensive investigation of the radiation was begun by Marie Curie, using pitchblende, a natural ore rich in compounds of uranium. This material showed an activity, measured by its ability to produce ionization, far greater than was to be expected on the basis of the amount of uranium it contained, and Mme. Curie suspected that this might be due to a new and much more highly active substance present in the ore. Pierre and Marie Curie then undertook a long series of repeated crystallizations of salts derived from pitchblende in order to concentrate the active ingredient.

Finally, from a ton of the ore, they obtained a small quantity of a new active element, which they named *polonium,* and, later, a minute amount (less than 0.02 gm) of a still more active element, *radium.* Further experiments by the Curies and by others soon led to the discovery of many other *radioactive substances.* For the most part, they are chemical elements occupying the last ten or so places in the periodic table.

19·15   Properties of the Rays

The physical nature of the radiations from radioactive substances was investigated very thoroughly by Rutherford[1] and his collaborators. Like X rays, these radiations cause fluorescence, affect a photographic plate, and produce ionization in air. However,

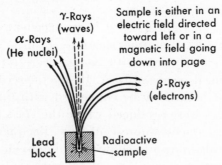

FIG. 19·17   The three types of radiation from radioactive materials.

the radiations from radioactive materials were found to be of three physically distinct kinds. Under the influence of transverse electric or magnetic fields, one type is bent very slightly in one direction, another type much more strongly in the opposite direction, and a third component not at all. This behavior of what are called respectively α (alpha), β (beta), and γ (gamma) rays is shown schematically (but not to scale) in Fig. 19·17.

The α rays are found to be streams of positively charged particles, and each of these particles has a mass number of 4 and carries a charge equivalent to 2 electron charges. *An α particle is, in fact, identical with the nucleus of an ordinary helium atom. The β rays turn out to be streams of fast electrons* with speeds

---

[1] Ernest Rutherford, brilliant and energetic experimental physicist, was a pupil of J. J. Thomson. His pioneer work in radioactivity and in atomic structure was of the greatest importance to the development of modern physics.

up to around 0.998c, while *γ rays are electromagnetic waves of which the wavelengths are generally shorter than those of X rays* and which therefore are more penetrating. The wavelengths have been measured by means of crystal gratings and by other methods. All radioactive elements emit either α or β rays, and either may be accompanied by γ radiation, but a given element does not generally emit all three types of rays. Radium itself is a notable exception, giving strong α radiation accompanied by weaker β and γ rays.

Of the three types of radiation the γ rays are the most penetrating and are able to go through as much as 20 cm of lead. Their physiological effects are similar to those of X rays but more pronounced because they are "harder." β rays can penetrate about 1 mm of lead, while the fastest α particles are stopped completely by a sheet of paper. Nevertheless, the speed of an α particle may amount to perhaps one-sixteenth of the speed of light and the corresponding energy to around 10 Mev.

Because of the large energies possessed by all three types of radiation, it is certain that they originate in the nucleus of the atom rather than in the external parts. An α particle is apparently a stable configuration that is ejected as a unit. Protons or neutrons are never thrown off individually by natural radioactive atoms. β particles (electrons) are not believed to be present in the nucleus as such, but each may be produced by the conversion of a neutron into a proton and an electron. Another part of the β radiation is thought to be due to the ejection of outer electrons of the radioactive atom through the action of γ radiation from the nucleus—a sort of γ-ray photoelectric effect. The γ radiation arises from the disturbance produced among the constituents of a decaying nucleus when a particle is emitted.

19·16 The Wilson Cloud Chamber

The passage of α or β particles through matter is accompanied by the formation of ions all along the path of the rays. Traveling through a gas, such particles may collide with and ionize tens of thousands of atoms before being brought to rest. The *Wilson cloud chamber,* devised by the English physicist C. T. R. Wilson in 1912, employs this ionizing ability to make visible the paths of α and β rays and their collision products. The underlying principle is the fact that, if the temperature of moist air is suddenly lowered, any ions present will act as centers around which condensation of water vapor begins. The chamber consists of a metal cylinder fitted with a piston (Fig. 19·18a). A small sample of radioactive material is mounted near one wall, and the interior of the chamber is illuminated from the side. When the piston is suddenly pulled down, the moist air contained in the cylinder is thus cooled and minute water droplets condense on the ions produced by the rays, thus making

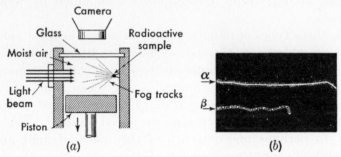

FIG. 19·18   Wilson cloud chamber and appearance of typical α- and β-ray tracks.

their paths visible. α particles cause heavy, straight "fog tracks," while β tracks are lighter and less continuous in appearance and are usually quite crooked owing to frequent deviations in direction by the atoms and molecules in the path of the rays (Fig. 19·18b). γ rays do not produce fog tracks directly.

19·17   Radioactive Transformations

A radioactive substance gives off heat continuously. Each gram of radium, for example, emits about 140 cal/hr, the heat being produced mainly by dissipation of the KE of the ejected particles and of the recoiling atoms. In 1902 to 1903, when Rutherford and Soddy advanced the idea that ejection of the particles was an accompaniment of the actual breaking down of atoms of the material, this seemed a concept of great novelty and boldness, for up to this time there had been no suggestion of the possibility that an atom could undergo any but the relatively slight changes involved in the process of ionization. Nevertheless, the consequences of these ideas were amply confirmed by experience.

When an atom of radium, for instance, *disintegrates*[1] by ejection

---

[1] The word "disintegration" as used in this connection does not mean complete decomposition of an atom into its ultimate parts but only the shedding of relatively small portions.

of an α particle from its nucleus, the latter will not only become four units lighter but will also thus lose two positive charges. This makes the atomic number of the nucleus $_{88}$Ra *smaller by two,* and it is now a nucleus of $_{86}$Rn (see Table 19·1). On the other hand, ejection of a β particle would leave the mass of a nucleus practically unchanged but by carrying off one negative charge would effectively *increase the atomic number by one,* and it would become a nucleus of the element following it in the table. Thus when a nucleus of uranium X_1 ($_{90}$UX$_1$), which is an isotope of thorium, disintegrates, it expels a β particle, becoming $_{91}$UX$_2$.

19·18 The Decay Law

It is found that the rate at which a given radioactive substance disintegrates is not influenced by external conditions but is a characteristic of the substance itself. Further, the rate at which material is transformed is not constant. Starting with a specified

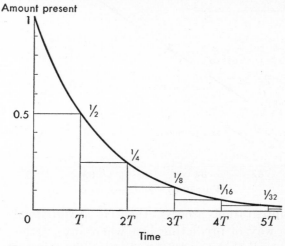

Fig. 19·19   Decay curve of a radioactive element.

amount of a radioactive element, the rate of decay will be greatest at first and will fall off steadily as the amount of the original substance dwindles. The interpretation of this fact is that *the breakdown of the atoms is governed by pure chance,* and hence the number breaking down in any short interval of time is proportional to the number of atoms present. This leads to a relation like that graphed in Fig. 19·19 for the amount remaining at any specified time. If we call the original amount unity, half of this quantity will be left after the passage of a certain time T; half of this (or one-fourth of the original amount) remains after time $2T$ has elapsed; the amount is again halved after $3T$, and so on.

The time T required for any initial amount to decrease to half is called the *half life* of the element. Its value varies enormously from one radioactive element to another; it may be anywhere from a few ten-millionths of a second to over 100 billion years. Radium has a half life of about 1590 years. The determination of a half life value that is either extremely short or extremely long must, of course, be undertaken by indirect methods.

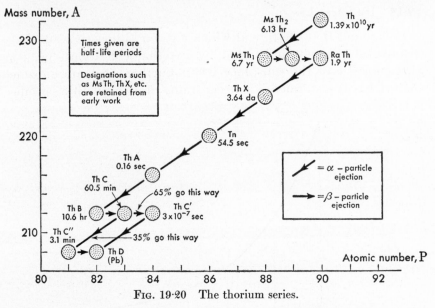

Fig. 19·20   The thorium series.

The disintegration process, then, is a *statistical* matter, and there is no way of predicting just when any particular atom will break down; all that can be done is to compute the total amount that will be left after a given time, provided only that the number of atoms remaining is not too small. The situation is analogous to basing life-insurance rates on mortality tables. By means of such statistics a company can predict with great exactness *how many* persons of a given age will die within, say, 1 year. But it cannot ascertain *which individuals* will die in that time.

Rutherford and his colleagues found that the disintegration product of a given atom may itself be radioactive and that the process of breakdown can be traced through a series of elements. Three such sequences were found, the uranium-radium series, the thorium series, and the actinium series. These begin, respectively, with U^{238}, Th^{232}, and U^{235}. Through a series of emissions of α and β particles, each ends up as a stable isotope of lead. A diagram tracing the course of the thorium series is shown in Fig. 19·20. The "branching" occurring here has a counterpart in each of the other series.

A fourth chain, the neptunium series, headed by Np^{237}, exists. The members of this series have short half-lives and would not be expected to occur in nature. Unlike the other three series, this one ends with bismuth rather than with lead.

SUMMARY

The details of the present chapter are difficult to summarize in a limited space, but the general conclusions to be drawn from this material are worth emphasizing.

The phenomena discussed all contributed to a drastic revision and significant extension of previous ideas concerning the nature of atoms. The discovery of the electron, treated in Chap. 18, furnished the first direct evidence for the divisibility of the atom and for its electrical constitution. The discovery of isotopes did away with the accepted idea that all atoms of a given chemical species are identical. Finally, radioactivity dispelled the notion of the permanence of the atom and showed that some varieties, at least, can change to other forms.

At the same time the phenomena of mass spectra, X rays, and radioactivity offered confirmatory evidence of things already known or suspected from purely chemical experience. Mass spectroscopy permitted the direct determination of the mass of individual atoms and also showed that only certain discrete masses and discrete ion charges exist. Moseley's law for X-ray spectra demonstrated conclusively the fundamental importance of atomic number; and the correlation of chemical changes in the radioactive series with the ejection of α or β particles furnished much evidence in support of our ideas of the constitution of atomic nuclei.

READING REFERENCES

1. Moulton, F. R., and J. J. Schifferes: "The Autobiography of Science," Doubleday, New York, 1945. For accounts of the work of Röntgen, Becquerel, the Curies, and Soddy, read pp. 484–502.
2. Gamow, G.: "The Birth and Death of the Sun," Penguin, New York, 1945. Written by one of the best living interpreters of science. Chapters II and III are of particular interest at this point.

382   MODERN INTRODUCTORY PHYSICS

3. Jauncey, G. E. M.: The Birth and Early Infancy of X-rays, *Am. Jour. Phys.*, Vol. 13, No. 6, pp. 362–379, 1945. A highly interesting narrative particularly for the light it throws on the way Röntgen's discovery was received.

4. Jauncey, G. E. M.: The Early Years of Radioactivity, *Am. Jour. Phys.*, Vol. 14, No. 4, pp. 226–241, 1946. Of equal value with the preceding reference.

5. Chalmers, T. W.: "Historic Researches," Scribner, New York, 1952. Read Chap. XII on positive rays and isotopes.

6. Curie, Eve: "Mme. Curie," translated by Vincent Sheean, Doubleday, New York, 1937.

EXERCISES

1. What is the percentage difference between the mass of a neutral atom of O^{16} and its ion O^{++}?

2. How many protons and how many neutrons are there in the nucleus of the neon isotope of mass 21 mentioned in the footnote on page 363?

3. A certain atomic nucleus contains 79 protons and 118 neutrons. What is its atomic number? Its mass number? What element is it?

4. A beam of cathode rays moving eastward passes through a strong magnetic field directed vertically upward. In what direction does the beam veer?

5. Electrons in an X-ray tube operating at 60,000 volts are stopped in a distance of 5×10^{-4} cm when they strike the target. Compute their average acceleration while being brought to rest.

6. An α particle is ejected from a radium atom with a speed of 1.5×10^9 cm/sec. According to the conservation of linear momentum what is the speed of recoil of the product atom?

7. Has the amount of radium in existence decreased appreciably since the dawn of civilization? For every gram of radium existing now, compute how many grams of radium existed in 6000 B.C. when the first settlements on the Nile were established.

8. The amount of a certain member of the thorium series remaining after $2\frac{3}{4}$ min is exactly one-eighth of the initial amount. What is the half life of this element? Referring to Fig. 19·20, which element is it?

9. A given radioactive nucleus emits an α particle, then two β particles in succession, and finally an α particle. What is the net change in atomic number? In mass number?

10. The energy of an α particle ejected from radium is of the order of a million times that involved, per atom, in an ordinary chemical reaction, such as combustion. This being true, why is it not possible to use a radioactive material as a practical source of heat?

Chapter 20

ORIGIN AND EARLY DEVELOPMENT
OF THE QUANTUM THEORY

The revolutionary changes in physical science that occurred at the beginning of the century were undoubtedly direct results of the important discoveries described in the preceding two chapters—X rays, the electron, radioactivity. But the development of modern physics is characterized by something far greater in scope than the mere uncovering of additional facts, and that is the advent of new points of view—new theories that were needed to account for the exceptional phenomena that presented themselves.

Modern theoretical physics advances largely under one or the other of two comprehensive programs—the *quantum theory* and the *theory of relativity.* The present chapter will be concerned mainly with an account of the origin and early development of the quantum idea. Curiously enough, this theory had its beginning in an attempt to explain certain phases of a phenomenon that was familiar experimentally—and to a great extent understood theoretically—long before the beginning of the century. The process in question is that of *ideal thermal radiation.* Before reading further you should go back and review Sec. 13·13 (page 232), where some fundamental aspects of this phenomenon are described.

20·1 The Quantum Hypothesis

Attempts at a theoretical explanation of the shape of the curves appearing in Fig. 13·13 were made by several investigators in the latter years of the last century, and although the results fitted the observations in part, there were serious disagreements with experiment. Examination of the proposed theories by competent critics revealed no errors, and it seemed that the established laws of physics had not been able to yield an explanation of what was observed.

Among those studying the problem was the German theoretical physicist Max Planck.[1] Planck had been able to devise an algebraic equation that fitted the experimental radiation curves, and he was encouraged to seek a theoretical basis for the empirical relation. He started with the assumption that an ideal radiating body contains in effect a large number of *oscillators,* each having a definite frequency of vibration and capable of sending out radiation of this frequency. The individual oscillators receive their energy from the source that is maintaining the temperature of the radiating body, and they dispose of this energy again in the form of radiation. In present terminology, these oscillators would be replaced by the various possible modes of vibration of the atoms and molecules of the material constituting the radiating body.

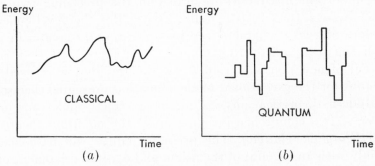

FIG. 20·1   Energy of an oscillator.

According to classical physics the process of absorption or radiation of energy is a *continuous* one. Thus the history of the energy possessed by an atom in a source of light would be represented by some kind of continuous curve like that of Fig. 20·1a. Wherever the curve rises, energy is being absorbed; where it descends, energy is being radiated.

The revolutionary aspect of Planck's work was this: In order to make the theory agree with the experimental radiation curve he had to abandon this idea of continuous energy exchange and assume instead that *each oscillator takes on and gives off energy in intermittent, discontinuous amounts,* which he called *quanta* (of energy). In contrast to the classical view, this situation would be represented roughly by the curve of Fig. 20·1b.

The theory showed that the size of a quantum of energy is not

[1] In 1918 he was awarded a Nobel prize for his work in originating and contributing to the development of the quantum idea.

the same for all oscillators but is proportional to the frequency of the radiation given off,

$$E = hn \tag{20·1}$$

where E is the energy of the quantum (in ergs), n is the frequency of the radiation (in vibrations per second), and h is a **universal constant,** now called **Planck's constant.** By comparing the computation with experimental results, Planck was able to arrive at a first rough value of this quantity, about 6.5×10^{-27} erg-sec.[1]

20·2 Significance of the Quantum Viewpoint

The quantum hypothesis represents a frank break with the doctrines of classical physics. It says, in effect, that an oscillating system can possess energy of amount 1, 2, 3, 4, . . . times hn but never fractional values. This pronouncement that energy can be given to or taken from such a system only in definite packets or granules is quite at variance with the idea of continuous flow of energy postulated by the older physics. And yet the quantum notion, which may be described as the **atomicity of energy,** fits neatly into place alongside two similar ideas with which you are already familiar—the atomicity of matter and the atomicity of electricity. Evidently we must face the fact that, when examined on a fine enough scale, all three of these aspects of nature show themselves to be discontinuous.

There is no reason to believe that the quantum idea does not apply to large-scale systems as well as atomic ones. Thus it is true that the energy of even a swinging pendulum or a weight oscillating at the end of a stretched spring must change discontinuously; but the frequencies involved are so low compared with those met with in atomic physics that the corresponding quanta, according to Eq. (20·1), would be small beyond all possibility of detection. In the same way the discontinuous nature of matter remains unrevealed in ordinary weighing, and that of electricity is too fine to be disclosed by the usual type of measurement of current.

It would be unscientific to reject the quantum theory merely on the ground that it is strange and unusual. It was soon recognized,

---

[1] According to Eq. (20·1) the dimensions of h are

$$\frac{\text{Energy}}{\text{Frequency}} = \frac{\text{ergs}}{\text{vib/sec}} = \frac{\text{erg-sec}}{\text{vib}} = \text{erg-sec}$$

since "vib" is merely a pure number.

even by many of Planck's critics, that here was a point of view that leads to results where the classical ideas are powerless. In what follows you will learn something of how the quantum theory has subsequently illuminated many fields of modern science, giving the quantity h a place alongside the velocity of light, the electron charge, the gravitational constant, and other fundamental constants of nature.

20·3 The Photoelectric Effect

Following its application to the ideal radiator, the quantum theory scored its second great success in explaining the *photoelectric effect*—the release of electrons from a substance by means of light. About 70 years ago, while experimenting with electromagnetic waves, Hertz noticed that a spark would jump a gap more

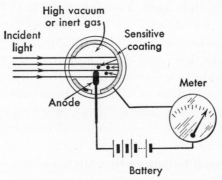

FIG. 20·2   A photocell (schematic).

readily when the negative electrode was illuminated with ultraviolet light. Subsequent experiments, viewed in terms of Thomson's discovery of the electron a decade later, led to the correct interpretation of the effect as the emission of electrons from the illuminated material. Electrons liberated in this way are referred to as *photoelectrons*.

The rate at which electrons are released from a given surface by light of a specified quality is found to be exactly *proportional to the intensity of the incident light.* This is the property that is most useful in connection with the practical applications of photoelectricity. A typical phototube, together with its electrical connections, is diagramed in Fig. 20·2. Electrons liberated from the surface of the cathode are attracted to the anode, and a current is thus made to flow through a detecting instrument. The photoelectric current begins the instant the light strikes the cell and stops the moment it is turned off, the delay time being of the order of a billionth of a second.

The fact that the number of photoelectrons produced each second is proportional to the intensity of illumination is plausible, but a puzzling fact is revealed when the *speeds* of the photoelectrons are measured. It is found that the electrons come out of the cathode with speeds varying from very small values up to a certain well-defined maximum but that this maximum speed *does not increase*

Table 20·1 The Photoelectric Effect—Sample Data

Color of light	Intensity, ft-c	Photocurrent, amp	Maximum electron speed, cm/sec
Blue	1	1.0×10^{-7}	8×10^7
	2	2.0×10^{-7}	8×10^7
Yellow	1	0.8×10^{-7}	6×10^7
	2	1.6×10^{-7}	6×10^7
Red	Any value	None	—

if the brightness of the light is increased. Electron emission is observed to begin at once, as mentioned above, and this is true no matter how weak the illumination; but no emission whatever takes place unless the frequency of the light exceeds a certain *threshold value* characteristic of the metal used. Finally, the higher the frequency of the incident radiation, the greater the top electron speed. These facts will perhaps be easier to keep in mind after examining the example given in Table 20·1.

Practical applications of photocells have become so common that it is almost unnecessary to list them. By leading the amplified output current into a suitable device, a cell may function as a burglar alarm, automatic door opener, inspecting and sorting mechanism, etc. Photocells are indispensable in sound motion pictures (Fig. 20·3), television, and picture transmission (see Ref. 4). The type of light-sensitive cell widely used as a light meter by photographers requires no battery. Such a *photronic cell* consists of a layer of copper oxide deposited on a plate of copper or of a film of selenium on an iron plate. The two elements are connected directly to a sensitive galvanometer, which may be calibrated in terms of illumination values (see Fig. 11·9, page 189).

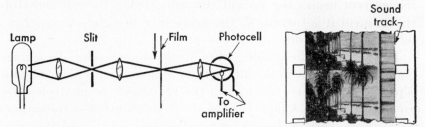

FIG. 20·3   Use of photocell in projecting sound motion pictures.

20·4   The Einstein Photoelectric Equation

An explanation of the experimental results with the photoelectric effect was not given until Einstein, in 1905, saw that here was another field where the quantum idea was capable of furnishing an answer. He realized that the wave properties of light were not able to account for the observations, in particular for the instantaneous release of photoelectrons by even very weak light. However, by thinking of a beam of light as a shower of localized packets of energy, or quanta, and assuming that each quantum, upon striking an atom, could release one photoelectron, an explanation could be devised. In addition, the kinetic energy of the photoelectrons could reasonably be assumed to depend only on some property of the quantum, such as the associated frequency.

Einstein made use of the same relation between energy and frequency, $E = hn$, to which Planck had been led in his work on radiation. Accordingly, the maximum kinetic energy of a photoelectron would be given by

$$\tfrac{1}{2} mv^2_{\text{max}} = hn - W \qquad (20\cdot2)$$

where W is the amount of work needed to pull the electron out of the surface of the material in question.

This equation says that the energy of the incoming quantum is used partly to remove an electron from the material and partly to give the detached electron kinetic energy.[1] It is known as *Einstein's photoelectric equation* and is amply confirmed by experiment. It represents one of the most celebrated relations in quantum physics.[2]

---

[1] As can be seen by transposing (20.2) to read $hn = W + \tfrac{1}{2}mv^2_{\text{max}}$.

[2] It is not generally remembered that the award of the Nobel prize to Einstein in 1921 was made primarily on the basis of his deduction of this result.

Subsequent experimental verification of this equation, especially through the careful work of Millikan in 1916, led to a more accurate value for the constant h. The best present value is

$$h = 6.624 \times 10^{-27} \text{ erg-sec} \qquad (20\cdot3)$$

Other investigators confirmed the relation for X rays and γ rays as well. It is found that a photoelectric effect exists not only for solids but also for liquids and gases.

20·5 Photons

Einstein's interpretation of the photoelectric effect brought about a profound change in our ideas concerning the nature of radiation. Even after Planck's theory of the discontinuous emission and absorption of radiation by matter had become familiar and generally accepted, light was still thought of exclusively as a wave motion. But Einstein's application of Planck's idea to photoelectricity implied that *the quantum retains its identity while traveling from source to destination* and finally goes intact into a single atom or molecule—that radiant energy consists of discrete packets not only when it is being emitted or absorbed but while traveling through space as well.

The Einstein view considers radiation as a process analogous to the firing of bullets from a machine gun rather than to the discharge of water from a pipe. Standing in opposition to this idea is the great array of well-grounded evidence for the wave nature of light reviewed in earlier chapters. Evidently a discrepancy exists between these two concepts. Additional discussion of the dilemma will be presented in Chap. 21.

A single quantum of energy, when in the form of radiation, is commonly called a *photon*. One sometimes sees the statement that photons are "corpuscles of light." This is an unfortunate term since it suggests a return to the ideas of Newton's theory of light. Newton's corpuscles were conceived to be material particles, while photons are to be thought of as *localized bundles of energy,* each having associated with it a certain number called the "frequency." The two concepts are not identical, as the discussion in Chap. 21 will show.

The photoelectric effect involves the release of electrons from a substance by radiation. What happens in an X-ray tube is precisely the inverse of this process—electrons impinging on a surface are able to release radiation. The striking fact is that this inverse phenomenon also obeys Einstein's equation, and X-ray wavelength measurements actually show that the frequency of the hardest X rays emitted by a tube operating at a voltage V (in ergs/esu) is given by

$$hn = eV = \tfrac{1}{2} mv^2 \tag{20·4}$$

Because of the high voltages used in X-ray work, the constant term corresponding to the work of escape W in Eq. (20·2) is negligible here. The maximum X-ray frequency corresponds to the sharp cutoff of the continuous X-ray spectrum, the point L in Fig. 19·15 (page 373).

20·6   Rutherford's Nuclear Atom

It has already been mentioned, on several occasions, that the nucleus of an atom is relatively very compact and contains all of the positive charge and virtually the entire mass of the atom. As a preliminary to discussing the next major triumph of the quantum theory—its application to the production of spectra—the direct evidence for our present idea of atomic structure will be presented.

Following his discovery of the electron, Thomson attempted to arrive at some concept of how the electrons and positive charges are arranged in an atom. In 1907 he proposed the plausible idea that the electrons are arranged in concentric rings within a globular mass of positive electricity. However, shortly afterward, two associates of Rutherford's, H. Geiger and E. Marsden, made some experiments on the passage of α particles through a thin sheet of metal. The results of these experiments suggested to Rutherford an entirely different picture of the atom—one in which the positive charge is confined to a very small region, with the electrons disposed in some way around it.

In the experiments in question a fine stream of fast α particles coming from a small sample of radioactive material was allowed to strike a thin metal foil. The idea was that the subsequent paths of the α particles might give some information as to the nature of the atoms of the metal. As Rutherford knew from some preliminary experiments he had performed earlier, most of the particles went straight through the foil, but some were turned aside, or "scattered," by a small amount. Geiger found, however, that a few particles were deflected through **very large angles** and that an occasional one almost doubled back in the direction from which it came.

The laboratory arrangement is shown in Fig. 20·4. The scattered α particles are detected visually by means of an instrument consisting of a small area of fluorescent material that is viewed in a low-powered microscope, and the whole assembly can be rotated to

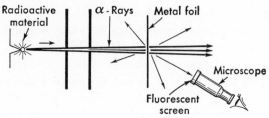

FIG. 20·4 Scattering of α particles—experimental arrangement.

various positions around the center of the foil. The impact of each scattered particle produces a tiny scintillation, or flash of light, on the screen—an exceedingly simple means of "seeing" individual α particles.

20·7 Conclusions from the Scattering Experiments

Rutherford, with characteristic insight, realized that the large-angle scattering was important; for if a sheet of metal a few ten-thousandths of a millimeter thick can turn back a projectile as massive (relatively) and as fast as an α particle, the nature of their interaction must differ fundamentally from that between a bullet and a piece of armor plate. He computed the number of particles that should, on the average, come off at various angles, basing his calculation on the view that the scattering was due to the repulsion of each particle by the concentrated, positively charged nucleus of an atom of the metal near which the particle happened to pass. Assuming the force to be given by Coulomb's law (page 274), the curved path of a particle could be computed. The closer the approach to the nucleus, the greater the angle of scattering (Fig. 20·5).

From a comparison of the experimental results with this theory he concluded that *all the positive charge of an atom, as well as practically all its mass, is confined to a region less than about* 10^{-12} *cm in diameter.* Evidence from chemistry and from the kinetic theory of gases shows that the diameter of an atom is of the order of 10^{-8} cm; hence this means that the nucleus has a diameter only about one ten-thousandth that of the whole atom. The electrons must be assumed to be distributed in some way in a globular region whose diameter is about 10^{-8} cm; and, particularly if the electrons are in motion, this would be the region of space from which any similar configuration (another atom) would be excluded.

This suggests that an atom is a very "open" structure. It explains, among other things, how an α particle can go right through hundreds of thousands of atoms without being stopped or deflected **unless** it passes close to a nucleus. The solar system is open in the same degree to the passage of comets, which are not deflected unless they happen to pass close to the sun or to a major planet.[1]

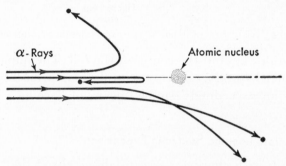

Fig. 20·5   Nature of α-particle deflection.

The scattering experiments also showed that the amount of positive charge on the nucleus increases with atomic weight. An improved version of the experiment, performed by James Chadwick in 1920, showed the proportionality between nuclear charge and atomic number—a conclusion that had been reached in the meantime from Moseley's work on characteristic X rays (page 374). In spite of remaining difficulties and a lack of completeness the picture of the atom was truly beginning to fit together.

20·8   Spectral Series; the Balmer Formula

The characteristic patterns of spectrum lines and bands obtained from various substances suggested from the very beginnings of the science of spectroscopy that a study of spectra might reveal something about the structure of the atoms or molecules responsible for

[1] Curiously enough, the ratio of the diameter of the sun to that of the orbit of Pluto, the outmost known planet, is of the same order of magnitude as the ratio of the size of the nucleus to that of the entire atom.

these radiations. Examination of the line spectra of the elements showed that, in the simpler cases at least, certain **series of lines** could be picked out that showed evident regularity in their arrangement. This regularity, often concealed in the spectra of the heavier elements, is particularly obvious in the spectrum of hydrogen (Fig. 13·8, page 226). The spacing in such a series decreases systematically from red to violet, the lines approaching a definite **series limit.**

The series of hydrogen lines represented in the figure is called the **Balmer series,** after the Swiss scientist who found (1884) that the following empirical formula would fit the wavelengths of the lines with great accuracy:

$$\lambda_A = 3645.6 \, \frac{m^2}{m^2 - 4} \tag{20·5}$$

Here λ_A is the wavelength in angstrom units, and the successive lines of the series are obtained by setting m equal to the integers 3, 4, 5, etc. Many years after the announcement of this relation, several other series of hydrogen lines were discovered. Some of these are in the infra-red, and one is in the ultraviolet; yet each set was found to be representable by an algebraic expression similar to that of Eq. (20·5).

The Balmer formula, as will be seen, has become the prototype of equations representing the line spectra of all the elements. Nowadays, however, the general relationship is usually written in the inverted form. For the whole set of hydrogen series, for example,

$$\frac{1}{\lambda} = R\left(\frac{1}{p^2} - \frac{1}{q^2}\right) \tag{20·6}$$

where R is a universal constant whose numerical value is 109,678 cm^{-1}. It is called **Rydberg's constant,** after a pioneer Swedish spectroscopist. In (20·6), p and q are both integers; p is a constant for a given hydrogen series, and q takes successive integer values for the several lines of the series. Thus $p = 2$ for the Balmer series, and $q = 3, 4, 5, \ldots$ in succession for the various lines. Further, if the above relation is multiplied throughout by the speed of light c, it takes the form

$$n = \frac{c}{\lambda} = \frac{cR}{p^2} - \frac{cR}{q^2} \tag{20·7}$$

the frequency n of each line is seen to be given as the difference of two numbers called **spectral terms.**

Even in the case of a very complicated spectrum it turns out that the frequency of any observed line can be expressed as the difference between two of a relatively limited set of terms. The array of terms represents a fundamental physical characteristic of the emitting atom or molecule, as spectrum theory later indicated.

20·9   Difficulties of a Planetary Atom; Bohr's Theory

The realization that all spectrum frequencies can be expressed in the form (20·7) stimulated numerous attempts to devise a model of the atom that would account for such a relation, but such efforts did not succeed. The frequencies capable of being emitted by a given atom are evidently related in a more complex way than are the various overtones of a simple acoustic system, and no mechanical system that was proposed seemed to satisfy the observations. The Rutherford model of the atom appeared to offer promise, but there was a grave difficulty. If the electrons were assumed to be at rest, a simple calculation showed that they could not remain in equilibrium but would fall into the nucleus.

On the other hand, if they were assumed to move in orbits about the nucleus, much like planets revolving about the sun, a new trouble arose; for a body moving in a curved path is subject to an *acceleration* (centripetal), and the theory of electromagnetism shows that when a charged body, such as an electron, is accelerated it *radiates* away electromagnetic energy. Thus on the basis of classical electricity an electron describing an orbit about a nucleus must continually lose energy and in consequence would, within a small fraction of a second, spiral into the nucleus. Such an atom could therefore not have a permanent existence.

It was at this point that a bold and entirely unprecedented theory was proposed by the young Danish physicist Bohr.[1] His accomplishment was the explanation of the spectrum formula by applying the quantum theory to the Rutherford model of the atom. But in order to do this he had to make assumptions that stood in outspoken contradiction to classical principles.

---

[1] Niels Bohr studied under Thomson and under Rutherford. He was the recipient of the Nobel prize in physics in 1922 for his important contributions to quantum theory. Virtually a prisoner of the Nazis during the Second World War, he was able to escape to England and then came to the United States, where he played a major part in the development of the atomic bomb.

Now it must not be assumed, as many of the uncritical are apt to, that the theorist can deliberately make the most bizarre assumptions that his imagination can contrive and "get away with it." Only in cases where the obvious and the ordinary fail to lead to results does a competent theoretical scientist resort to more unusual assumptions, and then he does this tentatively, treating his idea as a working hypothesis until it can meet the test of new observations.

While the Bohr theory, as first proposed in 1913, ultimately proved too restricted in its outlook and had to give way later to a more general approach, it represents the first successful application of quantum principles to the radiation from individual atoms and molecules. A general knowledge of what it involves is indispensable to the appreciation of the later forms of quantum theory.

20·10 Circular Orbits in the Hydrogen Atom

Taking the hydrogen atom as the simplest example, Bohr assumed that the single electron moves in a circle around the nucleus, which in this case consists of a single proton (Fig. 20·6). The general similarity between this arrangement and the motion of a planet around the sun suggests why the atom model used by Bohr is sometimes called a "planetary" atom.

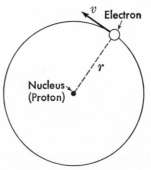

Fig. 20·6 Scheme of a planetary hydrogen atom.

The centripetal force holding a planet in its orbit is furnished by the gravitational attraction between planet and sun. In the atomic counterpart the centripetal force is the electrostatic attraction between the negatively charged electron and the positively charged proton. Since Rutherford's interpretation of the α-particle-scattering experiments indicated no departures from the validity of the inverse square force even at very small distances from the nucleus, Bohr equated the general expression for centripetal force to that given by Coulomb's law,

$$\frac{mv^2}{r} = \frac{e^2}{r^2} \quad \text{or} \quad mv^2 = \frac{e^2}{r} \tag{20·8}$$

Here e represents, as usual, the amount of charge on either the electron or the proton (in esu), m is the mass of the electron (in grams), v is its speed in the orbit (in centimeters per second), and r is the radius of the orbit (in centimeters). If the electron is to continue moving stably in its circle, this equation must always hold true.

While the above equation is valid from the point of view of classical **mechanics,** it contradicts classical **electrical** principles. As mentioned above, a charged body cannot—according to established theory—move in a circle without radiating energy. Even if it started in such a path, radiation would immediately begin to drain away its energy and it would promptly spiral into the center. It was at this point that Bohr found himself compelled to break with the classical theory and assume that *certain orbits do exist in which the electron can continue to move without radiating energy.*

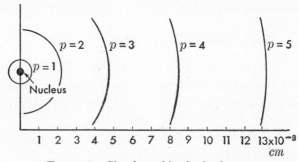

FIG. 20·7   Circular orbits for hydrogen.

The existence of a limited set of orbits suggested the quantum idea, and by restricting the possible group of stable (nonradiating) orbits in accordance with the quantum condition given by Eq. (20·1) it turned out that only those orbits are stable for which the **angular momentum** (page 145) of the electron is an integral number of times $h/2\pi$. As mentioned there, the angular momentum of a particle of mass m moving with a speed v in a circle of radius r is mvr. The above condition may then be stated

$$mvr = \frac{ph}{2\pi} \tag{20·9}$$

where p can take only the whole-number values 1, 2, 3, ... In order to find the radius of each of these allowed orbits, solve Eq. (20·9) for v, and substitute this value into Eq. (20·8). The result, solved for r, is

$$r_p = \frac{p^2 h^2}{4\pi^2 m e^2} \tag{20·10}$$

This expression shows that the radii of the stable orbits in which the electron can circulate without losing energy are proportional to $1^2, 2^2, 3^2, \ldots$ or $1, 4, 9, \ldots$. Some of these orbits are shown to scale in Fig. 20·7. If the known numerical values of h, m, and e are substituted into the expression (20·10), the result, with $p = 1$, turns out to be $r_1 = 0.53 \times 10^{-8}$ cm, which agrees surprisingly well with the radius of a hydrogen atom as found from the kinetic theory of gases. It is accordingly assumed that when the hydrogen atom is in its normal state the electron occupies the smallest of its allowed orbits.

20·11 Energy Relationships and Line Frequencies

An even more impressive agreement with known facts was revealed when Bohr went on to compute the energy relations in the atom. The crucial test that had to be met by the theory was the explanation of the observed spectrum lines. Bohr made the assumption that the electron can spontaneously jump from a larger to a smaller orbit and that in this process it is able to radiate energy. The radiated energy was assumed to be related to the frequency of the light by the quantum-energy formula $E = nh$.

Calculation shows that the energy of the electron in any stable orbit amounts to

$$E_p = -\frac{2\pi^2 m e^4}{p^2 h^2} \qquad (20\cdot11)$$

The negative sign implies that the energy is greater in the larger orbits. Thus if an electron jumps to a smaller orbit, its energy decreases and the difference is sent out in the form of light. Where does this energy come from initially? The electron, normally in the smallest orbit, must first be boosted to a higher orbit. This can be done in various ways. In an electric discharge tube this so-called *excitation* is accomplished by the impact of fast electrons moving through the gas. Or if light is sent through the gas, any photon having just the right amount of energy needed to raise the electron in an atom to one of the higher orbits will be absorbed and the transmitted beam of light will show an absorption line (page 229) at this frequency. Photons having any other frequency will be strictly ignored by the atom. In any event, once the electron in the atom has been elevated to one of the larger permitted orbits (it cannot stop anywhere in between), it is in a position to fall back into a smaller orbit.

Ordinarily an electron spends only about 10^{-8} sec in any one of its excited states before spontaneously dropping to a lower state. It may not go clear down to the smallest circle in a single jump but may do this in several steps. Each transition, however, produces radiation whose frequency is determined by $E = nh$, where E is the difference in energy of the initial and final orbits involved in a particular jump. The frequency of the light emitted by an atom when its electron goes from an orbit q to an orbit p is given by $n = (E_p - E_q)/h$; or, using Eq. (20·11),

$$n = \frac{2\pi^2 me^4}{h^3}\left(\frac{1}{p^2} - \frac{1}{q^2}\right) \qquad (20\cdot12)$$

Not only has this expression exactly the same form as the spectrum equation (20·7) (page 393), but when numerical values are substituted for m, e, h, and c the value of the Rydberg constant

$$R = \frac{2\pi^2 me^4}{ch^3} \qquad (20\cdot13)$$

turns out to be almost identical with that previously obtained by fitting the observed spectrum lines into the Balmer formula!

The Balmer equation itself is obtained by setting $p = 2$ in Eq. (20·12), which means that all lines of this series are produced by electron jumps ending in the second orbit. For example, an atom radiates light of a frequency corresponding to the first line of this series when, after excitation, its electron falls from the third to the second orbit; the second line of the series results from a jump from $q = 4$ to $p = 2$, and so on. When such events take place for myriads of atoms throughout a gas, the observed spectrum is produced.

The existence of other possible series of hydrogen, corresponding to final orbits for which $p = 1, 3, 4, 5, \ldots$, was surmised by Bohr, and members of four such series were actually found. Thus in spite of the highly arbitrary character of its assumptions the Bohr theory, by its surprisingly accurate numerical agreement with observation and its prediction of new facts, claimed serious attention throughout the scientific world and stimulated an enormous amount of investigation.

20·12 Extensions of the Bohr Theory

The simple situation on which the above theory was based was soon generalized and refined in attempts to explain additional details of spectra. For one thing, it was realized that the preceding computation ignored the fact that the nucleus as well as the electron would have a motion of revolution. Although a proton is about 1840 times as massive as an electron, the motion does not take place exactly around the proton but around an intermediate point that is at the center of gravity of the pair. When this circumstance is allowed for, the value of the Rydberg constant turns out to have a slightly different value (by less than 0.1 per cent), but this change even improves the agreement with experimental results!

This refinement of the theory also permitted it to be applied not only to hydrogen itself but to other *hydrogenlike* atoms as well. The helium atom normally has two orbital electrons; but one of these may be temporarily removed by ionization, and the resulting structure consists of a single electron revolving about a nucleus— the same *type* of structure as an atom of hydrogen. In the same way, a doubly ionized lithium atom, a trebly ionized beryllium atom, etc., are hydrogenlike; and when the above modification is made, their spectrum frequencies should be calculable by the Bohr theory. This turns out to be the case. The isotope of hydrogen of mass 2 ("heavy hydrogen," or *deuterium*) was discovered in this way. Faint spectrum lines adjoining those of ordinary hydrogen (H^1) were observed, and these fell at the places computed for the deuterium lines.

Another extension of the original circular-orbit theory, developed by the German theorist Sommerfeld, took into account the possibility of *elliptical orbits* for the electron. In the solar system the planets move in orbits of this shape, and the same possibility exists in the Bohr atom. When the calculation is carried through, it is found that each hydrogen spectrum line actually consists of a number of lines very close together. The agreement with observation is only fair. However, a further extension of the theory that attributes to the electron a *spinning motion* (page 315) about an axis of its own seems to account for the observed line patterns more satisfactorily.

20·13 Structure of Heavier Atoms

Guided by the observed spectral, chemical, and magnetic behavior of elements other than hydrogen, Bohr and Stoner worked out the general arrangement of the electrons in these atoms. A nucleus, you will recall, carries a positive charge equal to P electron charges, where P is the atomic number of the element. Surrounding the nucleus of a neutral atom there will be P electrons. It is assumed that the electrons are arranged in layers, or **shells,** around the nucleus. In general, more than one electron may occupy a given shell; and the problem is to determine for each element the way in which the electrons are apportioned among the various shells. The concept of electron shells is thus a more general one than that of orbits. A given shell is characterized by the energy associated with the electrons occupying it, and no details such as electron speeds, orbit shapes, etc., need be specified. In fact, the later, more general quantum theory dispenses with electron orbits altogether.

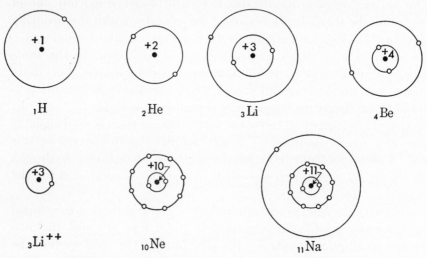

FIG. 20·8   Structure diagrams of some atoms and ions.

Moving down through the periodic table, electrons are added to the various shells in succession. In each shell there is a maximum number of possible electron places. Going outward from the nucleus, these numbers are 2, 8, 18, 32, 50, . . . , although for some of the heavier elements there are interruptions in the order in which the shells are filled, such departures being dictated by chemical evidence. Following hydrogen with its single electron comes helium, with its two electrons in the same shell, as indicated schematically in Fig. 20·8. The symmetry of this pair of electrons reflects the chemical inertness of helium. Next comes lithium. Positive ray experiments suggest, for example, that at most three electrons can be removed from an atom of this element. Two of these electrons occupy the same shell, as in the preceding element helium; the third is by itself in the next larger shell, making the whole structure resemble that of hydrogen. This single outer electron, which is available for sharing with another atom of suitable kind, accounts for the fact that a lithium atom has a chemical valence of 1.

With each of the next seven atoms another electron is added to the second shell until, when it contains altogether eight electrons, it is filled. This occurs for neon, the next of the inert elements (see figure). The following element, sodium, is again hydrogenlike in structure, for it has the two completed innermost shells containing two and eight electrons, respectively, and an additional single electron farther out (see figure). This structure is in keeping with such facts as the hydrogenlike nature of the spectrum and the valence of 1. In this general way, structural schemes for the atoms constituting the remainder of the list have been worked out, and the results are capable of explaining not only the chemical characteristics of the elements but their optical and X-ray spectra, magnetic behavior, etc. The details are very extensive and complicated and will not be given here.

20·14   Band Spectra

The general appearance of band spectra has been described in a previous chapter (page 231), and their connection with the molecules of compounds was pointed out. The quantum theory has been applied with success to the analysis of these spectra. A molecule may be held together in some cases by electrical attraction resulting from the fact that its constituent atoms are ionized, in other cases by the sharing of some of the outer electrons by the atoms. When an electric discharge is sent through a gas, the molecules may take up energy, not only in the form of electron excitation (boosting to higher orbits), but through the medium of increased rotation or vibration of the atomic centers. To take the simplest instance, that of a molecule composed of two atoms, such as carbon monoxide (CO)—the two atoms may vibrate back and forth along the line joining their centers, and the whole "dumbbell" may rotate around an axis normal to the line of centers (Fig. 20·9). Each of these motions, in addition to that of the electrons, is *quantized*— that is, made subject to a quantum condition. This means that a molecule can rotate or vibrate, not with any arbitrary frequencies, but only with certain definite ones. A change from a given state to one of lower energy involves the emission of a photon. Each electronic change gives rise to a whole set of bands, each vibrational change to a single band within such a group, and each rotational change to a single line in a band.

The analysis of band spectra furnishes a wealth of information concerning the structure, dimensions, and other properties of the molecules responsible for these radiations.

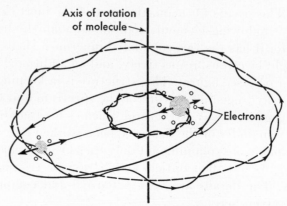

FIG. 20·9   A diatomic molecule.

20·15   Appraisal of the Bohr Theory

Despite its initial successes the Bohr model of the atom soon disclosed limitations which suggested that it might be too narrow in scope and too literal to become the basis of a general theory of atomic structure. Already in attempting to explain the details of the spectrum of hydrogen it was found necessary to resort to artificial "patching" of the original theory through the introduction of a motion of the nucleus, elliptic orbits, electron spin, etc.

Still other criticisms of the theory might be—and have been—leveled against it on logical and philosophical grounds. In the first place, in setting up his theory. Bohr helped himself to a peculiar mixture of classical and quantum concepts. He retained the classical laws of dynamics and of electrostatics but rejected the classical rule of electromagnetism concerning the radiation from an accelerated charged body. Later Sommerfeld, in developing the elliptic-orbit theory, had to introduce the relativistic variability of the mass of the electron (page 345) as well. In other words, it has been objected by some that the basic postulates of the theory are a mixture of classical, quantum, and relativity concepts.

Another feature of the theory for which it has been called to task is the mysterious nature of the assumed electron jumps. What happens to an electron while it is changing from one stationary orbit to another, and just how does the radiation of energy take place in such a process? One may well inquire whether or not it is legitimate or meaningful to raise such questions as these. Some light will be thrown on the problem in the next chapter.

On the positive side of the picture it must be remembered that it is easy to criticize a pioneering movement in the light of later and more complete knowledge—knowledge that might not have been revealed until much later if not for the incentive provided by the successes of the earlier efforts. Bohr's theory, while not the last word on the subject, did strike out in a significant new direction. It provided the basis and the stimulus for the development of more general forms of quantum theory to be described in the next chapter.

SUMMARY

Planck's hypothesis: Energy is sent out from an ideal radiator in discontinuous amounts called *quanta.* The energy of a quantum is given by $E = hn$.

Photoelectric effect: The release of electrons from matter by the action of radiation. Einstein applied the quantum idea to explain the observations. In doing this he was led to suggest that radiation is of a quantum nature even while traveling through a medium. A quantum of radiation is called a *photon.* It can be thought of as a "bullet" of radiant energy.

Scattering of α particles by matter showed that the nucleus of an atom is relatively small—of the order of one-thousandth of the atom diameter.

The Bohr theory: Bohr applied the quantum hypothesis to the planetary atom and succeeded in accounting for the spectrum of hydrogen. A photon was assumed to be radiated when the electron jumped from one stable orbit to a lower one. Refinements and extensions of the theory led to its application to the spectra of other atoms, to a general picture of the arrangement of electrons in the atoms of the various elements, to an explanation of X-ray and band spectra, etc.

READING REFERENCES

1. Taylor, Lloyd W.: "Physics, the Pioneer Science," Houghton Mifflin, Boston, 1946. For a more detailed treatment of many of the topics of this chapter read pp. 808–827.
2. Moulton, F. R., and J. J. Schifferes: "The Autobiography of Science," Doubleday, New York, 1945. Read pp. 536–547 on the work of Planck and of Bohr,

3. Born, Max: "The Restless Universe," Blackie, Glasgow, 1935. The Bohr atom is discussed in Chap. IV.

4. Zworykin, V. K., and E. G. Ramberg: "Photoelectricity and Its Applications," Wiley, New York, 1949. A detailed but not difficult treatment of this subject and many of its ingenious applications.

FILMS

"Electrons," Encyclopaedia Britannica Films. 16 mm, sound, 1 reel.
"Electronics at Work," Westinghouse Electric Corp. 16 mm. sound, 2 reels (transportation costs only).

EXERCISES

1. How much energy is contained in a quantum of visible light of wavelength 5000A? Compare this with the magnitude of the quantum of energy corresponding to a pendulum swinging with a frequency of 1 vib/sec.

2. A lamp is sending out radiation of a single wavelength, 5000A, at the rate of 0.10 watt. How many quanta are emitted each second?

3. Compare the wavelength of the hardest radiation obtained from an X-ray tube operating at 50,000 volts with that at 100,000 volts (compute relative values only).

4. Radiant energy of wavelength 4000A is falling on the surface of a photoelectric cell at the rate of 1.6×10^{-8} watt. How many quanta arrive per second? If the work of escape is 2.0 ev, what is the speed of the fastest photoelectrons released by this radiation?

5. From Fig. 19·16, page 374, estimate the wavelength of the shorter member of the pair of characteristic X-ray lines of copper, using the scale at the bottom of the diagram. What is the minimum PD, in volts, that must be applied to the tube in order to produce this line?

6. Compute the force acting on an α particle when it is 10^{-12} cm from the nucleus of an atom of gold ($P = 79$).

7. Discuss the extent to which the analogy between a Bohr atom and the solar system is valid. Are there "permitted orbits" in the latter? Spontaneous "jumps" between orbits? Does the spinning electron have a counterpart in the solar system?

8. Calculate the radius of the fourth circular Bohr orbit ($p = 4$) of a hydrogen atom. Compare the result with Fig. 20·7.

9. What is the speed of the electron in the smallest Bohr orbit of hydrogen? [Use $p = 1$ in Eq. (20·9).]

10. Referring to Eq. (20·5), compute the wavelengths, in angstrom units, of the first four lines of the Balmer series of hydrogen.

Chapter 21

WAVES AND PARTICLES; THE NEWER
QUANTUM THEORY

In Chap. 20 you were introduced to the idea of a photon as a localized bit of radiant energy. The photon may come into existence when energy is liberated by an atom or molecule of matter. It may be swallowed up again by matter in a phenomenon such as the photoelectric effect. One of the most striking pieces of evidence for the discrete nature of radiation was provided by experiments on the scattering of X rays.

21·1 The Compton Effect

In 1923, while studying the effects produced when a beam of X rays strikes a block of solid matter, A. H. Compton[1] discovered the effect that bears his name. He observed that when X rays are scattered from carbon their wavelength is slightly changed. The result stated in this simple way sounds extremely matter-of-fact; yet it was of the greatest importance for the support it gave to the photon concept.

The experimental arrangement is sketched in Fig. 21·1. A narrow beam of hard X rays of a single wavelength, allowed to strike a small block of carbon, was scattered out in various directions in much the same way as light from a searchlight or motion-picture projector is scattered by dust in the air. The scattered radiation was allowed to come into a Bragg crystal spectrometer (page 373), where its wavelength could be measured. According to the classical theory of radiation the scattered rays should have had the same wavelength as the incoming one. What Compton found, however, was that the scattered radiation contained, in addition, a new

---

[1] Arthur H. Compton, American physicist and educator, is noted for this discovery and also for his very extensive work on cosmic rays. In 1927 he shared the Nobel physics prize with C. T. R. Wilson (p. 377).

wavelength slightly greater than the original one—that besides the "unmodified" X-ray spectrum line there was present a "modified" line of which the wavelength increased with the angle at which the scattering took place. This is indicated by the small boxes in the figure.

No explanation could be devised on the wave theory, but Compton realized that the photon point of view would lead to a satisfactory description of what he observed. As you have seen, a photon has associated with it an amount of energy given by $E = hn$, where n is the frequency of the radiation. According to a result of the theory of relativity, such a packet of energy also possesses momentum of a given amount (see Sec. 21·10). If the incident photon is

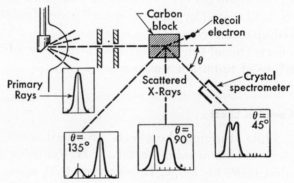

FIG. 21·1   The Compton effect.

then considered to be a "something" having energy and momentum, it may also be thought of as capable of colliding with and rebounding from matter. Yet a photon must not be imagined to be a particle in the ordinary sense, for a photon possesses energy and momentum and even existence only at one particular speed—that of light—and at no other.

If a photon strikes an electron and rebounds, it may communicate some of its energy to the electron and so have less energy afterward. But if its energy E is less, then its frequency n must also be less after collision, according to the relation $E = hn$, with the result that the scattered photons have lower frequency than the incident rays, as observed. When the mechanics of the situation is worked out numerically on the assumption that both momentum and energy are conserved, the result is in exact agreement with the observations. The unmodified wavelength, always present to some extent, is produced by photons scattered from electrons that are firmly attached to atoms of the scattering material. In such an instance, only negligible energy is handed over by the incident photon, and this means that the scattered photon has essentially the same wavelength as the initial one. But if a photon is scattered from a *free* electron in the material, the electron rebounds and much of the photon energy is transmitted to the electron. The result is that the photon has correspondingly less energy afterward.

The "recoil electrons" so produced are actually observed in a cloud chamber, and their speeds agree with the values computed from the equations. The *change* in wavelength of the photon in the Compton effect turns out to be independent of the initial wavelength, and this explains why the effect is observed only with hard X rays, where the wavelength difference is an appreciable fraction of the wavelength itself. For visible light the change would be far too minute to detect.

The Compton effect was later explained on the basis of the newer quantum theories, as mentioned below.

21·2   Dual Character of Radiation

When we considered such radiation phenomena as interference and diffraction, it was seen that their explanation compelled us to assume that light is propagated in the form of waves. On the other hand, phenomena like the photoelectric effect and the Compton effect and indeed all "quantum phenomena" lead unmistakably to the idea of photons. Attempts to reconcile the two pictures are generally unsuccessful. Einstein suggested that light waves act in a certain sense as guides for the travel of the photons and that the energy of radiation is not represented directly by the strength of the electric and magnetic fields in the wave, as Maxwell's (classical) theory asserts. Instead, it is assumed that these fields determine only the *probability* of finding photons at given places. There are inherent difficulties in such an interpretation and with others that have been proposed.

At one stage in the development of these ideas it was thought that perhaps interference experiments using very weak light might show some unusual effect—that each of the very small number of quanta used in, say, a diffraction experiment with a double slit would have to choose which of the two slits it would go through.

However, no unusual effects are found in such tests; it must be that any measurable effect requires a large enough number of quanta to make the average result the same as that obtained under ordinary conditions.

The only course open seems to be to face this *dualism* in the nature of light and to look upon waves and photons as two aspects of a single phenomenon that is not capable of description in terms of any mechanical model. The wave aspect appears to be adequate in describing the behavior of light as long as it is traveling through a medium, while the photon view seems to be required in dealing with the interaction of radiation with matter—that is, with the processes of emission and absorption of radiation. It is equally impossible to make any general statement to the effect that light "consists of" waves or that it "consists of" photons.

The existence of the disturbing wave-photon dilemma is remarkable enough in its own right, but the astonishing fact is that further developments revealed an exactly parallel dualism in the case of material particles.

21·3 Heisenberg's Quantum Mechanics

It was pointed out in Chap. 20 that the Bohr theory, with its nonradiating orbits and electron jumps, required repeated modifications in order to bring it into harmony with observation and that the conviction began to assert itself that the picture it presented was too literal and too special. Clearly the need for a new and better formulation was strongly indicated.

A successful attempt in this direction was made in 1924 by Heisenberg.[1] Proceeding on the assumption that the purpose of a physical theory is to provide the simplest possible connection between experimental data, he tried to construct a theory in which only *directly observable* quantities are utilized. In this class he placed the frequencies and intensities of spectrum lines, while he refrained from introducing such concepts as electron orbits, positions, or speeds that he regarded as mere constructs and not as observable data.

His original theory, which was later modified and extended by Born and Jordan (German) and by Dirac (English), consisted in

---

[1] Werner Heisenberg, German theoretical physicist, whose profound and penetrating work in quantum theory, begun when he was only twenty-three years old, won him the Nobel prize in physics in 1932.

a set of equations for finding the frequencies and intensities of spectrum lines and the energy levels in an atom. Heisenberg freed physical theory from the restriction of thinking about atomic processes in terms of a concrete mechanical model. His theory is infinitely more abstract than the Bohr theory and it makes no concession whatever to the intuitions. However, it scored the great triumph of accounting correctly for certain observed facts where the Bohr theory had given no result or a wrong one.

In formulating his theory Heisenberg made use of mathematical quantities of the type known as "matrices." For this reason the theory is usually called *matrix mechanics.* The use of the latter word may be unfortunate in this connection since the theory is not mechanical at all in the sense of being bound to a mechanical model of the atom. It goes without saying that the formal procedure is highly abstruse; nevertheless it is possible to gain at least a general idea of the matrix method even without a knowledge of higher mathematics. Reference 1 will be found excellent in this connection.

21·4 De Broglie's Wave Theory

At about the same time as the work of Heisenberg a significant new path in quantum theory was taken by the French theorist Louis de Broglie. His idea, in brief, was that not only radiation but matter as well may possess both wave and particle aspects. If Einstein's idea of photons guided by light waves is tenable, he reasoned, then perhaps material particles are also guided by or accompanied by some kind of wave. Thus, temporarily ignoring the fact that the wave-corpuscle duality for radiation remained unexplained, he boldly sought to explore the possibility that a similar duality might exist in the case of matter. In order to sketch the thread of his argument we must first consider a highly significant result deduced from the theory of relativity and called the Einstein *mass-energy relation.*

According to this relation, mass and energy are interconnected. *To every quantity of energy there corresponds an equivalent mass,* and *with every mass there is associated a certain intrinsic energy.* The quantitative relation is

$$E = mc^2 \tag{21·1}$$

where E represents the energy (in ergs), m is the equivalent mass (in grams), and c is the speed of light (in centimeters per second).[1] One implication of the principle is, for example, that whenever energy is supplied to a body (by heating it, by setting it into motion, etc.) its inertial mass increases. However, for any process at our disposal in the laboratory this increase is far too small to detect by ordinary means such as weighing. The occurrence of the large factor c^2 on the right-hand side of Eq. (21·1) shows why. Even if as much as 1,000,000 joules of energy is communicated to an object, its mass will increase by only

$$\frac{10^6 \times 10^7}{(3 \times 10^{10})^2} = 1.1 \times 10^{-8} \text{ gm}$$

In the reverse process, however, the conversion of even a minute quantity of mass can produce an enormous amount of energy. In modern nuclear transformation experiments both processes are actually observed, and the numerical values are in accord with Eq. (21·1). You will hear more of this in what follows.

To return to de Broglie's ideas: The light waves that Einstein assumed to act as guides for photons have a frequency given by the quantum relation $E = hn$. By using Eq. (21·1), this may be written

$$mc^2 = hn \qquad\qquad (21\cdot2)$$

where m may be described as the "equivalent mass of the photon."

The wavelength is always given by the wave equation $c = n\lambda$ (page 159); combining this with Eq. (21·2) yields $\lambda = h/mc$. If we make the assumption that electrons or other particles of matter behave in an analogous way, these must be accompanied by matter waves whose wavelength, by analogy, is

$$\lambda = \frac{h}{mv} \qquad\qquad (21\cdot3)$$

where v is the speed of the particle. For an electron that has fallen through a PD of 100 volts, the de Broglie wavelength turns out to be just over 1A, or of the order of size of X-ray wavelengths.

21·5 Detection of Matter Waves

De Broglie's suggestion is revolutionary indeed. Beginning with the discovery of the electron and of X rays, physicists took great

[1] Here again, as in all phases of relativity theory, the speed of light takes an important role.

pains to distinguish carefully between what were identified essentially as particles of matter and other things that were verified to have the properties of waves. Now they were being presented with the need for admitting that both matter and radiation partake of wave as well as particle qualities.

But experimental verification of the existence of matter waves was not long in coming. In 1927 the American physicists C. J. Davisson and L. H. Germer found that when electrons are allowed to strike a crystal they are reflected only in certain definite directions. It was mentioned above that the matter waves associated with electrons of moderate speed would have wavelengths of the same order of size as those of X rays, and

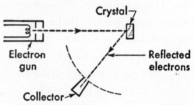

Fig. 21·2 Detecting the wavelike properties of electrons.

you have seen (page 371) that crystals are capable of acting as diffraction gratings for waves of this magnitude.

In the Davisson-Germer apparatus (Fig. 21·2), electrons coming from an electron gun strike a crystal of nickel, and the reflected electrons are detected by a collecting chamber, which is connected to a sensitive galvanometer. The whole assembly is in a highly evacuated vessel. The collector can swing in various directions, and it is found that at a certain angle the number of reflected electrons recorded increases greatly. Calculation of the wavelength that would be selectively reflected (diffracted) at this angle by the crystal yields a value agreeing with Eq. (21·3).

Fig. 21·3 Diffraction of matter waves. (*Courtesy of Dr. L. H. Germer.*)

Additional verification was obtained in experiments performed by G. P. Thomson, the son of J. J. Thomson. He succeeded in getting diffraction patterns by shooting electrons through thin metal foils (Fig. 21·3). In 1937, Davisson and Thomson were jointly awarded the Nobel prize in physics for this attainment. Similar diffraction effects with other particles such as helium atoms and even with hydrogen atoms were observed later by other experimenters.[1] There could no longer be any doubt that particles of ordinary matter had wavelike characteristics.

21·6 Schrödinger's Wave Mechanics

When the concept of matter waves is applied to the electrons belonging to an atom of matter, it is able to account in a vivid way for the stable or nonradiating states of the atom whose existence was assumed by Bohr (page 396). Suppose we compute the wavelength of the matter waves associated with the electron in a Bohr orbit. For simplicity, consider only circular orbits. According to Eq. (21·3) we shall need to know the value of mv for such an electron, and from Eq. (20·9) (page 396) this is given by $mv = ph/2\pi r_p$. Substituting in Eq. (21·2) gives

$$\lambda = \frac{h}{mv} = \frac{2\pi r_p}{p} \qquad \text{or} \qquad 2\pi r_p = p\lambda$$

But p represents any integer, and thus we see that the stable Bohr orbits are those around which whole numbers of matter waves of the electron will just fit. Otherwise stated, if an electron is a wave, then such a wave can continue to travel around a circle only if an integral number of wavelengths are contained in the circumference of the circle, so that the waves agree in phase after having gone completely around the orbit (see Fig. 21·4).

Extending significantly these considerations of de Broglie's, the Austrian theoretical physicist Erwin Schrödinger devised, in 1926, an original form of quantum theory that has come to be called *wave mechanics*.[2]

He started from a suggestive circumstance that exists in the case of light. In Chap. 11 you saw that for many purposes, such as the usual description of what happens in optical instruments like the telescope, light could be thought of simply as something that proceeds in straight lines (rays). Later you saw that more exact considerations make it necessary to replace this concept by the travel of waves. Schrödinger likened the classical mechanics of Newton to ray optics and asked himself what would correspond to the general *wave optics* of matter.

---

[1] The English physicist C. G. Darwin has suggested the name *wavicle* to replace the term "particle." The term has not found wide adoption, however.

[2] He shared the 1933 Nobel prize in physics with Dirac (p. 408).

Maxwell, in developing the electromagnetic theory of light (page 332), had arrived at a mathematical equation governing the behavior of electromagnetic waves. Similarly Schrödinger's pursuit of the ideas mentioned above led him to a form of wave equation describing the motion of matter. Both equations are of the type known to mathematicians as "differential." The Schrödinger rela-

tion involves a variable called the "wave function," whose possible values are determined by solving the equation. In an earlier discussion you learned that a mechanical system can vibrate only with certain definite frequencies—its fundamental and the various overtones.

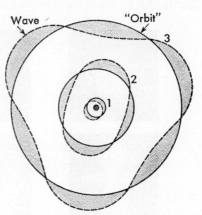

A solution of Schrödinger's equation always consists in a discrete set of *characteristic frequencies,* and these take the place of the stable states of Bohr's theory. In the latter theory, you will recall, the frequency of spectrum line is always determined by the *difference* of

FIG. 21·4 Stationary sets of electron waves correspond to Bohr orbits.

two energy values. In wave mechanics a line frequency is given directly as the *difference* between two of the characteristic frequencies of the wave function.

21·7 Interpretation of the Wave Function

Is it possible to form any idea of what the wave function represents physically? In the first place it is evident at once that matter waves are not the same thing as light (electromagnetic) waves. For one thing, we have seen that groups of matter waves may travel with *any* speed as long as this speed is less than that of light. Besides, matter waves are not radiated, but are associated with a particle. Schrödinger's earlier interpretation of the wave function was that it represents the density of electric charge at various places. On this basis the charge of an electron, for example, is not confined to a definite region but is "smeared out" through all of space; the charge density is quite large in the immediate neighborhood of a certain center but thins out rapidly in prescribed ways in different directions from such a center. Figure 21·5 is a pictorial representation of the way in which the charge of the single electron in a hydrogen atom may be distributed when the atom is in various energy states. To visualize the distribution in three dimensions, each picture should be thought of as rotated around a vertical axis.

An interpretation that has found more favor in recent years was developed largely by Born, Heisenberg, and Bohr. This view regards the particle as a localized object but assumes that the wave

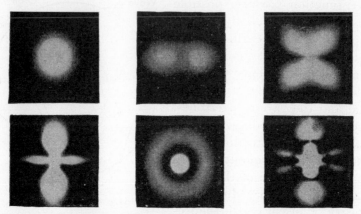

Fig. 21·5   Some possible distributions of the charge of the electron in a hydrogen atom. Each figure is to be imagined rotated about a vertical axis lying in the plane of the page. (*Courtesy of Prof. H. E. White.*)

function determines the *probability* of finding the particle at various places in space. In this sense the pictures of Fig. 21·5 then correspond to hypothetical "time-exposure" photographs of the electron.

21·8   Evaluation of the Newer Quantum Theory

Within a few months of the discovery of wave mechanics its complete mathematical equivalence with the Heisenberg theory was proved, so that while the two methods are very different in detail they are nevertheless capable of solving the same problems and giving identical results.

Wave mechanics seems to offer a more concrete picture and one that is easier to visualize than the purely mathematical symbols of matrix mechanics. For this reason the former method is preferred by most workers. However, this advantage disappears as soon as systems involving more than one particle are examined—even for the helium atom with but two electrons. Then it is necessary to deal with a space of *six dimensions*—a purely formal mathematical construct entirely incapable of being visualized in the way we think of ordinary space as consisting of the familiar three dimensions of length, breadth, and height.

With the continued development of the newer quantum theories their superiority to the Bohr theory and their wider applicability have become apparent. The new formulation not only succeeds in giving quantitatively the frequencies, intensities, states of polarization, etc., of spectrum lines but does so in a systematic and unified way without the introduction of semiempirical or entirely arbitrary assumptions as did the Bohr theory. In addition, many problems before which the Bohr theory was powerless have yielded to the newer quantum procedures. In particular the question of the forces holding together chemical molecules such as hydrogen (H_2) and the problem of radioactive disintegration might be mentioned. However, a great many questions connected with the interior of the nucleus are still lacking a theoretical explanation.

Important in a broader sense is the fact that the later quantum theory has shown the connection between the problem of matter and that of radiation and pointed out the fact that each of these aspects of nature possesses a duality. It provides us with a formalism that correctly represents atomic phenomena and asks in return only that we give up the hope of being able to visualize what goes on in the atomic world in terms of our ordinary large-scale experience.

21·9 The Principle of Indeterminacy

You have seen that, while common large-scale processes appear to be of a continuous nature, *elementary processes*—those dealing with individual electrons, photons, etc.—have a discontinuity characterized by Planck's constant h. It soon became apparent to theorists that this split might have some connection with the dual nature of waves and particles. In 1927, Heisenberg was able to enunciate a highly significant generalization, called the *principle of indeterminacy,* relating to the observation and measurement of elementary processes.

Whenever we measure something of ordinary size, a degree of inexactness or margin of error is involved. The extent of this inexactness depends on the nature of the method used. We feel confident that by taking pains to refine the method of measurement we could arrive at a result as accurate as desired. Heisenberg's contention is that this idea is wrong in principle!

To show this, he points out that in every process of measurement or observation there must be an actual physical interaction between the observer and what is observed. This interaction is, of course, far too small to trouble about in dealing with common objects, but the case is entirely different if we wish to observe, say, an electron in an atom. In order to "see" an electron, ordinary visible light could not be used; for an object can produce an appreciable effect (such as reflection) on a set of waves only if the dimensions of the object are not too small compared with the wavelength. Hence, in order to "observe" an electron, radiation of very short wavelength—γ rays—would have to be used. But what does this process imply in terms of the photon idea of radiation? In order to observe the electron, at least one photon would have to be reflected from it. In view of the extremely high frequency of γ rays these photons would have very high energy, since $E = hn$. Consequently, when a photon strikes the electron, there will be a Compton effect, and the electron will recoil with considerable speed; it may even leave the atom of which it was a part. This means that, if the electron is to be observed at all, the very process of observation alters what we are trying to observe!

If longer waves are used, the *position* of an elementary particle cannot be determined with exactness; if shorter waves are used, the *velocity* (or the momentum) that the particle had prior to the act of observation remains undisclosed. There is a fundamental inexactness, an uncontrollable or undefined element, inherent in all measurements connected with elementary processes. Heisenberg and Bohr analyzed many individual cases and always found the above conclusion to hold.

21·10   The Indeterminacy Relation

Heisenberg realized that this indeterminacy is fundamental in quantum theory and that it is responsible for our inability to visualize quantum processes. His considerations led him to an algebraic relation expressing the degree of indeterminacy involved in various types of measurement. The result may be arrived at as follows: The wavelength of any radiation is given by $\lambda = c/n$, and the indeterminacy of any measurement of length or position will be of this order of size. This may be expressed in symbols as

$$\Delta x \approx \frac{c}{n}$$

where the sign $\approx$ means that the two sides are not necessarily equal but are of the same order of magnitude.[1]

Further, the indeterminacy in the momentum of an elementary particle is of the same general magnitude as the momentum delivered by the impact of a photon. From Eq. (21·2) (page 410) the equivalent mass of a photon is given by hn/c^2, and hence its momentum would be this quantity multiplied by its velocity c. Then the indeterminacy in the momentum amounts to this mass multiplied by the velocity of the photon, or

$$\Delta M \approx \frac{hn}{c}$$

Multiplying the above two quantities together, we have

$$\Delta x \, \Delta M \approx h \qquad\qquad (21·4)$$

This is Heisenberg's indeterminacy relation. It expresses the fact that, *the more closely we determine the position of a particle, the less accurately are we able to specify its momentum,* and vice versa. This relation contains the true significance of Planck's constant h and shows its general importance in quantum theory: h is not only the factor that relates the energy and frequency of radiation; more generally, it is the constant of nature that regulates the limit of accuracy attainable in any kind of measurement.

21·11 Complementarity

What has been said concerning particles is equally true for light waves. Even the most minute amounts of radiant energy are able to interfere; hence it must be concluded that what we look upon as the intensity of light waves is simply a quantity giving the probability with which we can expect to find photons at a given place. No *single* experiment exists, however, by which both the wave and corpuscle aspects of light—or of electrons—can be verified. In the case of radiation, if we wish to fix the path of the photons, we can attempt to do so only by letting the light pass through narrow slits; but, by so doing, diffraction is introduced, and the wavelike property of light makes itself felt.

Bohr, in 1928, first formulated such conclusions in a general

[1] It may be read "is of the order of."

statement that has been called the most significant philosophical result of modern physics. It is known as the *principle of complementarity* and may be stated as follows:

Every experiment that allows us to observe one aspect of a phenomenon deprives us of the possibility of observing a complementary aspect.

The two complementary features may be the position and momentum of a particle, the wave and corpuscle characteristics of radiation or of matter, etc.

Considerable caution is needed in wording and interpreting a statement of such generality. According to Frank,[1] in phrasing the indeterminacy relation we must be careful to avoid saying that "it is impossible to measure the position and velocity of a particle simultaneously," for this statement implies that there exist *definite* positions and velocities, but that we are powerless to find them. A better approach is provided by Bohr's later formulation of the complementarity idea in which he discusses experimental arrangements where the expressions "position of a particle" and "velocity of a particle" can never be used *at the same time.* One or the other may be employed, but not both simultaneously,—the two statements are *complementary* descriptions. This formulation avoids the danger of thinking of a "real" world whose details somehow elude us.

21·12 Causality in Classical Physics

In Chap. 1 the concept of the uniformity of nature was briefly touched upon (page 8). Now, with a background of the main contributions of quantum theory, this idea can be, and must be, extended. Closely bound up with the constancy of natural law is the concept of *causality.* In experimenting with elementary processes, physicists attempted to proceed in much the same way as their predecessors in investigating the phenomena of classical physics. They sought out measurable quantities, determined their magnitude, and tried to bring the resulting information together in the form of scientific laws. It was felt that the same possibilities for observation were present in the field of elementary phenomena as had long been known to exist in the case of large-scale processes. With the recent developments in quantum theory, however, has come the realization that this idea may need drastic modification.

[1] See reference on p. 484.

Classical physics evolved largely from mechanics, and it was tacitly assumed that all the events taking place in space and time had the objective character that we associate with ordinary mechanical phenomena. The aim of physical science was taken to be the setting up of laws that would predict exactly the future configurations of the universe. In particular it was assumed without question that forces such as gravitation hold even in the smallest imaginable portions of space and that exactly the same natural laws are valid everywhere and at all times. Newton's laws had been applied to astronomy and had succeeded in predicting with exquisite exactness the future positions of the planets. Since atoms were regarded simply as material particles, why should it not be possible to predict the future arrangement of any set of atoms, too?

Early in the nineteenth century the great French mathematician and physicist Laplace made the much-quoted statement that an omniscient mind, knowing the position and velocity of every atom at any one instant, could deduce the entire course of events in the universe, both past and future. In accepting the Heisenberg indeterminacy concept we recognize that this view is no longer valid even in principle. The Laplace statement assumes that the universe is, even down to its smallest units, a machine in which all the parts are deterministically interlocked—that strict causality holds in the sense that every event is rigorously determined by the preceding one—something that the indeterminacy principle denies for elementary processes.

21·13 Causality and Probability

If strict causality is not valid in the realm of elementary phenomena, what takes its place? We know that large-scale physical phenomena obey what seem to be rigorous laws that enable us to make reliable predictions. Hence it appears that nature must possess some kind of regularity despite the indeterminacy of elementary phenomena. But what is the nature of this regularity? The answer is that *the orderliness we observe in an experiment on a finite scale is statistical in nature.* It may be that *all* physical laws are based on probability.

You have met the idea of probability in connection with physical phenomena on several occasions earlier in this book. In discussing the molecular constitution of a gas (Chap. 8), it was pointed out that we could not hope to follow the career of each individual molecule but that we could nevertheless describe with accuracy certain average properties of large numbers of molecules, such as their average speed or the average frequency of collision. In dealing with radioactivity, we found that, while no prediction could be made regarding the time when a given atom would disintegrate, a quite exact figure could be deduced for the rate at which atoms of a given kind would break down. Metaphorically it may be said that we can predict the "climate" of physical situations even if we do not know the state of the "weather."

But there is a fundamental difference between the meaning of the probability concept as applied to these large-scale cases and its significance for elementary processes. In the kinetic theory of gases, for example, the need for using statistical methods was seen to be a consequence of the very large numbers of molecules dealt with and the practical impossibility of following the course of each one. However, no doubt was felt as to the possibility of computing the motion of every molecule at least *in principle*—it was held merely to be too complicated but not necessarily impossible (to Laplace's all-knowing being). However, the statistical nature of quantum physics is a different matter. In the latter the *processes* themselves are statistical in character. Chance rules elementary events, and it is only in the large-scale phenomena that myriads of separate occurrences merge to give results of such high probability that we can regard them as practically certain.[1]

Gradually certain principles begin to take shape as a result of our consideration of some of the implications of the quantum idea. In place of the rigorously determined world of classical physics we are presented with a quite different picture—one in which the puzzling facts of discontinuity, duality, indeterminacy, and the impossibility of constructing visualizable models of phenomena are all bound up together. Many physicists and many philosophers have found great difficulty in accepting the newer ideas.[2]

On the other hand, some thinkers have received these concepts with great enthusiasm and have even gone so far as to attempt to apply them to an understanding of life processes, free will, social

---

[1] The difficulty mentioned in the first paragraph of Sec. 21·11 does not present itself in the field of large-scale phenomena. For example, no particles are ever observed in connection with radio waves, and diffraction does not manifest itself when baseballs are thrown at a picket fence.

[2] Einstein was among them.

phenomena, theological questions, etc. A discussion of these lines of thought is, of course, outside the scope of this book.

SUMMARY

Compton effect: The change in wavelength of X rays scattered from matter. Important because it can be interpreted in terms of the collision of photons with electrons.

Heisenberg's matrix theory: A mathematical scheme for treatment of quantum processes exclusively in terms of observable quantities.

Matter waves: De Broglie's idea that a moving particle has associated with it a wave of length $\lambda = h/mv$. Such waves were detected experimentally by diffracting elementary particles by means of crystals.

Wave mechanics: Schrödinger's extension of the matter-wave concept. It makes use of a wave function interpretable as giving the probability of finding a particle, such as an electron, at various points in space. This theory was shown to be mathematically equivalent to matrix mechanics.

Indeterminacy: Heisenberg's principle, which denies the inherent possibility of speaking of exact values of both position and momentum of an elementary particle simultaneously.

Complementarity: Bohr's general statement of the impossibility of observing two complementary aspects of a phenomenon in a single experiment.

Causality and probability: Indeterminacy denies the regulation of elementary processes by causality. The observed regularity of large-scale phenomena is a statistical one.

READING REFERENCES

1. Hoffmann, B.: "The Strange Story of the Quantum," Harper, New York, 1947. An extremely well written nonmathematical exposition of the nature of quantum theory. Not for rapid reading, but rewarding to one who goes through it slowly and thoughtfully.
2. Jordan, P.: "Physics of the Twentieth Century," translated by Eleanor Oshry, Philosophical Library, New York, 1944. A critical discussion, mainly from a philosophical point of view, of the newer physics.
3. Reichenbach, H.: "Atom and Cosmos," translated and revised by E. S. Allen, Macmillan, New York, 1933. The substance of a series of radio talks by one of the most distinguished living philosophers of science. "It aims to give insight into the physicist's way of thinking."
4. Compton, A. H.: The Scattering of X-ray Photons, *Am. Jour. Phys.*, Vol. 14, No. 2, pp. 80–84, 1946. Some reflections on this effect by its discoverer.

5. Moulton, F. R., and J. J. Schifferes: "The Autobiography of Science," Doubleday, New York, 1945. Read passages from the writings of de Broglie, Schrödinger, and Heisenberg, pp. 547–557.
6. Darrow, K. K.: The Quantum Theory, *Sci. American*, Vol. 186, No. 3, pp. 47–54, 1952. An easy introduction to the earlier developments.

EXERCISES

1. A γ-ray photon of wavelength 0.261A collides with a free electron, and its wavelength is thereby changed to 0.273A. With what speed does the electron, originally at rest, recoil? (*Hint:* Write the expression for conservation of energy in this process, using $hn = hc/\lambda$ for the energy of a photon of wavelength λ. For the electron mass use $m_0 = 9.11 \times 10^{-28}$ gm.)

2. A good chemical balance can detect mass differences of about 10^{-5} gm when weighing objects whose mass is of the order of 1 kg. Would it be possible to detect the loss in mass of a piece of hot iron, corresponding to its loss of energy on cooling? Use Eq. (21·1), and compute for a 1-kg ball of iron. Assume it to cool from the solidification temperature to that of the room, a difference of about 1500 C°. The specific heat of iron is about 0.11.

3. What is the de Broglie wavelength of a molecule of oxygen moving with a speed of 50,000 cm/sec? Of an electron whose speed is $0.5c$? Are both these wavelengths capable of being detected experimentally?

4. What is the de Broglie wavelength of a 500-gm baseball thrown with a speed of 25 m/sec?

5. When Davisson and Germer accelerated electrons in their apparatus, the associated matter waves were found to have $\lambda = 1.65A$. What was the speed of these electrons, expressed as a percentage of c?

6. If the position of a certain electron can be determined only to the nearest angstrom unit (10^{-8} cm), what will be the order of size of the uncertainty in its speed, expressed as a fraction of c?

7. Assuming that in a certain experiment an elementary particle can in effect be observed at intervals no shorter than 10^{-12} sec, what is the order of magnitude of the uncertainty of the particle's energy? (*Hint:* Energy and time are complementary quantities, and $\Delta E \, \Delta t \approx h$.)

8. If the uncertainty in the energy of a particle in an atomic nucleus is of the order of 100 Mev, what is the corresponding uncertainty of its location in time? Assuming the particle to be moving with essentially the speed of light, what is the indeterminacy of its position? Notice that this turns out to be of the order of the diameter of a nucleus. (1 ev = 1.60×10^{-12} erg.)

Chapter 22

NUCLEAR DISINTEGRATION

The phenomenon of natural radioactivity described in Chap. 19 and its interpretation on the basis of modern concepts of the structure of matter gave science its first example of the change of one variety of atomic nucleus to another. These disintegrations are confined to a relatively small number of elements. In the present chapter you will see how, through the use of both high-speed particles from radioactive atoms and artificially energized particles, it was discovered how to bring about nuclear changes under controlled conditions and of eminently greater number and variety than before. The discussion will begin with a brief treatment of the main features of the most energetic of all natural processes—cosmic rays.

22·1 Discovery and Early History of Cosmic Radiation

It has been known for a long time that an electroscope will gradually lose its charge at a rate faster than can be accounted for by leakage across the insulating support. This discharge has been traced to the existence of ions in the surrounding air, of which there are normally several hundred per cubic centimeter.

At the beginning of this century it was believed that the ionization was caused solely by radioactive materials in the earth's crust. However, by carrying electroscopes aloft in balloons, it was found that the ionization increased with height. At an altitude of $5\frac{1}{2}$ mi, Hess[1] found the effect to be 8 times as great as at sea level. After studying his observations, he announced: "The results . . . are best explained by the assumption that a radiation of very great penetrating power enters our atmosphere from above . . . ." The phenomenon was soon named *cosmic radiation.*

Extensive experiments were begun in the 1920's by Millikan and

[1] Victor Hess, Austrian-born American physicist. He was awarded a Nobel prize for his discovery of cosmic rays.

his coworkers and, somewhat later, by A. H. Compton and others associated with him. Extremely numerous measurements of the rays have been made at many localities at various levels in the atmosphere and even below the earth's surface. Self-recording electroscopes have been sent up in free balloons as high as 100,000 ft.[1] Detectable amounts of radiation have been found below as much as 2000 ft of rock, which is equivalent in absorbing power to about a 1-mi thickness of water.

These investigations showed that the general radiation consists of two main parts—a soft, or more easily absorbed, part and a harder, or more penetrating, component. The soft component is completely stopped by the equivalent of a few feet of water. The hard component has greater penetrating power than the hardest known γ rays.

Naturally one of the first questions that arose in connection with cosmic rays was that of their character and origin. At the present time neither aspect of this question has been given an unequivocal answer, but with the accumulation of much additional experimental information certain interpretations have acquired a high probability of being correct. As for the nature of the radiation two possibilities were recognized from the very first. It may consist either of high-speed electrified particles or of electromagnetic waves (or photons) of very high frequency. The basic questions are, "What is the nature of the primary radiation, where does it come from, and what is the source of its tremendous energy?"

22·2 Instruments for Detection and Observation of the Rays

Penetrating radiations of either kind may be detected in several ways, as already described in connection with X rays, γ rays, β particles, etc. Besides the electroscope, the cloud chamber, and the photographic plate an instrument developed by Rutherford, Geiger, and Mueller and usually called a *Geiger counter* is frequently used. In principle and construction it is not very different from the ionization chamber described on page 370 (see Fig. 19·10).

The Geiger instrument (Fig. 22·1) has a fine wire extending down the axis of a metal cylinder. The tube is filled with argon or other gases at about one-tenth of atmospheric pressure. A PD of the order of 1000 volts is maintained between the wire and the

---

[1] Lately, instruments carried in the heads of high-altitude rockets have been able to record data at several times this height.

cylinder. The value is adjusted so that a small increase of PD would start a discharge in the gas. If a fast particle or other ionizing ray comes into the gas, the few ions it produces are accelerated in

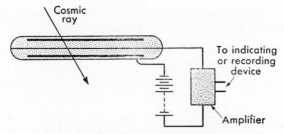

FIG. 22·1 The Geiger counter.

the field between wire and cylinder. In less than a billionth of a second, enough additional ions are produced by collision (in the manner described on page 339) to cause a momentary current in the outside circuit. This operates a device that records the event. Thus a Geiger tube is sensitive enough to count individual photons or particles. A tube of the usual size will register one to two counts per second at sea level.

In order to determine the intensity of cosmic radiation in various directions, two or more tubes may be connected to form a *cosmic-ray telescope*. The tubes are mounted in a frame that holds them in a single plane with their axes parallel (Fig. 22·2). The tubes are connected to a so-called "coincidence circuit," which can be arranged to register only when every tube or a selected combination of tubes is traversed by a ray. The entire arrangement may be pointed in various directions, and it is found that many more counts are registered when the plane of the tubes is nearly vertical than for any other direction, showing that the rays come mainly from overhead.

A cloud chamber placed in a strong magnetic field may be used to obtain more detailed information about each ray—such as its energy, and its mass and the sign of its charge if it is a particle. Counters placed on either side of the chamber can be made to trigger a circuit that operates the

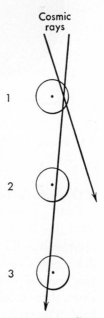

FIG. 22·2 Cosmic-ray telescope (schematic).

chamber each time a ray passes through it, so that the radiation almost literally takes its own picture (Fig. 22·3).

It turns out that the energy values in some cases exceed 10^{17} ev, so that cosmic rays constitute by far the most energetic processes known. The total rate at which the earth receives energy in this form is computed to be a few thousandths of an erg per square centimeter per second, or nearly the same order of magnitude as the light received from the stars.

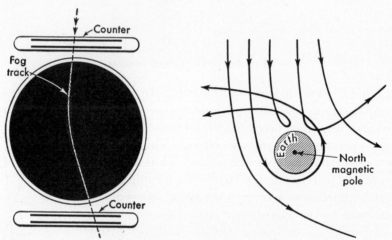

FIG. 22·3 Cloud chamber equipped with counters for automatic operation.　　FIG. 22·4 Deflection of charged particles by the earth's magnetic field.

22·3 Primary and Secondary Rays; the Positron

Observations show that the *primary cosmic rays*—the radiations coming in from beyond the earth's atmosphere—must consist at least partly of charged particles. A moving electrified particle that approaches the earth will be acted upon by the earth's magnetic field. Some of the particles may be turned back without reaching the ground at all (Fig. 22·4), while those that succeed in getting through will have their distribution changed by the action of the field. The observations are in accord with the idea that the primary rays are mainly protons having energies above a billion electron volts. Mixed with the protons are smaller amounts of high-energy nuclei of other elements.

The entry of the primary rays into the atmosphere gives rise to several other effects. Beginning about 1930, a great number of investigations were undertaken using the cloud chamber in a magnetic field—the method outlined on page 425. Contrary to what would be expected for cosmic rays, many of the particles that made tracks resembling those of electrons seemed to have passed through the chamber from below rather than from above. In order to account for the observed direction of bending under the assumption that they came from above, the suggestion was made that these particles were really protons.

In 1932, the young American experimenter Carl Anderson was able to show that these tracks were caused by a previously unob-

served particle carrying a positive charge and having a mass much less than that of a proton. He obtained a photograph, represented by the draw-ing of Fig. 22·5, of the passage of a particle through a sheet of lead placed across the chamber. Inasmuch as the curvature of the path is noticeably greater below the lead plate, he con-cluded that the particle must have come from above, losing some of its speed in going through the metal.

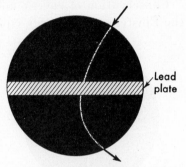

FIG. 22·5   Fog track of a posi-tron. (*After Anderson.*)

By using the known direction of the motion, of the bending, and of the field, the right-hand rule (page 317) shows that the charge of the particle must be positive.[1] The appearance of the track showed that the mass and amount of charge must be the same as for an electron. Anderson called the particle a "positive electron." Later the name *positron* attained general use, the word "electron" (unless otherwise qualified) continuing to mean the negative kind. Others confirmed Anderson's discovery and found additional sources of these particles. They can now be produced in the labora-tory in the form of intense beams.

22·4   Pair Production

Positrons have only a transient existence, for they soon combine with negative electrons, which are very numerous as constituents of atoms as well as in the unattached state. This is probably why the positron remained undiscovered so long. Quantum theory had predicted that if a high-energy photon (γ ray) were to pass into

[1] In the figure, the field is directed down into the page. Satisfy yourself that the charge is positive by applying the rule to this situation.

the strong electric field near an atomic nucleus the photon would be annihilated and in its place a pair of (oppositely) electrified particles having equal masses would come into being. Such particles were looked for and found in cloud-chamber experiments chiefly by Blackett in England and by Anderson in this country. Figure 22·6 represents what happens in a typical case when γ rays pass into the cloud chamber. The figure shows how two tracks originating at a single point in the chamber are made to curve in opposite directions by the magnetic field.

Conservation of energy and of momentum, taken together with the Einstein mass-energy equivalence (page 409), hold for the pair production process. Part of the energy hn of the incoming γ ray is converted into the combined mass of the two charged particles—the positron and the electron—and any excess is in the form of KE of these particles. Thus these observations furnish direct evidence for the conversion of energy into mass. Moreover, they provide one of the best proofs of the equality in mass of the positron and electron. Notice that electric charge is also conserved in the process. The initial photon has, of course, no electrification, and the charges of the positron and electron together also add up to zero.

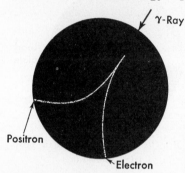

FIG. 22·6 Pair production: electron and positron "materialize" from a γ ray.

What is the wavelength of the softest γ ray that can cause pair production? This will be a photon of just enough energy to account for two electron masses, with no KE. According to Eq. (21·1) (page 409) we should have $hn = 2mc^2$, or $n = 2mc^2/h$, and with $\lambda = c/n$ this gives

$$\lambda = \frac{h}{2mc} = \frac{6.62 \times 10^{-27}}{2(9.11 \times 10^{-28})(3 \times 10^{10})} = 1.2 \times 10^{-10} \text{ cm}$$

or 0.012A.   This wavelength is in the region corresponding to hard γ rays.

Unlike electrons, positrons appear to have only a transient existence. They are annihilated by a process that is the reverse of the above. Thus a positron can combine with an electron to produce one or more photons of γ radiation. The commonest occurrence is one in which two photons of equal frequency are produced. If the initial KE of the positron and electron can be neglected, the wavelength of each of these radiations will be 0.024A.

22·5 Mesons

Cloud-chamber photographs of cosmic-ray events occasionally show tracks that cannot be attributed to protons, electrons, or positrons. About twenty years ago it was established that these tracks are caused by particles whose mass is somewhere between that of the electron and the proton. The new particles have been collectively called *mesons*. About ten years ago it was shown conclusively that two kinds of mesons, with distinct masses, exist in cosmic radiation. They are called μ mesons and π mesons, respectively.

Mesons either are neutral (in the case of one variety of π meson), or carry a positive or negative charge of amount e (see Table 22·1). Moreover, they are unstable, decaying spontaneously like radioactive materials of very short half life. The products may include other mesons, electrons, positrons, or γ rays.

Table 22·1   Properties of μ and π Mesons

Particle	Charge	Mass, in terms of electron mass	Half life, sec
μ^+	$+e$	207	1.5×10^{-6}
μ^-	$-e$	207	1.5×10^{-6}
π^+	$+e$	273	2×10^{-8}
π^-	$-e$	273	2×10^{-8}
π^0	0	262	Less than 10^{-13}

In addition to μ's and π's, a number of other mesons have been observed in cosmic ray records taken during the past few years. They range in mass from about half that of a nucleon to values considerably greater than the latter. The characteristics of these heavier mesons are not yet well established.

It was mentioned earlier that cosmic rays have been found to belong to two rather distinct energy groups, one much more penetrating than the other. It is now fairly certain that the harder radiation consists of fast μ mesons plus a few residual protons, while the soft component is made up of slow μ mesons, electrons, and photons. The mesons and other secondary rays are thought to be produced largely by interaction of the primary particles with terrestrial matter. Most of the mesons originate at altitudes of more than 10 mi. The virtual absence of π mesons from the radiation at ground level is due to both their rapid decay and the capture of the negative ones by atomic nuclei.

The question of the source of energy of the primary cosmic rays is still very much open. The energy has variously been ascribed to an initial cosmic explosion; to magnetic fields in space, in certain

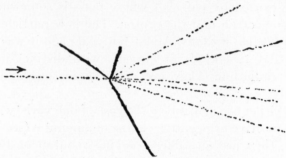

FIG. 22·7 A cosmic-ray particle entering from the left disintegrated a nucleus. The fragments produced these tracks on a photographic plate.

stars, or even in sunspots; or to still other causes. The relatively recent achievement of artificial meson production by means of particle accelerators may clear up some of the puzzling questions concerning mesons.

22·6 Rutherford's Transmutation of Nitrogen

We now go back to a highly significant experiment conceived by Rutherford in 1919. This experiment was the first step in a long line of investigations that enlarged our understanding of the nucleus and led, among other things, to the attainment of the fission process to be described in the next chapter.

The interpretation of natural radioactivity (Chap. 19) as the spontaneous breakdown of atomic nuclei suggested to Rutherford the possibility of causing nuclear disintegrations artificially by letting fast particles strike atoms of matter. As his "projectiles" for bombarding the nuclear fortress, Rutherford used α particles produced by the natural radioactivity of radium C. These were allowed to pass through various gases in the apparatus diagramed in Fig. 22·8. The radioactive source was located in the chamber, and a sheet of metal foil thick enough to stop all the α particles was placed across the opening. Just outside this window were placed a fluorescent screen and a microscope with which scintillations could be observed (page 391).

With oxygen or carbon dioxide in the chamber at normal pressure, no scintillations were observed; but when nitrogen was used, scintillations were seen even when the distance of the source from the window was as much as six times as great as the range of the α particles. The only explanation that Rutherford could propose was that the α rays in some way disintegrated the nitrogen nuclei and that long-range particles were emitted in the process. Magnetic-deflection experiments showed that these particles were

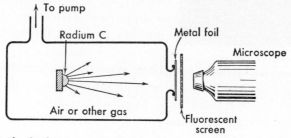

FIG. 22·8   Rutherford's apparatus for observing the effect of α particles on a gas.

probably protons, and this was later confirmed by other work. In a short time it was found that about a dozen other elements in the early part of the periodic table (page 360) similarly could be made to give off protons.

22·7   Cloud-chamber Identification of the Particles

Blackett in England and Harkins in the United States were among the first to investigate these disintegrations by means of the cloud chamber. On the average about one photograph in 50,000 showed an α particle colliding with a nitrogen nucleus, as sketched in Fig. 22·9. The bundle of tracks is produced by the α's, and in one case it is seen that such a track branches sharply. It produces a short, heavy spur, caused by the rebound of the struck nucleus, and a long, thin track left by the proton. The fact that there is no continuation of the α track indicates that this particle entered the nucleus and remained a part of it, ejecting a proton in the process.

Cloud-chamber photographs such as these are usually taken in stereoscopic pairs—that is, two pictures are taken simultaneously from different angles in order to be able to determine the true lengths of the paths and their relative position in space. Measurement of such photographs showed that momentum was conserved in these processes. In some cases the total KE of all the particles after impact was less than that of the incident α particle, but in certain others it turned out to be greater. Rutherford surmised that the extra KE in the latter case came from the internal energy of the struck nucleus.

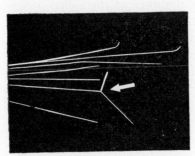

You are already familiar (page 365) with the fact that a given kind of atomic nucleus may be denoted by writing its chemical symbol with a subscript indicating the atomic number P and a superscript giving the atomic-mass number A. With these symbols, nuclear reactions can be represented by equations similar

Fig. 22·9   Collision of an α particle with a nitrogen nucleus.

to ordinary chemical equations. The disintegration of nitrogen by α particles is written as follows:

$$_2He^4 + {}_7N^{14} \rightarrow ({}_9F^{18}) \rightarrow {}_8O^{17} + {}_1H^1 \qquad (22·1)$$

The α particle is represented by $_2He^4$, since it is identical with a helium nucleus, and the proton is symbolized by $_1H^1$, it being a hydrogen nucleus.[1]

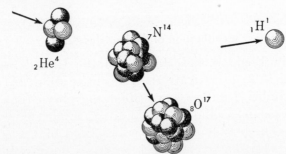

FIG. 22·10   Transmutation of a nitrogen nucleus by an α particle.

The intermediate compound nucleus $_9F^{18}$, which is believed formed by combination of the quantities on the left, is highly

[1] As pointed out earlier, the external electrons are usually ignored in writing nuclear reactions. The masses of the colliding nuclei are ordinarily very large compared with those of the atomic electrons. If a nucleus is hit with great energy, its electron complement may be detached as a result of this action, but it soon picks up electrons again after coming to rest.

unstable and breaks down into the products on the right. The intermediate product is often omitted entirely in writing the equation. This temporary nucleus must have an atomic number $P = 9$, since by the principle of conservation of charge it must carry $2 + 7$ electron charges (positive). It is therefore an isotope of fluorine, and its atomic-mass number must be the sum of those of the α particle and the nitrogen nucleus, or 18. When this compound nucleus sheds a proton, the remaining particle must then have a charge of 8 units and a mass of 17 units; it is therefore a nucleus of the relatively rare oxygen isotope of mass 17. Figure 22·10 is an attempt—much too literal—at representing the action.

22·8 Mass-Energy Conservation in Nuclear Reactions

It should be noted that when we say that the sum of the mass numbers of the initial particles must equal the sum of the final particles we are not necessarily stating that mass is exactly conserved in such a reaction, since the integers representing the atomic-mass numbers are not exactly equal to the actual atomic masses. The principle of the conservation of mass is superseded by the larger principle of conservation of mass and energy (page 409). Equations such as (22·1) should, strictly speaking, be written in the form

$$M + K = M' + K' \qquad (22\cdot2)$$

where M and M' represent the total mass of all participants before and after the reaction, respectively, and K and K' are their total kinetic energies before and after, all quantities being expressed in the same units. It is usual to change everything to mass units in writing nuclear equations. Still another useful way of writing this type of equation is

$$M = M' + E \qquad (22\cdot2a)$$

where $E = K' - K$, the **reaction energy** of the process. In a particular case this quantity may be positive, indicating that energy is liberated in the process, or it may turn out to be negative, in which case some of the initial particle energy is "frozen" in the form of mass. If the mass-energy equivalence is satisfied in nuclear reactions, this reaction energy E should be equivalent to the difference in masses of the original and final particles. This turns out to be quite accurately true in all of the many instances where the energies have been measured, and nuclear transformations furnish one of the best confirmations of the correctness of $E = mc^2$. Let us see how this works out numerically for the reaction represented by Eq. (22·1).

The value of E computed from observations amounts to

$$-2.02 \times 10^{-6} \text{ erg} = -1.26 \text{ Mev}$$

the minus sign indicating that the total KE of the particles is smaller after the reaction than before. We must compute the mass (in amu) equivalent to the above amount of energy. By definition, 1 amu is equal to $\frac{1}{16}$ of the mass of an atom of O^{16}, or $1/(6.02 \times 10^{23})$ gm. Further, by $E = mc^2$ the energy equivalent to this mass will be $(3.00 \times 10^{10})^2/(6.02 \times 10^{23})$ ergs. According to page 351,

$$1 \text{ ev} = 1.60 \times 10^{-12} \text{ erg}$$

so that

$$1 \text{ amu} = \frac{(3.00 \times 10^{10})^2}{(6.02 \times 10^{23})(1.60 \times 10^{-12})} = 9.31 \times 10^8 \text{ ev}$$

or

$$1 \text{ amu} = 931 \text{ Mev} \tag{22·3}$$

a relation that is useful in many nuclear computations.

Returning to the example at hand, -1.26 Mev will be equivalent to $-1.26/931 = -0.00135$ amu. Using nuclear masses based on the mass-spectrograph values for the atoms involved in the reaction, we get the following:

Initial		Final	
$_2He^4 =$	4.00279	$_1H^1 =$	1.00758
$_7N^{14} =$	14.00366	$_8O^{17} =$	17.00011
	18.00645		18.00769
			−0.00135
			18.00634

The agreement is very satisfactory; the two figures differ by only a few parts in a million. The results of such comparisons not only confirm the correctness of the mass-energy principle but also show that atomic-mass values determined by the mass spectrograph are identical with those obtained from nuclear reactions.

22·9 The Neutron

The discovery of this particle, an entity already referred to many times in talking of atomic nuclei, came about as the result of an interesting series of events. In 1930 the German experimenters Bothe and Becker found that when the metal beryllium was struck by α particles a very penetrating type of radiation capable of passing through several inches of lead was emitted. It was assumed that this radiation was of the nature of very hard γ rays. In 1932 the Joliot-Curies,[1] in examining the absorption of these rays, made a puzzling but important discovery. When paraffin or water was placed in the path of the rays, their strength was observed to increase, rather than to decrease as one would expect. The Joliot-Curies found that long-range *protons* were ejected from the

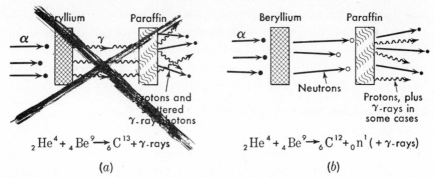

$$_2He^4 + {}_4Be^9 \rightarrow {}_6C^{13} + \gamma\text{-rays}$$

(a)

$$_2He^4 + {}_4Be^9 \rightarrow {}_6C^{12} + {}_0n^1 (+ \gamma\text{-rays})$$

(b)

FIG. 22·11 Original and revised interpretations of the reaction of α particles on beryllium.

absorber, and they assumed that γ rays from the beryllium were releasing these protons by a Compton-effect process. This is represented schematically in Fig. 22·11a.

But Chadwick, working in England, was not satisfied with this interpretation. A computation based on his further experiments convinced him that a γ ray capable of accounting for the long-range protons could not possibly be produced by the method that was used. He found, however, that agreement with observation resulted if he assumed that the penetrating rays were composed of particles having about the same mass as a proton but carrying no charge, since they produced no visible tracks in a cloud chamber and were not deflected by magnetic fields.

[1] J. F. Joliot (later Joliot-Curie) and his wife Irène Joliot-Curie, daughter of Pierre and Marie Curie.

The new particles are called **neutrons**.[1] The symbol is $_0\mathrm{n}^1$. The best value of the neutron's mass is 1.0089, as compared with 1.0076 amu for the proton. The neutron is thus about $2\frac{1}{2}$ electron masses heavier than the proton. An interesting fact about the neutron is that, when outside an atomic nucleus, it is unstable, having a half life of about 12 min.

The reaction occurring when α particles strike beryllium is now known to produce neutrons in the manner represented in Fig. 22·11b. These neutrons, striking a block of paraffin or other material containing many hydrogen atoms, knock some of the latter out with high speed. Because they are charged, the protons produce ions and can therefore be observed in the cloud chamber. Many other reactions have been observed in which α particles produce neutrons by transforming elements near the beginning of the periodic table. The great penetrating power of neutrons is ascribable to the fact that, having no electrification, they are not slowed down by producing ionization as they penetrate a substance. Unless it makes a direct collision with another particle, a neutron will not have its velocity changed in passing through matter.

22·10   Reactions Produced by Electrically Energized Particles

To Rutherford's way of thinking, the logical next step after succeeding in attaining disintegration with natural projectiles was to attempt to produce nuclear changes by means of artificially energized particles. At his suggestion, Cockcroft and Walton undertook to accelerate protons for such purposes and in 1932 succeeded in disintegrating lithium atoms by this means. Hydrogen ions accelerated by a PD of about 250,000 volts were allowed to hit a target of lithium metal. It was found that α particles, each having an energy of about 8.6 Mev, were produced. This energy, which for the two particles produced amounts to about 100 times the energy possessed by the incident proton, is liberated in the reaction—at the expense, of course, of part of the initial mass.[2] The reaction goes as follows:

$$_1\mathrm{H}^1 + {}_3\mathrm{Li}^7 \rightarrow {}_2\mathrm{He}^4 + {}_2\mathrm{He}^4 \tag{22·4}$$

[1] The 1935 Nobel prize in physics was awarded to Chadwick for his discovery.
[2] At the time it was thought that such reactions could be used as sources of large quantities of energy, but it was soon realized that the collisions were too few for such purposes. Nuclear fission (Chap. 23) was to prove a more feasible source.

The reaction produces a net amount of energy equal to about $17.2/931 = 0.0185$ amu. The nuclear masses involved in the reaction are

Initial	Final
$_1\text{H}^1 = 1.0076$	$_2\text{He}^4 = 4.0028$
$_3\text{Li}^7 = 7.0166$	$\times 2$
$\overline{8.0242}$	$\overline{8.0056}$
	$+0.0185$
	$\overline{8.0241}$

and again a close numerical check with the mass-energy law is found.

Similar reactions were found to occur when protons were allowed to strike a number of other elements, such as boron, chlorine, and sodium. Reactions have also been observed in which an incident proton produces a γ-ray photon rather than a pair of α particles. For example, a proton of sufficient energy may be captured by a lithium nucleus, forming a compound nucleus that is in an excited state. This nucleus then reverts spontaneously to its normal state by emitting a photon,

$$_1\text{H}^1 + {}_3\text{Li}^7 \rightarrow {}_4\text{Be}^8 + \gamma \text{ ray} \qquad (22 \cdot 5)$$

22·11 Particle Accelerators; the Cyclotron

The success of the Cockcroft-Walton experiment stimulated many other attempts to devise ways of producing high-speed particles for use in nuclear research. In addition to direct methods using high voltages (see Ref. 2) and the betatron described on page 368, one other device requires discussion. This is the *cyclotron,* developed by the American physicists E. O. Lawrence and M. S. Livingston beginning about 1930. In this machine a relatively moderate voltage is applied many times over to a stream of charged particles until they attain energies of considerable magnitude—in the largest present installations several hundred mega-electron volts.

The instrument (Fig. 22·12) makes use of two hollow metal half cylinders called "dees" because of their shape. They are enclosed in a vacuum chamber placed between the pole pieces of a strong electromagnet. A source of ions, such as protons, deuterons, or α particles, is located at the center. High-frequency alternating voltage is applied to the dees by means of a powerful oscillating circuit. An ion moving in a horizontal plane will be bent into a circular path by the magnetic field. If, each time such a particle crosses from one dee to the other, the charge of the dee it is about to enter could be arranged to be opposite in kind to the ion charge, the particle would be accelerated in crossing the gap. If this were done many times over, the particle would soon acquire a high energy as it continued to revolve in its circular path.

Consider the factors that determine the path of each ion. According to Eq. (17·3) (page 319) the force acting on an ion of charge Q esu and moving with a speed v cm/sec in a plane normal to a magnetic field of strength H oersteds is $HQv/(3 \times 10^{10})$ dynes. The

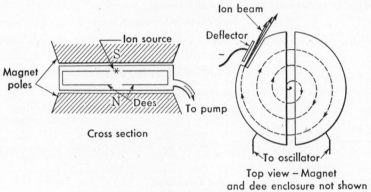

Ion beam

Deflector

Ion source

Magnet poles

S

Magnet poles

N Dees

To pump

Cross section

To oscillator

Top view – Magnet and dee enclosure not shown

Fig. 22·12   Diagram of essential parts of a cyclotron.

particle will move in a circle of radius r cm determined by equating the above force to the centrifugal force Mv^2/r, where M is the mass of the ion in grams,

$$\frac{HQv}{3 \times 10^{10}} = \frac{Mv^2}{r} \qquad \text{or} \qquad v = \frac{HQr}{(3 \times 10^{10})M} \qquad (22 \cdot 6)$$

Having traveled through half a circle inside one of the dees, the ion comes to the gap. Assume the ion to be charged positively. If the charge on the dee that it is just leaving is now positive while that on the dee it is about to enter is negative, the ion will be accelerated while crossing the gap and will move in a slightly larger circle in the second dee, as you can see from the last equation. Having described half this circle, the particle again comes to a gap and is again given an acceleration, for in the meantime the potential difference across the dees has changed sign. The ion continues to describe larger and larger circles as it goes from one dee to the other.

22·12 Conditions for Synchronism; Other Accelerators

The ingenious feature of the cyclotron is that conditions can be readily adjusted to make the revolving particles automatically maintain synchronism with the alternating PD applied to the dees, for the time required for the ion to make a half turn is independent of the size of the circle. This is easily seen as follows: The time t taken by a particle having a speed v to describe a semicircle of radius r is given by $\pi r/v$. Substituting the value of v from Eq. (22·6) yields

$$t = \frac{3 \times 10^{10}\pi M}{HQ} \tag{22·7}$$

This expression for t contains only the charge and mass of the ion and the strength of the applied magnetic field but does not involve r. By adjusting the value of H, t can be made the same as the half period of the oscillator. When the ions have completed a sufficient number of turns and approach the outer edge of the dees, an electric field applied to a deflecting plate swerves them away from the circular path and out through a thin window, where they are allowed to strike a target and produce the effects desired.

The voltage applied to the dees may be of the order of 10,000 or 100,000 so that after making a few hundred or a few thousand revolutions the ions may emerge with energies of as much as several hundred mega-electron volts. The oscillator frequency is of the order of ten million cycles per second. In one of the largest present installations the pole pieces of the magnet are more than 15 ft in diameter.

A limit to the particle speed attainable with the cyclotron is imposed by the relativistic dependence of the mass of the particle on its speed (page 345). This has the effect of spoiling the constancy of v indicated by Eq. (22·6), with the result that for speeds approaching that of light the ions get badly out of step with the applied voltage and the instrument does not function. This trouble can be surmounted by gradually decreasing the frequency of the applied PD as the ions proceed outward and acquire speed. The instrument—modified in this way by introducing, in effect, frequency modulation—is called a *synchrocyclotron.*

In another form of machine the strength of the magnetic field is also varied during the time the particles are accelerated. This is called a *synchrotron*. It is largely used for accelerating protons, and so is often called a *proton synchrotron*. The magnet in such a machine is shaped like a race track in plan and has a cross section shaped like the letter **C**. The particles move along in the space between the arms of the **C**, acquiring their energy as they repeatedly traverse the race track.

FIG. 22·13   The Brookhaven Cosmotron, showing the doughnut-shaped magnet, over 70 ft in diameter. In the foreground is seen part of the concrete radiation shield that surrounds the machine.

Three examples of these giant machines are worth at least brief mention. The first two are already in operation, while the third is still under construction.

1. The Cosmotron at Brookhaven National Laboratories, near New York City. Designed to give protons energies of 2.5 to 3 Bev (billion electron volts).
2. The Bevatron at the University of California. Designed for 5 to 7 Bev. This machine was the first to produce mesons artificially. Recently, the *antiproton*—the negative counterpart of the proton—was produced by this device.
3. An alternating gradient synchrotron at Brookhaven. It is expected to reach 25 to 35 Bev.

22·13 Some Deuteron Reactions; Branching

The use of the cyclotron made it possible to bring about a large number of reactions using high-energy deuterons (deuterium nuclei). One or two examples may be of interest:

$$_1H^2 + \ _7N^{14} \rightarrow \ _6C^{12} + \ _2He^4 + 13.4 \ Mev \qquad (22·8)$$

The production of α particles in this reaction was verified and their energy measured by using a cloud chamber. The other product, ordinary carbon, was identified by writing and balancing the reaction equation.

When deuterons impinge on beryllium metal, intense beams of fast neutrons can be produced and these are of great utility in causing other nuclear changes. The reaction equation is

$$_1H^2 + \ _4Be^9 \rightarrow \ _5B^{10} + \ _0n^1 + 4.1 \ Mev \qquad (22·9)$$

In some instances the bombardment of a given material with high-speed particles produces two or more alternative reactions. An example is the capture of a deuteron by a lithium nucleus. The ensuing disintegration may proceed according to one or the other of the following schemes, with either protons or α particles as products:

$$\begin{aligned} _1H^2 + \ _3Li^6 &\rightarrow \ _3Li^7 + \ _1H^1 + 4.9 \ Mev \\ _1H^2 + \ _3Li^6 &\rightarrow \ _2He^4 + \ _2He^4 + 22.2 \ Mev \end{aligned} \qquad (22·10)$$

Note that the energy released in the second process is several times larger than in the first.

22·14 Induced Radioactivity

While the Joliot-Curies had narrowly missed the discovery of the neutron, their work on the disintegration of various elements by means of α particles led them, in 1934, to make one of the most significant discoveries in recent physics. Following Anderson's identification of the positron, a number of investigators found that these particles were emitted from a variety of elements when bombarded by fast ions. It was generally assumed that these positrons were produced in a direct nuclear reaction or that the primary action released γ rays, which then produced electron-positron pairs (page 427).

When the Joliot-Curies allowed α particles to strike boron or aluminum, they found that positrons appeared but that the positron emission did not stop when the source of α's was removed. In each instance the positron activity was found to fall off as time passed exactly in the manner in which a natural radioactive element decays (page 379), the half life being of the order of several minutes. The experimenters concluded that, as a result of the α-particle bombardment, atoms of the target metals had been converted into radioactive isotopes of other elements, which then disintegrated into stable atoms of another kind by giving off positrons. This was fully verified. Such processes are referred to as *induced radioactivity*.

The initial reaction in the case of aluminum, say, is

$$_{13}Al^{27} + {}_2He^4 \rightarrow [{}_{15}P^{30}] + {}_0n^1 \qquad (22\cdot11)$$

where the square brackets indicate that the isotope of phosphorus that forms is radioactive.[1] The radioactive decay of the phosphorus nuclei then goes according to the equation

$$[{}_{15}P^{30}] \rightarrow {}_{14}Si^{30} + {}_{+1}e^0 \qquad (22\cdot12)$$

the symbol $_{+1}e^0$ denoting a positron—that is, an entity having a charge of $+1$ and a mass that is essentially zero compared with 1 amu. The nucleus $_{15}P^{30}$, being radioactive and of short half life, is not found in nature, but the stable nucleus Si^{30} is.

Induced radioactivity differs from natural radioactivity in one important respect: In the former, only electrons or positrons are emitted, never α particles. Gamma rays may be produced in either type of activity, however.

22·15   Radio-isotopes and Their Applications

Lawrence exposed common salt (sodium chloride) to a beam of high-energy deuterons from the cyclotron and found that radioactive atoms of sodium were produced and that fast protons were also given off. The reaction goes

$$_1H^2 + {}_{11}Na^{23} \rightarrow [{}_{11}Na^{24}] + {}_1H^1 \qquad (22\cdot13)$$

The target, once removed from the deuteron beam, was found to

[1] This is not to be confused with the use of ordinary parentheses in an equation such as Eq. (22·1) where we are dealing with unstable atoms that disintegrate almost immediately after they are formed instead of decaying at random over a period of time after the manner of natural radioactivity.

be emitting ordinary electrons and γ rays due to the decay of the unstable sodium.

$$[_{11}Na^{24}] \rightarrow {}_{12}Mg^{24} + {}_{-1}e^0 + \gamma \text{ ray} \qquad (22\cdot14)$$

The process has a half period of about 15 hr. The nucleus $_{11}Na^{24}$ is called *radiosodium;* it is not found in nature.

Many of the isotopes formed as a result of induced radioactivity began to find significant applications in biology and medicine almost from the time of their discovery. For one thing, some of these isotopes are used as *tracers* in experiments on plants and animals. Nearly all the common chemical elements can now be obtained in the form of radioactive isotopes, or *radio-isotopes*. The active atoms enter into the same chemical reactions as the normal atoms. They can be built into compounds and allowed to take part in biochemical processes. The distribution of the element in space and time can then be followed by means of sensitive Geiger counters or other detectors of radiation. Radio-isotopes thus furnish the biologist with a powerful tool for investigating fundamental processes occurring in living matter.

Evidence indicates that radiocarbon (C^{14}) is formed[1] by the action of cosmic rays and that there are enough of these atoms built into the structure of the body to constitute one of the major sources of radiation to which we are exposed.

At the present time more than 1000 different nuclear reactions are known, and over four-fifths of this number lead to induced radioactivity. You have seen several instances of how induced radioactivity may be produced by bombardment by both α rays and by artificially energized particles. In some cases, too, it may be induced by γ rays. But the most prolific source of radio-isotopes is the atomic reactor, to be described in the next chapter.

SUMMARY

Cosmic rays: Extremely penetrating radiation coming from outer space and capable of causing ionization and other effects. Distribution of the radiation near the earth indicates that the primary rays are mainly protons with energies above 1 Bev.

The *positron* is a positive electron. It originates in cosmic rays and in nuclear reactions in the laboratory. It is impermanent, converting itself into radiation by uniting with an ordinary electron. The opposite process—*pair production*—also occurs.

[1] The reaction is $_0n^1 + {}_7N^{14} \rightarrow {}_6C^{14} + {}_1H^1$, followed by the decay $_6C^{14} \rightarrow {}_7N^{14} + {}_{-1}e^0$ with a half life of about 5600 years.

Mesons are impermanent particles apparently with several distinct masses ranging from about one-tenth to several times the mass of a nucleon. They may carry a charge of $+e$, $-e$, or 0. Mesons are produced in cosmic rays and also in high-energy particle accelerators.

Artificial nuclear transformations may be produced when particles from radioactive elements or from particle accelerators strike atomic nuclei. The total mass-energy is conserved in such reactions.

Neutrons are particles having about the same mass as protons but no charge. They enter into the composition of all atomic nuclei (except $_1H^1$).

Induced radioactivity results when unstable nuclei, or *radio-isotopes*, formed by the addition of incident particles (or photons), decay spontaneously and at random over a period of time.

READING REFERENCES

1. Leprince-Ringuet, L.: "Cosmic Rays," Prentice-Hall, New York, 1950. A good descriptive account.
2. Macmillan, E. M.: High Energy Physics, *Am. Scientist*, Vol. 43, No. 3, pp. 420–430, 1955. New particles and the machines that create them.
3. Wendt, Gerald: "You and the Atom," Morrow, New York, 1956. A brief, highly readable presentation of the newer developments and their implications. Read Chaps. 6 and 7 at this time.
4. Colton, F. B.: Man's New Servant, the Friendly Atom, *Natl. Geographic Mag.*, Vol. 105, No. 1, pp. 71–90, 1954. A popular treatment, well illustrated. Read, at this point, the parts dealing with the applications of radio-isotopes.
5. Atomic Power, special number of the *Unesco Courier*, Vol. 7, No. 10, March, 1955, UNESCO Publications Service, New York. A splendid series of articles on all phases of atomic science.

FILMS

"Atom Smashers," Encyclopaedia Britannica Films. 16 mm, sound, 1 reel.

"Atom and Industry," Encyclopaedia Britannica Films. 16 mm, sound, 1 reel.

See free pamphlet, "Film Helps," obtainable from Educational Section, American Museum of Atomic Energy, Oak Ridge, Tenn. Lists a large number of films obtainable without rental cost from the AEC.

EXERCISES

1. The sensitive area of a certain Geiger counter is about 3 in.^{2} and it records a background count of about 40 per minute. Assuming that

your body presents an effective area of 2 ft² to cosmic radiation (including rays coming in obliquely), about how many rays pass through you per second? Biologists have suggested that this may be the cause of certain cellular changes and even of mutations in organisms.

2. It is estimated that about 10^{20} primary cosmic-ray particles hit the whole earth every minute. If the average energy of the primaries is about 6 Bev, calculate the average intensity of the radiation received, in ergs per square centimeter per second. Compare with the statement at the end of Sec. 22·2, page 426.

3. Prove the statement at the top of page 429 regarding the wavelength of each of the two photons produced by destruction of a positron when it encounters an electron.

4. Trace the origin of the word "meson" by looking up the meaning of the Greek word *mesos*. How should "meson" be pronounced?

5. Because of the relatively small mass and speed of the bombarding proton show that the two α particles produced in the reaction of Eq. (22.4) must come off in opposite directions with equal speeds.

6. With what energy (in mega-electron volts) does a proton emerge from a cyclotron after making 1,000 rev if the maximum PD across the dees is 7,000 volts? (Remember that the particles are accelerated *twice* in each revolution.)

7. In Exercise 6 the oscillator has a frequency of 5 megacycles/sec. How long a time is required to give each proton the specified energy? What must be the strength of the magnetic field that is used? [*Hint:* The mass of a proton is 1840 times that of an electron, and e/m for an electron is 5.28×10^{17} esu/gm. Use Eq. (22·7).]

8. At what energy would a synchrotron have to operate in order to produce a proton-antiproton pair? In practice, the energy would have to be considerably greater than this minimum value, since the bombarding particle cannot deliver all its KE to the target nucleus.

9. When α particles are used to bombard ordinary sulfur atoms, protons are emitted and chlorine atoms are left behind. Write the reaction equation.

10. The impact of α particles on ordinary nitrogen does not always go according to Eq. (22·1) but may yield, instead, a neutron and an atom $_9F^{17}$. Write the reaction equation.

11. The radioactive silver atom $_{47}Ag^{106}$ can disintegrate in two ways, (1) either emitting a positron and leaving an atom of palladium, or (2) emitting an electron and leaving an atom of cadmium (see pp. 360, 361). Write the reaction equation for each of these changes.

12. Compute the reaction energy, in mega-electron volts, for the transformation described in Exercise 9. Is this quantity of energy positive or negative? What does this signify concerning the possible use of this reaction as a source of "atomic energy"?

Chapter 23

THE STRUCTURE OF THE NUCLEUS

Up to the time of the discovery of natural radioactivity, science's concern with the structure of the atom was confined mainly to the external envelope of electrons. In particular, the tremendous variety of known chemical reactions involves only this outer part of the atomic complex. In natural radioactivity and in the various types of artificially promoted change described in preceding chapters, it is the *nucleus* of the atom that is involved. While the number and variety of reactions known to nuclear chemistry do not yet approach those of ordinary atomic chemistry, no person living today should require much persuasion to recognize the importance of nuclear changes. Experimental information in this field is now being amassed at a wholly unprecedented rate, and it is one of the foremost problems of contemporary theoretical science to try to formulate a theory that will correlate these data and lead to an understanding of the nature of the atomic nucleus.

In this final chapter an attempt will be made to describe the present state of this decidedly unfinished task of physics and to discuss the new and most spectacular types of nuclear change—fission and fusion—and some of their broad consequences.

23·1 Nuclear Binding Forces

Prior to the discovery of the neutron, all atomic nuclei (except H^1) were assumed to consist of protons and *electrons,* the latter being present in just the right number to ensure the electrical neutrality of the atom as a whole. For example, the nucleus of ordinary oxygen, O^{16}, would on this basis contain 16 protons in order to account for its mass of 16 amu. In addition, there would be 8 electrons, which would add nothing appreciable to the mass but would reduce the net charge of the nucleus to $+8e$, so that it could hold by attraction the required 8 external electrons of this atom. However, it was not long before theory indicated that an electron existing in a nucleus would have to possess energy many times greater than that of the most energetic β particles ever found to be ejected from radioactive nuclei.

The difficulty was soon resolved by the discovery of the neutron, and now it is generally held that nuclei are made up of protons and neutrons in the manner described earlier (Chap. 19). It is then further assumed that, when an electron is emitted from a nucleus in the form of a β particle, it is in some manner created at the instant of departure, say, by one of the neutrons in the nucleus changing into a proton (see page 377). Similarly, if a positron is emitted, a nuclear proton must change into a neutron. A satisfactory theory of nuclear structure must not only explain the mechanism of such processes but also account for the fundamental but puzzling fact that a nucleus can hold together at all! In the light of this circumstance, it must be assumed that *strong forces of attraction exist between the nuclear particles;* otherwise, there could be no stable nuclei.

From experiments such as those of Rutherford on the scattering of α particles (page 391) we know that the constituents of a nucleus must be confined to a roughly spherical region whose radius is of the order of 10^{-12} cm. These same experiments showed that there is a force of repulsion between an α particle and a nucleus, given by Coulomb's law, which holds even when the particles approach as close as about three times this distance from the nucleus. It must be concluded, then, that inside the nucleus Coulomb's law for the repulsion between like charges cannot hold but must be replaced by some kind of force of attraction. This prospect comes as not too great a shock when it is remembered that Coulomb's law has been verified only in experiments on the ordinary scale but cannot be checked in any direct manner for distances as small as that cited above. Reciprocally, anything we succeed in finding out about electrostatic forces on a nuclear scale will not in the least prevent us from continuing to use Coulomb's law to compute the attraction of two charged balls in the laboratory.

A free neutron shows no attraction for other particles, which is what would be expected on the basis of its lack of charge. When a *fast* neutron collides with an atomic nucleus, it usually rebounds "elastically"—that is, with no loss of energy.[1] But the neutrons and protons that are inside a nucleus apparently do attract each

[1] This is not true, however, for slow neutrons, as will be seen below.

other. A theoretical explanation proposed by Heisenberg can best be described by saying that he assumes the neutron and the proton to be two different states of the same particle and that the nuclear particles are capable of changing momentarily back and forth between these two states. Experimental evidence for the existence of these "exchange forces" has been obtained.

23·2 Nuclear Potential Barrier

About 1928 the Russian-born American physicist George Gamow proposed a way of thinking about the nucleus in terms of the potential energy of a positively charged particle approaching from the outside. Such a particle, coming toward a nucleus, would find

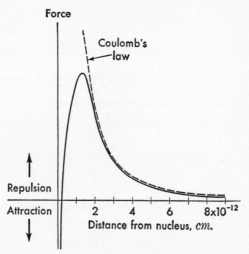

FIG. 23·1   Force between a nucleus and a positive particle.

itself opposed by a Coulomb force of increasing magnitude as long as the distance was not too small. This force law is represented graphically by the dashed curve of Fig. 23·1. However, this law, which indicates that the respulsive force becomes infinite for very close approach, cannot continue to represent what happens down to distances as small as 10^{-12} cm. From what you have seen above, the force to which the approaching positive particle is subject must change to one of *attraction* as soon as it comes close enough to the nuclear center. Gamow adopted the idea that at a certain distance of approach the force curve begins to depart from the Coulomb form and dips over sharply, as represented in the figure by the solid curve. Where this curve lies below the horizontal axis, the force is one of attraction.

In place of depicting the variation of force with distance, it is more useful to represent the variation of the PE of the particle in the field of the nucleus. The energy curve has the same general shape as the force curve. The field of the nucleus may be better visualized by thinking of the energy as gravitational rather than

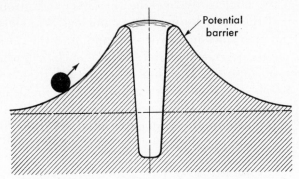

FIG. 23·2   "Crater" model of a nucleus.

electrostatic PE. Imagine a curve similar to Fig. 23·1, revolved about the vertical axis, so that it generates a surface resembling a volcanic cone and its central crater (Fig. 23·2). If a ball is rolled toward this crater, we have the counterpart of an atomic particle approaching a nucleus. If the approaching ball is not moving very fast or not heading directly for the crater, it will roll part way up the side of the cone and roll off again, in the manner of an α par-

ticle scattered by a nucleus in Rutherford's experiment (Fig. 23·3). If the ball is sent directly toward the crater with enough energy to surmount the *potential barrier,* it will drop into the cra-ter and become a constituent of the nucleus.

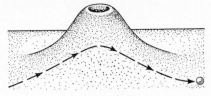

FIG. 23·3   "Scattering" of a positive particle by a nucleus.

There is one respect in which this mechanical model falls short of representing the facts. Nuclear experiments show that, even when the positive particles projected toward a nucleus have en-ergies less than that corresponding to the height of the potential barrier, a certain fraction of these particles is nevertheless captured by the nucleus. It must be assumed, then, that a given probability exists for the *penetration of the potential barrier* by such particles. Such an action, sometimes called the "tunnel effect," is totally mysterious on classical grounds but has been explained satisfactorily by wave mechanics.

23·3 The Waterdrop Model; Resonance

Bohr proposed (1937) an extension of our conception of the structure of the nucleus by likening the latter to a drop of water. The motion of the particles in a heavy nucleus is analogous to the motion of the molecules in a drop of liquid, and the potential barrier corresponds to the superficial "skin" (surface tension) at the free surface of a liquid. Ejection of a particle from the nucleus proves to be closely similar to evaporation of molecules from a drop, and it is even possible in a certain sense to speak of the "temperature" of a nucleus. If a fast particle enters from the outside,

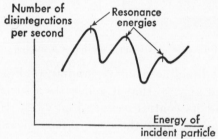

FIG. 23·4   Illustrating resonance capture of incident particles.

its energy soon becomes distributed among the members of the newly formed nucleus, raising the effective nuclear temperature. In the process, one of the constituents of the original nucleus may acquire enough energy to send it out over the barrier, disintegration taking place as a result.

It would be expected that the probability of interaction between an incident particle and a nucleus would vary in a regular way with the energy possessed initially by such a particle. While this turns out to be generally true, there are many cases in which the number of particles captured is found to increase markedly around certain values of the energy of the bombarding particle (Fig. 23·4). These are called *resonance energies.* Their existence suggests that the particles in a nucleus arrange themselves at various energy levels, analogous to the energy states of the electrons that surround the nucleus (page 397). If a particle approaches the nucleus with an energy corresponding to one of these levels, its chance of entering and remaining in the nucleus is much increased. Here again is an instance where the crater model must be supplemented by the idea that the incoming particle has wavelike properties. If its energy (and hence its wavelength) are just right, it will be taken up by a nucleus just as a sound wave of appropriate wavelength can be taken up by a tuning fork. The process is one of resonance (page 172).

Unlike protons, α's, or other charged particles, neutrons are not faced by a barrier as they approach a nucleus. Because it has no

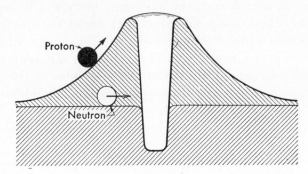

FIG. 23·5 Different behavior of potential barrier toward positive and neutral particles.

electrical charge, a neutron approaching a nucleus may have very low energy and yet succeed in entering. A proton coming toward a nucleus may in effect be confronted with the necessity of surmounting a steep cone, while a neutron approaching the same nucleus is able to roll along on a level plane and merely drop into the crater, as depicted in Fig. 23·5. This way of looking at the matter is in harmony with the fact that neutrons are particularly effective agents for bringing about nuclear transformations.

23·4 Reactions Using Slow Neutrons

The Italian-born American physicist Enrico Fermi and his co-workers discovered (1934) that certain atoms could be disintegrated by even very slow neutrons. A common way of producing fast neutrons is bombardment of beryllium metal by a beam of deuterons from the cyclotron according to the reaction of Eq. (22·9) (page 441). Fermi chanced to observe that the activity induced in certain metals was greatly increased when the target material was surrounded by a substance rich in hydrogen—for example, paraffin or water. He concluded that the fast neutrons were slowed down by successive impacts with hydrogen nuclei (protons) and that certain atomic nuclei are able to absorb slow neutrons much better than they absorb fast ones.

With regard to the first point it is not difficult to see that a neutron colliding elastically with a stationary *heavy* nucleus would not have its speed much reduced—it would merely rebound with almost all of its original energy. But if a moving object makes a head-on collision with another object of about the *same mass,* which is originally at rest, the impinging body will be reduced to rest and the struck body will go off with about the speed that the first object had when it approached.[1] After a number of collisions with protons a fast neutron will have had its KE reduced to the average KE of thermal motion of the molecules of the material. At ordinary temperatures this amounts to only about $\frac{1}{40}$ ev, whereas the initial energy of the neutrons produced in the reaction discussed above is over 4 Mev, or almost 200 million times greater.

Concerning the second point—the greater ease of absorption of slow neutrons by certain nuclei—it is found that the kind of resonance absorption discussed above exists for neutrons as well as for charged particles. When the energy of the impinging neutron is about right, it can be absorbed, boosting the nucleus to a higher energy level. In reverting to its lower energy state, the nucleus then disposes of the excess energy in the form of a γ ray.[2]

23·5 Discovery of Nuclear Fission

With the availability of much information on neutron-produced nuclear reactions, Fermi and his coworkers decided, in 1934, to try the effect of neutrons on heavy elements such as thorium and uranium ($P = 90$ and 92). The very first trials using uranium produced β-ray activity with several different half-life periods, and the experimenters thought that they had succeeded in producing nuclei of elements heavier than that of uranium, which was at that

---

[1] See Exercise 2 at end of chapter.

[2] Hundreds of reactions of this kind are known. An example is

$$_{47}Ag^{107} + {}_{0}n^1 \rightarrow [_{47}Ag^{108}] + \gamma \text{ ray}$$
$$[_{47}Ag^{108}] \rightarrow {}_{48}Cd^{108} + {}_{-1}e^0 \qquad \text{half life 2.3 min}$$

time the last element in the periodic table. To see why they drew this conclusion, recall (page 379) that when a nucleus gives off a β particle its nuclear charge, and thus its atomic number P, effectively increases by one and it becomes a nucleus of the succeeding element in the table. Fermi and his group attributed the observed β activities to successive disintegrations of a given atom, which would lead to *transuranic elements* (that is, "beyond uranium") for which $P = 93, 94, 95$, etc. Similar observations were soon made in France and in Germany. The formation of transuranic elements was generally accepted as the explanation of all these results.

In 1939, careful work on the chemical separation of the products showed that the above view was incorrect. Tests revealed that one of the product materials was either radium ($P = 88$) or barium ($P = 56$). Both elements are found in the same column of the periodic table (see page 360) and hence are similar in their chemical behavior. They can be separated at least partly, however, by a long series of crystallizations. When this was done, it was found that the β activity went along with the barium rather than with the radium. Other radioactive materials present were identified as various elements that, like barium, are not far from the middle of the periodic table. The results led to the striking conclusion that *neutron bombardment can cause a uranium nucleus to break apart, producing two or more fragments of moderate size.*

The novelty of this view lies in the fact that, without exception, all the nuclear disintegrations previously encountered among the heavier elements (including those of natural radioactivity) involved only the sloughing off of relatively small portions from the parent nucleus. Here, on the other hand, the nucleus splits into pieces of comparable mass. The term *fission* was suggested for such changes. The fission reaction can take place in many ways, and radio-isotopes of dozens of elements have been identified in the fission products from thorium and uranium (see Fig. 23·6). The primary fission products decay by emitting neutrons or electrons until a stable configuration is reached.

The word "fission" is well chosen, for the process suggests the biological action of the same name by which certain plants and animals, such as paramecia, divide to form new individuals. Also, the waterdrop model of the atomic nucleus provides a visualization of fission. Because of the existence of attractive forces a nucleus would be expected to be roughly spherical in shape, much as the surface forces cause a small raindrop to take on such a form. The entry of a neutron into a heavy nucleus causes an instability that sets the "drop" into a violent state of vibration. The drop may elongate and pinch off into two globules. An important feature is that, when these come apart at high speed, several smaller drops—neutrons—may be thrown off, too.

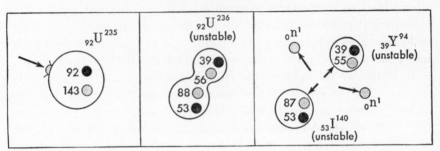

Fig. 23·6 A fission reaction. The unstable product nuclei may have atomic numbers from about 30 to 65.

The most impressive fact about fission, recognized almost from the start, is the colossal quantity of energy released in the process—an energy of the order of 200 Mev.

23·6 Chain Reactions

Experiments showed that the fission of uranium could be brought about by fast neutrons having energies greater than about 1 Mev or by slow ones of less than perhaps 1 ev, but not by neutrons of intermediate energy. An isotope of uranium having β activity was produced by the resonance absorption of neutrons at about 25 ev, but neutrons of this energy caused no fission. Bohr suggested that very slow ("thermal") neutrons are able to cause fission in the uranium isotope of mass 235 only but not in U^{238}, which is about 140 times more abundant in natural uranium. The radioactivity mentioned he ascribed to the 238 isotope. This idea was confirmed by experiments performed in this country using minute samples of the two isotopes, which had been separated by the mass spectrograph.

The realization that the fission of a nucleus might release more than one neutron suggested the possibility of a *chain reaction*. If each of the two or three neutrons now known to be produced in a fission were itself able to cause such a disintegration in another nucleus, the number of neutrons would increase rapidly, fission would proceed at an increasing rate, and in a very short time the whole sample of fissionable[1] material would be transformed, releasing tremendous amounts of energy.

Such was the state of knowledge in this field in 1942 when the United States government began large-scale support of investigations looking toward possible military uses of nuclear energy. Meanwhile, a policy of voluntary secrecy had been in force for some time, and the public was not to know the story of the work leading to the production of the atomic bomb until the release of the official Smyth Report (Ref. 2) in the summer of 1945.

23·7   The Nuclear Reactor

A chain reaction does not occur in natural uranium, for the neutrons emitted in the fission of U^{235} have high speeds and are captured by the much more abundant U^{238} before they can produce appreciable fissions in the lighter uranium isotope. The suggestion was made that the neutrons might be made to slow down before they have much chance of finding 238's by mixing natural uranium with some substance rich in hydrogen—the procedure mentioned on page 452. But calculation showed that this would not slow them soon enough to prevent the greater part from being absorbed in the inactive 238 as they passed through the 25-ev resonance energy. In order to make this scheme work, it was found that the concentration of U^{235} in the uranium sample would have to be about doubled. Accordingly, for this purpose, a number of the isotope-separation processes described on page 363 were set up experimentally at Oak Ridge, Tenn.

Meanwhile, it was suggested that small pieces of natural uranium be disposed throughout a mass of some material capable of slowing the neutrons—a *moderator,* as it is called. This will work where a uniform mixture of uranium and moderating substance fails, for the following reason: Neutrons originating in one of the pieces of uranium will soon find their way into the surrounding moderator, where they will be slowed down without danger of capture by

---

[1] The more correct adjective is "fissile," but the clumsy form "fissionable" has established itself quite firmly. In the same way, "nuclear" would be a better adjective than "atomic" in such phrases as "atomic energy" and "atomic bomb," but the usage is already too set to make any widely accepted change possible.

238's. But by this time they will probably enter another lump of uranium, where they can produce fission of a 235 nucleus.

The first such atomic pile, or *nuclear reactor,* was successfully operated by Fermi and his group in the winter of 1942. It contained over 6 tons of uranium and used highly purified graphite as a moderator. The energy output of the pile can be readily controlled because of the circumstance that there is some delay in time before some of the fission-produced neutrons are released from their parent nuclei. By making the pile only large enough so that it can maintain a chain reaction, its activity will increase very slowly

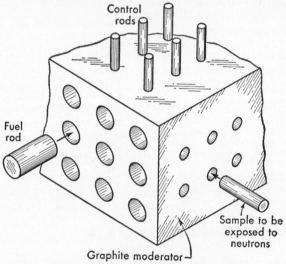

Fig. 23·7   A nuclear reactor (schematic).

because of the delay in neutron emission. Projecting into the pile are several movable control rods made of cadmium metal, which is a strong absorber of neutrons. When these rods are drawn out beyond a critical point, the activity of the reaction begins to increase, as measured by the amount of heat and the number of neutrons produced. By occasional manipulation of the rods the activity can be held at a desired level. The possibility of using nuclear reactors as commercial sources of power was eagerly seized upon from the very first. We shall have more to say about this later.

23·8   Production of Neptunium and Plutonium

The capture of neutrons by U^{238} was represented above as a detrimental feature of the operation of a nuclear reactor. Actually this process proved of great value in realizing the military goal of the atomic project, which was not the generation of power but the production of a weapon.

The first of the transuranic elements—No. 93, now known as *neptunium*—is provided in a nuclear reactor. This element is produced by the resonance capture of low-energy neutrons by U^{238}. A new uranium isotope of mass 239 forms, and γ radiation is given off.

$$_{92}U^{238} + {_0}n^1 \rightarrow [_{92}U^{239}] + \gamma \text{ ray} \tag{23·1}$$

The U^{239} then decays by emitting a β particle, leaving a nucleus of neptunium.

$$[_{92}U^{239}] \rightarrow [_{93}Np^{239}] + {_{-1}}e^0 \qquad \text{half life 23 min} \tag{23·2}$$

As indicated by the square brackets, neptunium is also radioactive. By emitting a β particle it becomes a nucleus with $P = 94$, now called *plutonium,* according to the following reaction:

$$[_{93}Np^{239}] \rightarrow [_{94}Pu^{239}] + {_{-1}}e^0 \qquad \text{half life 2.3 days} \tag{23·3}$$

This isotope of plutonium is α-active, the product nucleus being U^{235}; but the period is extremely long.

$$[_{94}Pu^{239}] \rightarrow {_{92}}U^{235} + {_2}He^4 \qquad \text{half life 24,000 years} \tag{23·4}$$

As mentioned above, the primary objective in constructing a nuclear reactor was to produce a bomb. Pu^{239} is useful in one form of atomic bomb for the reason that neutrons of any speed can make it undergo fission and it is constantly being produced in the operation of a nuclear reactor. Moreover, plutonium is a different chemical element from uranium and hence is separable from the latter by the relatively simple methods of chemistry. On the other hand, to obtain U^{235} in usable form for a chain reaction requires the difficult and costly process of isotope separation, as mentioned earlier.

When it became apparent that a nuclear reactor could be made to operate successfully, a gigantic plant for plutonium production was built at Hanford, Wash., in 1943. This establishment contained the reactors, dissipating hundreds of thousands of kilowatts of power in the form of heat. It also housed the necessary chemical separation plant for extracting the plutonium from them.[1]

[1] While the extraction process is simple from a chemical standpoint, great precautions are needed for the protection of personnel when the separation is done on an engineering scale. The intensely active materials must be handled entirely by remote control (see Refs. 4, 5 at end of preceding chapter).

23·9 The Atomic Bomb

You have seen, then, that a self-maintaining chain reaction is possible in a nuclear reactor using natural uranium—a mixture of isotopes 234, 235, and 238. The reactor is large, and the energy release takes place comparatively slowly and steadily. For a bomb, the requirement would be sudden (explosive) release of great quantities of energy in a small space. It turns out that this will have to depend almost entirely on fission brought about by fast neutrons and that the substance used as bomb material might be either uranium, enriched with additional 235, or plutonium. Another fissile substance, U^{233}, was produced from thorium for the first time in 1942.

There is another point of the utmost importance in connection with the production of fissile materials, whether for use in a reactor or in a bomb, that must be mentioned. How can we be sure that a sample, once manufactured, will not be accidentally touched off? Stray neutrons are continually present, due to the action of cosmic rays, radioactivity in the earth's crust, and other causes. Such a neutron, entering a mass of fissile material, could conceivably initiate a reaction that would spread explosively through the whole mass.

The answer is to be found in the fact that probability of fission increases with the mass of vulnerable material present and decreases with the chance of escape of neutrons from the sample. Under given circumstances (kind of fissile material, shape of sample, etc.) the mass will increase in proportion to the *cube* of any linear dimension of the sample, while the surface area of the piece—which determines the chance of escape of neutrons—increases only as the *square* of this dimension. If a sample is very small, its surface will be relatively large for the amount of material present and an explosive reaction will be prevented by the large rate of escape of neutrons into the surrounding regions. There will be a certain *critical size* below which the rate of escape and loss by nonfission capture of neutrons is less than their rate of production by fission. Such a sample will be safe. But if enough of such smaller specimens are brought together into one piece, the number of neutrons will multiply rapidly and an explosion will result. Thus there is no such thing as a scale-model fission bomb. The critical size must be attained before it will work at all. Figures on the magnitude of the critical mass have not been disclosed, but it is probably several kilograms.

While most of the physical facts and principles concerning fission were common scientific knowledge at the time the United States entered the war, the myriad details of developing a practicable bomb remained to be worked out. For carrying out the underlying calculations and tests the laboratory at Los Alamos, N.M., was set up in 1942 and placed under the direction of J. R. Oppenheimer.

There is little else that need be said here regarding the bomb. Apparently the weapon contains two (or more) samples of sub-critical size, and these are thrust together suddenly by the firing mechanism, producing an unstable mass. As soon as the explosion gets under way—perhaps in something less than a ten-millionth of a second—the mass begins to disperse and this prevents the effective fission of all the material. This effect is counteracted to a certain extent by surrounding the active material with a strong casing of some dense metal, which acts to reflect neutrons back into the dispersing mass as well as to delay the expansion until higher temperatures and pressures can be built up. Some additional details will be found in the Smyth Report (Ref. 2).

23·10 Source of Stellar Energy

An interesting question of long standing to which nuclear physics is now able to give a plausible answer is that of the origin of the stupendous quantities of energy that the sun and the stars are continually pouring into space. Each gram of the sun's mass is releasing energy at the rate of nearly 2 ergs/sec. This, to be sure, does not sound impressive—a gram of radium and its decay products evolves energy at nearly a million times this rate. However, because of the great mass of the sun, its *total* energy output is enormous, amounting to about 3.8×10^{33} ergs/sec. This means that, even at the earth's distance, each square yard of area exposed perpendicularly to the sun's rays receives energy at the rate of nearly 2 hp.[1]

Many attempts have been made to account for the production of this great quantity of energy, but none of the suggested sources

[1] If none of this were lost in passing through the atmosphere, it would mean a share of nearly half a million horsepower for each inhabitant of the earth—a fact that should give pause to those who scarcely had heard of energy before the advent of the atomic bomb!

proved adequate (see Ref. 3). With the discovery of nuclear trans-
mutations, however, it was realized that here was available an
energy source of the correct order of magnitude. Nearly two decades had to elapse before enough detailed knowledge of nuclear
processes was accumulated to lead to a definite theory. In 1939,
Weizsäcker in Germany and Bethe in the United States succeeded
almost simultaneously in explaining stellar energy production by
the process of combination of four hydrogen atoms to form an atom
of helium.

In order to satisfy the conservation of charge, the above reaction
must be looked upon as the combination of 4 protons and 2 electrons to yield an α particle. The total mass of the initial particles
will be $(4 \times 1.0076) + (2 \times 0.00055)$, or 4.0315 amu. The mass
of the α particle is 4.0028, so that there is a decrease in mass of
0.0287 amu. According to Eq. (22·3) (page 434) this is equivalent to
an energy yield of 0.0287×931, or about 27 Mev.

It turns out that two different sequences of intermediate reactions can take place. In the cooler stars, a deuteron, an He^3, and
finally an He^4 are formed. In the hotter stars, nitrogen or carbon
nuclei are involved in the intermediate reactions but are left in
their original state at the end of the process—they serve merely
the function of what chemists call *catalysts,* or agents that promote
a reaction without themselves undergoing permanent change. In
any case the net effect is the formation of helium nuclei from
hydrogen.

With an energy output of nearly 2 ergs/gm/sec the corresponding loss of solar mass, computed by using $E = mc^2$, is found to be
over $4\frac{1}{2}$ million tons each second. Nevertheless, even if the present
rate were maintained, this would mean only about a 1 per cent decrease in the sun's mass in the course of 150 billion years.[1]

The process in which nuclei of hydrogen or other light atoms
combine to form heavier nuclei is called nuclear *fusion*. It will be
described in more detail below.

23·11   Fission and Fusion Compared

You have seen that two types of nuclear reaction, fission and
fusion, are capable of releasing extremely large quantities of
energy. We can understand how this comes about by comparing

[1] Some of the hotter stars are expending energy at roughly 2000 to 3000 times
the sun's rate.

the potential energy stored up in the nuclei of various elements. Figure 23·8, based on experimental results, is one way of showing this information. The curve shows that the lightest as well as the heaviest nuclei are much less stable than those of intermediate weight. In a mechanical analogue, the arms of the curve may be thought of as the sloping sides of a valley, the various nuclei being boulders embedded in the slopes. A boulder that becomes detached will tumble to the bottom of the valley, giving up its initial gravitational PE in the process. But a boulder originally at or near the bottom can give up little if any energy.

In the nuclear case, if one of the heavier atoms such as uranium should undergo fission and change to, say, barium and krypton,

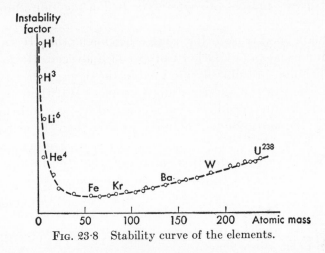

FIG. 23·8   Stability curve of the elements.

considerable energy would be given off, as we know is the case. But the figure suggests that even greater amounts of energy would become available if light nuclei on the steeper side of the curve were to undergo fusion and change to heavier nuclei.

There is an important difference, however, between fission and fusion. This has to do with the method of starting and maintaining the reaction. The presence of a single neutron in a mass of fissile material can start a chain reaction which spreads through the whole mass. The entry of a neutron into a fissile nucleus sets the nucleus into vibration, as described on page 450. The pinching-off process is helped by the electrostatic repulsion between the protons in the two lobes of the "drop." On the other hand, in order to bring two positive-charged nuclei close enough together to permit them to fuse, they would have to be given very high speeds. This means that the material would have to be brought to very high temperature, at least locally, in order to start the reaction. For this reason, fusion is also referred to as *thermonuclear reaction.* It becomes plausible that fusion can occur in the interior of a star, where the temperature is many millions of degrees.

23·12   The Thermonuclear Reaction

How can a thermonuclear reaction be started in an experiment conducted on earth? The fission reaction provides an answer. The temperature attained momentarily in a fission bomb probably exceeds that in the center of the sun. A fission bomb might then be used as a "match" to ignite the fusion reaction among light nuclei.[1]

There are good reasons for using other nuclei than H^1 in making a thermonuclear bomb. Other isotopes of hydrogen, H^2 and H^3, as well as lithium, presumably are used in the devices already tested.

In addition to the one mentioned on page 461, there is another fundamental difference between fission and fusion. To bring about fission, an amount of active material greater than the critical mass must be assembled; there is no way of "scaling down" a fission bomb. We have no indication, however, that the fusion reaction is limited in this way. In principle, any amount of fusible material can react, once the process is initiated. Intensive experimentation is now under way to find a way of producing the controlled release of energy by nuclear fusion, analogous to the controlled release of fission energy in a reactor.

23·13   Radio-isotope Production and Uses

In the preceding chapter, some of the uses of radio-isotopes as tracers were mentioned (page 443). The actual yield of such isotopes when made in particle accelerators such as the cyclotron is extremely small, and it takes an expenditure of several billion electron volts to produce a single neutron. It is true that for tracer purposes only small amounts of radio-isotopes are sufficient, but

---

[1] The fact that a fusion reaction had actually been accomplished was first made public in this country in 1950. Subsequently, "thermonuclear devices" have been tested from time to time by American authorities in remote areas of the Pacific Ocean. Several explosions of this type are known to have occurred in other countries since 1953.

other highly important applications become available if the production of such isotopes can be made more efficient.

The nuclear reactor supplies the solution to this problem. Because more neutrons are produced in fission than are needed to keep the fission process going, a high concentration of neutrons is available for transforming materials inserted into the reactor into new radio-isotopes.[1] The U.S. Atomic Energy Commission keeps about 150 radio-isotopes in stock and can supply them to qualified users at comparatively low cost.

Radio-isotopes are finding increasing use in many forms of medical therapy. Diseases of the thyroid gland are treated by giving the patient a weak solution of radioiodine to drink. Most of this isotope is taken up selectively by the thyroid, where the emitted β rays reduce the abnormal activity of the gland. Radioboron and radiophosphorus are among other isotopes that are useful in therapy. Radium, which has long been used for the treatment of tumors and cancer, is now being widely replaced by cesium or cobalt which has previously been activated in a reactor. One hospital has a radiocobalt source, costing only a few thousand dollars, equivalent in strength to a kilogram of radium which would cost perhaps $100,000,000. Other interesting details of these applications will be found in the references at the end of this chapter.

23-14   Nuclear Power

While the production of useful radio-isotopes in a nuclear reactor is important, it must be remembered that the primary product is energy. The kinetic energy of fast fission and secondary fragments is merely heat energy. Delivered at a steady, controlled rate, it can be used for industrial and technological power production through the use of some ordinary type of heat engine (such as a steam engine or turbine) coupled with an electric generator. A single pound of U^{235} can give as much energy as the combustion of 1300 tons of coal. This, together with the fact that the world's supply of coal, oil, and natural gas may not last for more than a few hundred years at present rates of consumption, makes the prospect of atomic power an attractive one.

The fuel costs and even the expense of periodic purification of the active materials would be negligible fractions of the total

[1] The neutron flux in the core of a reactor is tremendous, amounting to something of the order of 10^{12} to 10^{14} neutrons/cm^2/sec.

cost of power so produced; but there are two other factors which offer difficulties. One is the fact that the original cost of a nuclear plant would be about double that of a conventional steam plant using coal. However, this gap will probably be closed in the future; and, in regions where natural fuels are expensive, the nuclear plant may come into its own before long. Some industrial power installations are now in operation or being planned in this country and in several others. The number is certain to increase within the next few years.

The other obstacle to the rapid development of commercial nuclear power is the matter of radiation hazard. All active materials must be handled by remote control, and operating personnel and

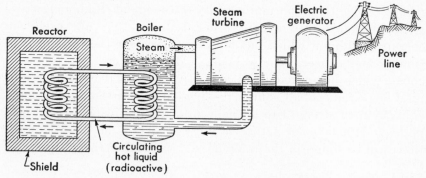

FIG. 23·9   Nuclear power plant (schematic).

people living nearby must be assured adequate protection from harmful neutron and γ radiations. This requires, among other things, the use of massive metal or concrete shields surrounding the reactor (see Fig. 23·9). While it is feasible, at present, to propel submarines, ships, and perhaps even trains with nuclear engines, it may be some time before this can be done for automobiles or aircraft (see Ref. 5).

23·15   Nuclear and Other Energy Sources Compared

In connection with the discussion of the practical utilization of nuclear power, it may be of interest to compare the amounts of energy that can be made available from various sources, both chemical and nuclear. The results, computed on an equal-weight basis and expressed to the nearest power of ten, are collected in Table 23·1.

The first entry in the table represents, as to order of magnitude, the energy that can be released by chemical processes such as the combustion of coal or the metabolism (combustion) of food by an animal. This quantity is relatively small compared with the others, since it originates in changes affecting only the outer parts of atoms—the electrons.

The next two items involve "nuclear energy" and are of the order of hundreds of thousands or millions of times greater than anything chemical action can yield. But perhaps the most concentrated energy source is matter itself in the process of annihilation according to Einstein's $E = mc^2$ (page 409). Up to the present

Table 23·1 Energy Obtainable from 1 Gm of Matter by Various Processes

	Mev
Chemical change	10^{17}
Nuclear fission	10^{22}
Hydrogen fusion	10^{24}
Complete annihilation	10^{27}

time, the only instances where this seems to occur is in the mutual destruction of a positron and an electron, or of a proton and an antiproton. Such events are so "diluted" in space and time that they do not come into consideration as practical methods of energy production on earth. If, however, a means should be discovered for carrying out the annihilation process, every speck of matter in the universe would be potential fuel.

SUMMARY

Nuclear binding forces: Particles making up a nucleus exert strong forces of mutual attraction, which differ fundamentally from Coulomb forces.

Potential barrier: To an approaching charged particle, the nucleus appears to be surrounded by a steep "hill." There exists a certain chance that the barrier may be penetrated rather than surmounted. Neutrons are not usually opposed by a barrier.

Fission: The disintegration of a heavy nucleus into two or more fragments of comparable size. First observed for uranium under neutron bombardment. Large amounts of energy are released in the process.

Nuclear chain reaction: A self-propagating nuclear process such as fission in which each disintegration produces more than one neutron and a certain percentage of these cause further fissions, etc.

Nuclear reactor: A structure consisting of pieces of some suitable active material (uranium, plutonium) embedded in a *moderating* substance that slows neutrons so that they can produce changes in the fissile nuclei present.

Neptunium and plutonium are new elements produced in the nuclear reactor according to the equations on page 457.

The fission ("atomic") *bomb* operates by the bringing together of a mass of fissile material large enough to support a chain reaction. The resultant fission process releases a vast amount of energy in a very short time.

Stellar energy can be accounted for adequately in terms of nuclear reactions. The effective change seems to be the combination of four hydrogen atoms to form an atom of helium. *Thermonuclear reactions of* this type are used in the *hydrogen bomb.*

Beneficial uses of nuclear energy include the utilization of reactor-produced isotopes in medicine and other sciences and the development of plants for generating industrial power.

READING REFERENCES

1. See Refs. 3, 4, and 5 at the end of the preceding chapter (page 444).
2. Smyth, H. D.: "Atomic Energy for Military Purposes," Princeton University Press, Princeton, N.J., 1945. The famous Smyth Report is particularly interesting for its description of the immense task of organizing the A-bomb project.
3. Gamow, G.: "The Birth and Death of the Sun," Penguin, Baltimore, 1945. A fascinating description of nuclear processes in the stars.
4. Hecht, S., and E. Rabinowitch: "Explaining the Atom," Viking, New York, 1954. A lucid account of the whole development of the atom concept.
5. "Peaceful Uses of Atomic Energy," Report of the Panel on the Impact of the Peaceful Uses of Atomic Energy to the Joint Committee on Atomic Energy, Vol. I, GPO, Washington, D.C., January, 1956.
6. Bethe, H.: What Holds the Nucleus Together? *Sci. American,* Vol. 189, No. 3, pp. 58–63, September, 1953.

FILMS

"Atomic Energy," Encyclopaedia Britannica Films. 16 mm, sound, 1 reel.
"The Nuclear Reactor," McGraw-Hill. 16 mm, sound, 1 reel.
See also listings at end of preceding chapter (p. 444).

EXERCISES

1. If Coulomb's law were to hold for charged particles within a nucleus, how great would be the repulsion between two protons assumed to be effectively 10^{-13} cm apart?

2. In order to understand how a neutron can be effectively slowed down by collisions with particles of small mass, such as protons, consider the central impact of a particle of mass 1, moving with a speed v, with a stationary particle of the same mass. Choose letter symbols for the speeds after impact, and write the equations for conservation of energy and conservation of momentum. Then use these two relations to show that the impinging particle is stopped dead, the struck body going on with a speed equal to v.

3. A reactor is developing energy at the rate of 10,000 kw. If an average of 200 Mev is released per fission, how many atoms of U^{235} undergo fission each second?

4. What mass of U^{235} would the reactor of the previous problem use in one month of continuous operation at this level? (1 amu = 1.66 $\times$ 10^{-24} gm.)

5. Check the value of the third entry in Table 23·1, page 465, using the reaction energy given on page 460 and the fact that a hydrogen atom has a mass of about 1 amu.

CONCLUSION

You have come a long way since beginning your study of physics and have been introduced to what may seem an almost countless number of facts even in this short introductory treatment. It is hoped that the journey, admittedly not an easy one at every stage, has proved worthwhile. It is proper to ask yourself at this point what lasting gain you may have got in return for your efforts. If this had been a more conventional science course, it would also follow that the measurement of accomplishment would be a simpler matter—so many facts remembered, so many experimental skills acquired, so much preparation for a profession in which the technical results of this subject are put to use. But in a course such as the present one, intended to contribute to the general education of the student, evaluation of gain and accomplishment is more difficult.

Just what should you now expect to have as part of your intellectual equipment that you did not have before? Is it factual information, an appreciation of the accomplishments of scientific effort, a reverence for nature as evidenced by physical laws, a "feeling" for the behavior of inanimate things, or something else? Perhaps the answer is that the most valuable and lasting benefit one might derive from a first nontechnical college course in science is an appreciation of the utility of the scientific way of attacking problems and an awareness of the possibility of applying such methods to the resolution of difficulties in other fields of human endeavor.

The first chapter of this book presented a brief exposition of the nature of the scientific enterprise. It is understandably difficult for the average person to appreciate the intrinsic nature of science, for he is apt to be bewildered by the many-sidedness of this highly complex enterprise. For instance, the most obvious way in which science touches our lives is through its myriad technical products, which quite literally surround us. To many, that is all there is to science. But the far more important, if less tangible, features of science are its spirit and methods. This quintessence of science—the aspect that is most likely to outlive the gadgets of the moment—is taken to be embodied in the word *research* in a view advanced by Wendt.[1] His interpretation of the word stresses:

. . . exploration and penetration into the unknown, and implies too that it [research] is not limited to science alone but has its place in all human affairs. Thus research is a much broader and deeper thing than science. Indeed, what we have defined as science is the product of research in the study of nature. Civilization is concerned with science as the implement of research but the real source of civilization and its changes is the research spirit and the research method.

Precisely because the research method seems to hold great promise for the solution of problems other than those we customarily think of as belonging to formal science, this procedure is something that every educated person must make part of his own way of thinking and his own attitude toward life. With this in mind the research features have been given a prominent position in this book. Perhaps you will take away with you enough of an idea of the meaning of the term to make possible its application to your own problems.

Recent advances in technology based on scientific discoveries have hurtled us into a new period in history far more critical for humanity than any previous one. If any single piece of evidence was needed, the discovery of how to release subatomic energy on a large scale brought home to thoughtful persons the realization that social problems and science are now inextricably linked. To blame science for this most stupendous of its offshoots would be futile. Rather, the solution to our difficulties, if we are to survive, is to learn to apply scientific thinking to our social and political problems.

It is a matter of vital concern that all of our people, and especially our elected agents in government, realize that the conduct of practical affairs should be guided by the scientific method; that is, by critical examination and evaluation of actual experience rather than by raw emotion, vested authority or wishful thinking. This calls for an educational program in which science must have an important function, for people must understand the scientific method before they can use it—and surprisingly few, even among the highly educated, now do understand it.[2]

[1] Gerald Wendt, American chemist, educator, and distinguished interpreter of science, in "America Now," edited by H. E. Stearns, Scribner, New York, 1938.

[2] Herrick, C. Judson, Scientific Method and Human Values, *Am. Scientist*, Vol. 34, No. 2, pp. 239–245, 1945.

In the same sense, Conant[1] reminds us that:

In a democracy, political power is widely diffused. National policy is determined by the interaction of forces generated and guided by hundreds of thousands if not millions of local leaders and men of influence. Eventually within the limits imposed by public opinion decisions of far-reaching importance are made by a relatively few. These men are almost accidentally thrown into positions of temporary power by the forces working throughout our benignly chaotic system of political democracy. Because of the fact that the applications of science play so important a part in our daily lives, matters of public policy are profoundly influenced by highly technical scientific considerations. Some understanding of science by those in positions of authority and responsibility as well as by those who shape opinion is therefore of importance for the national welfare.

Wendt summarizes the outlook for the broader application of the unique procedure developed by man's investigation of nature in this way:[2]

The same impartial, unprejudiced method of study which has mastered the natural environment can also master our present social environment. Research must be conceived not as the technical study of electrons and atoms, that is, of nature, but as the best use of human intelligence to improve the conditions under which we live.

The nineteenth-century English mathematician and philosopher W. K. Clifford[3] gives us a fitting and cogent closing thought:

Remember, then, that scientific thought is the guide of action; that the truth at which it arrives is not that which we can idly contemplate without error, but that which we may act upon without fear; and you cannot fail to see that scientific thought is not an accompaniment or condition of human progress, but human progress itself.

[1] Reference 6, p. 13.
[2] Wendt, in "America Now," *op. cit.*
[3] Quoted in Bronowski (Ref. 19, p. 14).

APPENDIXES

VALUES OF SOME FUNDAMENTAL PHYSICAL CONSTANTS

Speed of light	$c = 2.9979 \times 10^{10}$ cm/sec
Constant of gravitation	$G = 6.670 \times 10^{-8}$ dyne-cm^2/gm^2
Avogadro's number	$N = 6.025 \times 10^{23}$ atoms/mole
	$= 2.690 \times 10^{19}$ atoms/cm^3 of a gas at standard temperature and pressure.
Electron charge	$e = 4.8024 \times 10^{-10}$ esu
	$= 1.6020 \times 10^{-19}$ coulomb
Mass of the electron at rest	$m_0 = 9.106 \times 10^{-28}$ gm
Ratio of electron charge to mass	$e/m = 1.7594 \times 10^8$ coulombs/gm
Planck's constant	$h = 6.624 \times 10^{-27}$ erg-sec
Mass of proton at rest	$M_p = 1.672 \times 10^{-24}$ gm
Mass ratio, proton to electron	$M_p/m_0 = 1836.6$
Atomic-mass unit	1 amu $= 1.660 \times 10^{-24}$ gm
Electron volt	1 ev $= 1.60 \times 10^{-12}$ erg
Mass-energy equivalent	1 amu $= 931$ Mev

SUMMARY OF ELECTRICAL UNITS USED IN THIS BOOK

Quantity of Charge

One *esu:* Of such size that the force between two small bodies each bearing 1 esu of charge and placed 1 cm apart in a vacuum is equal to 1 dyne. 1 esu $= 2.08 \times 19^9$ electron charges.

One *coulomb* (practical unit) $= 3 \times 10^9$ esu, approximately.

Current

The time rate of passage of charge past any point in a conductor. $I = Q/t$.

One *ampere* (practical unit) $= 1$ coulomb/sec.

Electric-field Strength

The magnitude of the force acting on a unit charge placed at the point in question. The direction of the field is that of the force on a positive charge. A field of unit strength is one in which a charge of 1 esu experiences a force of 1 dyne.

Potential Difference

Measured by the work done on a unit charge in moving it, against the field, from one point to another. Two points in a field have a PD of 1 cgs unit if 1 erg of work is done on 1 esu of charge in moving it between them.

One *volt* (practical unit) = $\frac{1}{300}$ of 1 cgs unit of PD, approximately.

Capacitance

The constant ratio of the charge on a conductor to its potential.

One *farad* (practical unit) = capacitance of a conductor whose potential increases by 1 volt when its charge is increased by 1 coulomb.

Resistance

The constant ratio of the PD applied at the ends of a solid conductor to the current flowing through it, the temperature remaining constant.

One *ohm* (practical unit) = resistance of a conductor in which the application of a PD of 1 volt maintains a current of 1 amp.

$$I_{\text{amp}} = \frac{V_{\text{volts}}}{R_{\text{ohms}}}$$

SIMPLE MATHEMATICAL OPERATIONS

Proportion and Variation

In the study of physics and in the expression of its laws there frequently arises the need for stating the exact relation between two or more quantities. In fact, most physical laws find their only adequate expression in this form. Such statements often involve the concept of *proportion.* In ordinary affairs we hear such expressions as "The greater the effort, the greater the gain" or "Less risk is involved if the investments are more diversified." In science an attempt is made to express quantitatively the nature of the variation of one quantity with one or more other quantities.

Direct Proportion. Probably the simplest example of a relation between the magnitudes of two quantities is that in which the first quantity is directly proportional to the other. In simple terms this implies that, if one quantity is doubled, the related quantity also becomes doubled; if one increases threefold, the other increases in value three times, etc. We may say that "y is proportional to x," where x and y are the things concerned. For example, x might represent the cost of one article of a given kind, and y might be the cost per dozen, per gross, or per hundred.

The statement "y is proportional to x" may be put in symbols in a number of ways. Using $\propto$, the sign of proportion, the direct shorthand expression is

$$y \propto x \qquad \text{(A·1)}$$

Another way of expressing the same fact, and one that lends itself to computation, is

$$y = kx \qquad \text{(A·2)}$$

where k is a constant. This means that any y value is obtained by multiplying the corresponding x value by a number k which has a constant numerical value throughout the problem. Thus if y represents the distance covered by an airplane traveling at constant speed and x is the elapsed time, we might have the following set of values:

x, hr.........	1	2	3	4	5	etc.
y, mi.........	250	500	750	1000	1250	

Any y divided by the corresponding x is equal to 250 mi/hr, and hence this is the value of k [Eq. (A·2)] appropriate to this example. That is,

$$y = 250x \qquad \text{(A·3)}$$

If the value of any pair of entries in the above table is known, we may express the statement of direct proportion in still another way,

$$\frac{x_1}{y_1} = \frac{x_2}{y_2} \qquad \text{(A·4)}$$

to be read, "x_1 is to y_1 as x_2 is to y_2." Here x_1 and y_1 and x_2 and y_2 represent any two pairs of values. If any three of the above quantities are known, the fourth may be found. For example, how far will the airplane in the preceding example go in 3 hr 24 min? Using any known pair of values of time and distance, say, the second pair in the table, we can write Eq. (A·4) in the form

$$\frac{2}{500} = \frac{3.4}{y}$$

Cross-multiplying (that is, clearing of fractions) yields $2y = 3.4 \times 500$, or $y = 850$ mi.

Note that the relation expressed by Eq. (A·4) can also be written in any of the following ways:

$$x_1 y_2 = x_2 y_1 \qquad \frac{x_1}{x_2} = \frac{y_1}{y_2} \qquad \frac{y_1}{x_1} = \frac{y_2}{x_2} \qquad \text{(A·5)}$$

The numerical example could have been solved also by using Eq. (A·3). Substitution gives $y = 3.4 \times 250 = 850$ mi.

If two quantities x and y are in direct proportion, then a graph of y against x will be a *straight line* passing through the origin of the coordinate system. Plotting experimental data and obtaining points that lie, within experimental error, on a straight line through the origin is a convenient way of recognizing the existence of such proportionality between the two variables. Figure 4.5, page 60, illustrates the direct proportion between the speed and the time for a body starting from rest and moving with constant acceleration.

Sometimes, as in the case illustrated by Fig. 4·8, page 63, the straight lines do not pass through the origin. Then the relation between the variables must be written $y = a + kx$, where a and k are constant. Shifting the origin by an amount a will again give the simple proportionality relation $y = kx$.

Quadratic and Higher Proportion. As you know, the circumference of a circle is proportional to its radius. This fact is expressed by the formula

$$C = 2\pi r \tag{A·6}$$

where C is the circumference and r is the radius. The preceding equation expresses this proportionality in the form of Eq. (A·2), with k equal to $2\pi \; (= 2 \times 3.1416 \cdots)$.

If now the question is how the **area** of a circle is related to its radius, the answer is expressed by the geometric relation

$$A = \pi r^2 \tag{A·7}$$

This formula is slightly more involved than the previous one. Here we have one quantity, A, proportional to the **square** of another quantity, r. This means that, if the radius is doubled, the area of the circle becomes 2^2, or 4, times as great as before; 3 times the radius means 9 times the area, etc. Corresponding to Eqs. (A·1) and (A·4), we could write this fact

$$A \propto r^2 \quad \text{or} \quad \frac{A_1}{A_2} = \frac{r_1^2}{r_2^2} \tag{A·8}$$

Example: How much more paint does it take to cover a disk 10 ft in diameter than to cover one that is only 2 ft in diameter? Since areas are proportional to squares of diameters (or to squares of radii),

$$\frac{A_1}{A_2} = \frac{10^2}{2^2} \quad \text{or} \quad \frac{A_1}{A_2} = 25$$

The ratio of diameters is 5, the ratio of the areas is $5^2 = 25$, so that 25 times as much paint will be needed.

The volume of a sphere is proportional to the **cube** of the radius (or diameter).

$$V = \tfrac{4}{3}\pi r^3 \tag{A·9}$$

Double the radius, and the volume increases $2^3 = 2 \times 2 \times 2 = 8$ times; treble the radius, and it increases 27 times. Thus the diameter of the sun is about 100 times the earth's. The volume of the sun is therefore about 1,000,000 times that of the earth.

It is a general fact that the surface areas of geometrically similar bodies are proportional to the squares of corresponding dimensions and that their volumes are proportional to the cubes of corresponding dimensions. For instance, if an airplane model is built to a linear scale of 1 to 20, the wing area of the actual plane will be 400 ($= 20^2$) times that of the model. The cabin space (volume) will be $20^3 = 8000$ times that of the model.

Inverse Proportion. Two magnitudes x and y so related that

$$\frac{x_1}{x_2} = \frac{y_2}{y_1} \tag{A·10}$$

are said to be **inversely proportional** to each other. Alternative ways of expressing this are

$$x \propto \frac{1}{y} \qquad x = \frac{k}{y} \qquad xy = k \tag{A·11}$$

where k is a constant.

In this kind of relation, in contrast with previous examples, one quantity **decreases** as the other increases. For instance, when the temperature of a gas is held fixed, the volume occupied is inversely proportional to the applied pressure (Boyle's law, page 124). This means that, if the pressure is doubled, the new volume becomes half of the old; if the initial pressure is trebled, the volume changes to one-third its initial value, etc.

Inverse Square Proportion; Other Forms. In physics an important form of relation between two quantities x and y is expressed by

$$\frac{x_1}{x_2} = \frac{y_2^2}{y_1^2} \tag{A·12}$$

The quantity x is said to be **inversely proportional to the square** of y. By using our other forms of writing proportions, this would be expressed

$$x \propto \frac{1}{y^2} \qquad x = \frac{k}{y^2} \qquad \text{or} \qquad xy^2 = k \tag{A·13}$$

where k is a constant. The force of gravitational attraction between two particles of matter is inversely proportional to the square of their distance apart. Doubling the distance makes the force one-fourth as great, and reducing the original distance to one-third increases the force nine times, etc.

In addition to the above forms, which are among those most frequently used in elementary physics, many other types of variation may be met with. In particular, several forms may be combined as in an expression like $a = kbc^2 \sqrt{d}/e^3$.

A good reference on the common sense of the subject of proportion is W. W. Sawyer, "Mathematician's Delight," Chap. VIII.

The Laws of Exponents

Many of the algebraic expressions used in physics involve quantities that are raised to certain powers. Thus, in the relation stated at the end of the last section, c is raised to the second power (square), e to the third power ("e cubed"), and d occurs under the square-root sign, which is equivalent, as you will see, to its being raised to the one-half power. A simple integral *exponent* applied to a quantity is merely a shorthand notation indicating that the quantity is to be raised to the indicated power —that is, to be multiplied by itself the indicated number of times. For instance, A^4 is a compact way of indicating $A \cdot A \cdot A \cdot A$. Stated differently, the power, or exponent, 4 used here indicates that A is to be used as a factor four times over.

The following rules then result for exponents that are integers:

1. If two or more quantities, each a power of the same base, are *multiplied,* the product is the base raised to a power equal to the *sum* of the separate powers. Thus $2^2 \times 2^3 = 2^5 = 32$.

2. If one power of a given quantity is *divided* by a smaller power of the same quantity, the quotient is given by the base raised to a power equal to the exponent of the dividend *minus* the exponent of the divisor. For example, $3^5/3^2 = 3^3 = 27$.

3. If a number given as a power of a certain base is raised to another power, the result is equal to the base with an exponent equal to the *product* of the two exponents. Thus

$$(2^4)^3 = 2^{12} = 4096$$

The meaning of these rules for operations with exponents can readily be extended to include negative and fractional powers. Then the general rules become

$$(1) \quad A^m A^n = A^{m+n}$$
$$(2) \quad \frac{A^m}{A^n} = A^{m-n} \qquad \qquad \Big\} \quad (\text{A·14})$$
$$(3) \quad (A^m)^n = A^{mn}$$

These rules hold when either m or n or both are any rational numbers. The exponent *zero* also has a meaning. Inasmuch as A^m/A^m always equals unity, it follows from rule 2 of Eqs. (A·14) that $A^m/A^m = A^{m-m} = A^0 = 1$. That is, any quantity with the exponent 0 is equal to 1.

Triangles

Similar Triangles. Corresponding sides of any two geometrically *similar* figures are *proportional*. This fact is particularly useful in connection with triangles. For instance, in certain problems in Chap. 3 dealing with vectors there occur two triangles having their sides respectively parallel or two triangles with corresponding sides perpendicular to each other. In either case the triangles are *similar,* and their *sides are proportional.* Calling the two triangles ABC and $A'B'C'$, we may thus write

$$\frac{AB}{A'B'} = \frac{AC}{A'C'} = \frac{BC}{B'C'}$$

Right Triangles. The sides of a right triangle are related very simply by the theorem of Pythagoras, which says that

$$c^2 = a^2 + b^2 \tag{A·15}$$

where c is the hypotenuse and a and b are the sides adjoining the right angle. If the lengths of any pair of sides are known, the third side may be computed from this relation.

There are particular sets of *integer* values for the sides a, b, and c that satisfy Eq. (A·15). Two of the most common combinations are 3, 4, 5 and 5, 12, 13. Equal multiples of these numbers will of course also satisfy Eq. (A·15)—for example, a right triangle can be constructed with sides of length 6, 8, and 10.

Basic Ideas of Trigonometry

Trigonometry deals more formally with the relations between the sides and angles of triangles. The size of any acute angle may be specified in terms of certain ratios between the sides of a right triangle of which the given angle is a part. These ratios are called *trigonometric functions* of the angle. We shall restrict attention to the two most frequently used ones, called the *sine* and *cosine,* respectively.

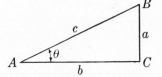

In the figure, θ is the angle to be described, and ACB is a right triangle constructed on it. The sine of theta, written $\sin \theta$, is defined as the ratio of the opposite side BC to the hypotenuse AB. The cosine of theta, written $\cos \theta$,

FIG. A·1 Right-triangle relationships.

is the ratio of the adjoining side AC to the hypotenuse AB. Thus,

$$\sin \theta = \frac{a}{c} \tag{A·16}$$

$$\cos \theta = \frac{b}{c} \tag{A·17}$$

Values of $\sin \theta$ and $\cos \theta$ have been computed for all values of θ and collected in convenient tables for reference. An abbreviated table of these functions is found on page 483. It is evident from Fig. A·1 that for acute angles the range of values of the two functions will be

	$\theta = 0$ deg	$\theta = 90$ deg
sin θ...........	0	1
cos θ...........	1	0

For certain special angles, the values of sine and cosine can be found without recourse to tables. Thus sin 45° = cos 45° = $1/\sqrt{2}$, sin 30° = cos 60° = $\frac{1}{2}$, etc.

The sine and cosine of any angle are simply related. From the figure, $a^2 + b^2 = c^2$. Dividing through by c^2, we have

$$\left(\frac{a}{c}\right)^2 + \left(\frac{b}{c}\right)^2 = 1 \qquad \text{or} \qquad \sin^2 \theta + \cos^2 \theta = 1 \qquad (A·18)$$

(This is to be read: "Sine-squared theta plus cosine-squared theta . . . .") Thus, if the value of either the sine or the cosine of an angle is known, the other may easily be computed.

Deduction of Bernoulli's Equation for the Pressure of a Gas [1]

An ideal gas consists of molecules of negligible size that exert no forces on each other except at the instant of collision. The molecular collisions must be assumed to entail no change of KE (see text, page 119).

Imagine a swarm of such moving molecules confined in a rectangular box (Fig. A·2a). Let m be the mass, in grams, of each molecule and let n represent the number of molecules in each cubic centimeter of the box.

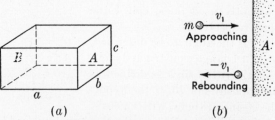

FIG. A·2　Mechanics of gas molecules in motion.

Consider a molecule that is about to strike wall A of the container (Fig. A·2b). Designate by v_1 the component of this molecule's velocity that is directly toward the wall. There will in general be two other independent velocity components in the plane perpendicular to v_1, but these will have no effect on the interaction of this molecule with the wall in question.

[1] See pp. 114, 115 of the text.

The effect of the collision with the wall is to change the (vector) momentum of the molecule, sending it in the reverse direction with a velocity $-v_1$. The molecule experiences, at collision, a momentum change amounting to

$$\Delta M_1 = mv_1 - (-mv_1) = 2mv_1 \qquad \text{(A·19)}$$

The molecule in question may be thought of as bounding back and forth continually between walls A and B, always moving with speed v_1. Actually, a given molecule will make many collisions with other molecules before going very far; but its momentum will be handed on just as if it had traversed the whole length of the box and collided with the opposite wall directly.

Consider the collisions of the single molecule with wall A. The time taken to go from A to B and back to A again will be $\Delta t = 2a/v_1$. Then the rate of change of momentum on the part of this single molecule will be, according to Eq. (A·19),

$$\frac{\Delta M_1}{\Delta t} = \frac{2mv_1}{2a/v_1} = \frac{mv_1^2}{a} \qquad \text{(A·20)}$$

But, according to Newton's second law, the rate of change of momentum is equal to the (average) force on this molecule, and the equal and opposite reaction on the wall is a force whose magnitude, in dynes, is simply

$$f_A = \frac{mv_1^2}{a} \qquad \text{(A·21)}$$

At any instant, the molecules of the gas have a wide range of speeds and are moving in all conceivable directions. Statistically, however, this amounts to assuming that $\frac{1}{3}$ the total number are effectively moving in each of the three principal directions.[1] With this in mind, the total force on the wall A can be computed. The effective number of molecules encountering this wall is $\frac{1}{3}$ the number per unit volume multiplied by the entire volume of the box, or $\frac{1}{3} n(abc)$. Multiplying this by the force exerted in each collision, (A·21) gives the total force

$$F_A = \frac{1}{3} nmv^2(bc) \qquad \text{(A·22)}$$

where v^2 now represents the average of the squares of the speeds of the individual molecules. Dividing by bc gives the force per unit area, or the pressure on the wall, as

$$p = \frac{1}{3} nmv^2 \qquad \text{(A·23)}$$

This result is independent of which face of the box was under consideration. It represents the pressure exerted on any portion of the container.

[1] A more detailed analysis proves this rigorously.

The Centripetal-force Formula

In order to derive Eq. (9·5), page 143, consider a small change in the position of a particle of mass m that is describing a circle with the uniform speed v (Fig. A·3). The speed of the particle is the same at all points in the path; but in moving on a circle the body is continually changing its direction, and because of this the **vector** velocity is changing. When the particle is at P_1, its velocity is P_1N_1, and when it is at P_2, the velocity is represented by P_2N_2. The vector difference, indicated as Δv in the diagram at the right, is the change in velocity. It is directed toward the center as shown.

If, now, we can calculate the size of Δv, we need only divide it by the time during which this change took place in order to get the centripetal acceleration. Finally we can appeal to $f = ma$ to find the force needed to

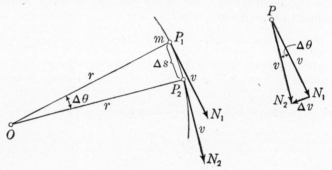

Fig. A·3   Particle moving in a circle.

produce this acceleration, which is what we set out to do. If $\Delta\theta$ is the angle between the radii to P_1 and P_2, then the angle between PN_1 and PN_2 is also $\Delta\theta$, for each velocity vector is perpendicular to the corresponding radius. In the limiting case where $\Delta\theta$ is small, OP_1P_2 is essentially a triangle and is similar to the vector triangle PN_1N_2. Equating the ratios of the sides, $\Delta v/v = \Delta s/r$, or

$$\Delta v = \frac{v}{r}\Delta s$$

Dividing both sides of this relation by Δt, the interval of time during which the particle moves from P_1 to P_2, we get

$$\frac{\Delta v}{\Delta t} = \frac{v}{r}\frac{\Delta s}{\Delta t} \qquad\qquad (A·24)$$

But $\Delta v/\Delta t$ is, in the limit, the acceleration directly toward the center, and $\Delta s/\Delta t$ is the speed v of the particle in the circle. Making these substitutions gives $a = v^2/r$, and using $f = ma$ then gives the value of the centripetal force

$$f_c = \frac{mv^2}{r} \qquad (A\cdot 25)$$

as in the text.

Simple Harmonic Motion

The analytical description of SHM is readily obtained with the help of the reference circle (pages 150 to 152).

The displacement of the vibrating particle is the projection of the displacement of the point that moves on the circle (Fig. A·4). Using the notation of trigonometry, it amounts to

$$x = a \cos \theta \qquad (A\cdot 26)$$

Similarly, the x component of V gives the instantaneous speed of the vibrating particle. From Fig. A·4a,

$$\frac{v}{V} = \frac{y}{A} = \frac{\sqrt{A^2 - x^2}}{A} \qquad (A\cdot 27)$$

Now V is expressible in terms of the period T. The point P, going at the constant speed V, covers a distance equal to the circumference of

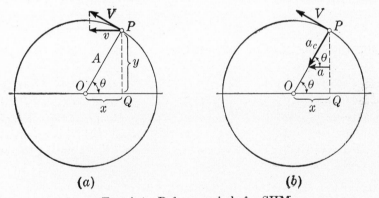

(a)   (b)

Fig. A·4   Reference circle for SHM.

the circle in time T. Thus $VT = 2\pi A$, or

$$V = \frac{2\pi A}{T} \qquad (A\cdot 28)$$

Using this value of V, (A·27) becomes

$$v = \frac{2\pi}{T} \sqrt{A^2 - x^2} \qquad (A\cdot 29)$$

This result can also be written

$$v = \frac{2\pi A}{T} \sin \theta \qquad (A\cdot 30)$$

The instantaneous acceleration of the particle is the projection (Fig. A·4b) of the *centripetal acceleration* V^2/A of the point P [see just above Eq. (A·25)]. Thus

$$\frac{a}{a_c} = -\frac{x}{A} \qquad (A\cdot 31)$$

the minus sign indicating that a is contrary in direction to x. Using $a_c = V^2/A$, this last expression becomes

$$a = -\frac{V^2}{A^2}x$$

or, by (A·28),

$$a = -\frac{4\pi^2}{T^2}x \qquad (A\cdot 32)$$

The restoring force acting on the particle is $f = ma$, or

$$f = -\frac{4\pi^2 m}{T^2}x \qquad (A\cdot 33)$$

This equation is of the form $f = -kx$, as it must be for SHM (page 149), and here we see that $k = 4\pi^2 m/T^2$. Solving this for T, we have

$$T = 2\pi \sqrt{\frac{m}{k}} \qquad (A\cdot 34)$$

which is the same as (9·10), page 151.

VALUES OF SIN θ AND COS θ

Angle θ, deg	$\sin \theta$	$\cos \theta$	Angle θ, deg	$\sin \theta$	$\cos \theta$
0	.000	1.000	46	.719	.695
1	.017	.999	47	.731	.689
2	.035	.999	48	.743	.662
3	.052	.999	49	.755	.656
4	.070	.998	50	.766	.643
5	.087	.996	51	.777	.629
6	.105	.995	52	.788	.616
7	.122	.993	53	.799	.602
8	.139	.990	54	.809	.588
9	.156	.988	55	.819	.574
10	.174	.985	56	.829	.559
11	.191	.982	57	.839	.545
12	.208	.978	58	.848	.530
13	.225	.984	59	.857	.515
14	.242	.970	60	.866	.500
15	.259	.966	61	.875	.485
16	.276	.961	62	.883	.469
17	.292	.956	63	.891	.454
18	.309	.951	64	.899	.438
19	.326	.946	65	.906	.423
20	.342	.940	66	.914	.407
21	.358	.934	67	.920	.391
22	.375	.927	68	.927	.375
23	.391	.921	69	.934	.358
24	.407	.914	70	.940	.342
25	.423	.906	71	.946	.326
26	.438	.899	72	.951	.309
27	.454	.891	73	.956	.292
28	.470	.883	74	.961	.276
29	.485	.875	75	.966	.259
30	.500	.866	76	.970	.242
31	.515	.857	77	.874	.225
32	.530	.848	78	.978	.208
33	.545	.839	79	.982	.191
34	.559	.829	80	.985	.174
35	.574	.819	81	.988	.156
36	.588	.809	82	.990	.139
37	.602	.799	83	.993	.122
38	.616	.788	84	.995	.105
39	.629	.777	85	.996	.087
40	.643	.766	86	.998	.070
41	.656	.755	87	.999	.052
42	.669	.743	88	.999	.035
43	.682	.731	89	.999	.017
44	.695	.719	90	1.000	.000
45	.707	.707			

LIST OF ALL READING REFERENCES MENTIONED IN THE TEXT

Books

Andrade, E. N.: "Isaac Newton," Parrish, London, 1950.

Anthony, H. D.: "Modern Science and Its Background," Macmillan, London, 1948.

Armitage, A.: "The World of Copernicus," Mentor Books, New York, 1947.

Bernal, J. D.: "The Social Function of Science," Routledge, London, 1939.

Born, Max: "The Restless Universe," Blackie, Glasgow, 1935.

Bragg, W. H.: "Concerning the Nature of Things," Harper, New York, 1925.

Bragg, W. H.: "The Universe of Light," Macmillan, New York, 1933.

Bragg, W. H.: "The World of Sound," G. Bell, London, 1925.

Bragg, W. L.: "Electricity," Macmillan, New York, 1936.

Bridgman, P. W.: "The Nature of Physical Theory," Princeton University Press, Princeton, N.J., 1936.

Bronowski, J.: "The Common Sense of Science," Heinemann, London, 1951.

Butterfield, H.: "The Origin of Modern Science, 1300–1800," Macmillan, New York, 1951.

Cajori, F.: "A History of Physics," Macmillan, New York, 1929.

Chalmers, T. W.: "Historical Researches," Scribner, New York, 1952.

Cohen, M. R., and I. E. Drabkin: "A Source Book in Greek Science," McGraw-Hill, New York, 1948.

Conant, J. B.: "Modern Science and Modern Man," Columbia University Press, New York, 1952.

Conant, J. B.: "On Understanding Science," Yale University Press, New Haven, Conn., 1947.

Cosslett, V. E.: "The Electron Microscope," Sigma Books, London, 1947.

Crew, Henry: "The Rise of Modern Physics," William & Wilkins, Baltimore, 1935.

Crowther, J. G.: "The Social Relations of Science," Macmillan, New York, 1941.

Curie, Eve: "Mme. Curie," translated by Vincent Sheean, Doubleday, New York, 1937.

Dingle, H.: "The Scientific Adventure," Philosophical Library, New York, 1953.

Eddington, A. S.: "The Nature of the Physical World," Macmillan, New York, 1928.

Frank, Philipp: "Between Physics and Philosophy," Harvard University Press, Cambridge, Mass., 1941.

Freeman, Ira M.: "Invitation to Experiment," Dutton, New York, 1940.

Gamow, G.: "Atomic Energy in Cosmic and Human Life," Macmillan, New York, 1946.

Gamow, G.: "The Birth and Death of the Sun," Penguin, Baltimore, 1945.

Harrison, G. R.: "Atoms in Action," Morrow, New York, 1939.

Harsányi, Zsolt: "The Star Gazer," translated by Paul Tabor, Putnam, New York, 1939.

Hayakawa, S. I.: "Language in Action," Harcourt, Brace, New York, 1941.

Hecht, S., and E. Rabinowitch: "Explaining the Atom," Viking, New York, 1954.

Hoffman, B.: "The Strange Story of the Quantum," Harper, New York, 1947.

Holton, G.: "Introduction to Concepts and Theories in Physical Science," Addison-Wesley, Cambridge, Mass., 1952.

Jaffe, B.: "Men of Science in America," Simon and Schuster, New York, 1944.

Jeans, J. H.: "Science and Music," Macmillan, New York, 1938.

Jeans, J. H.: "The Universe Around Us," 4th ed., Macmillan, New York, 1944.

Jordan, P.: "Physics of the 20th Century," translated by Eleanor Oshry, Philosophical Library, New York, 1944.

Krogdahl, W. S.: "The Astronomical Universe," Macmillan, New York, 1952.

Leprince-Ringuet, L.: "Cosmic Rays," Prentice-Hall, New York, 1950.

Lodge, O.: "Energy," Benn, London, 1928.

Lodge, O.: "Pioneers of Science," Macmillan, New York, 1910.

Loeb, L. B., and A. S. Adams: "The Development of Physical Thought," Wiley, New York, 1933.

Luckiesh, M.: "Light, Vision and Seeing," Van Nostrand, New York, 1944.

Magie, W. F.: "A Source Book in Physics," McGraw-Hill, New York, 1935.

Michelson, A. A.: "Studies in Optics," University of Chicago Press, Chicago, 1927.

Mills, John: "A Fugue in Cycles and Bels," Van Nostrand, New York, 1935.

Minnaert, M.: "Light and Colour in the Open Air," Dover, New York, 1954.

Mott-Smith, M.: "This Mechanical World," Appleton-Century-Crofts, New York, 1931.

Moulton, F. R., and J. J. Schifferes: "The Autobiography of Science," Doubleday, New York, 1945.

Payne-Gaposchkin, C.: "Introduction to Astronomy," Prentice-Hall, New York, 1954.

Perrin, Jean: "Atoms," translated by D. L. Hammick, Constable, London, 1923.

Reichenbach, H.: "Atom and Cosmos," translated and revised by E. S. Allen, Macmillan, New York, 1933.

Ruhemann, M.: "Power," Sigma Books, London, 1946.

Russell, Bertrand: "The Scientific Outlook," Norton, New York, 1931.

Sawyer, W. W.: "Mathematician's Delight," Penguin, Baltimore, 1946.

Schrödinger, E.: "What Is Life?" Macmillan, New York, 1945.

Sedgwick, W. T., and H. W. Tyler: "A Short History of Science," Macmillan, New York, 1939.

Skilling, W. J., and R. S. Richardson: "Astronomy," Holt, New York, 1939.

Smyth, H. D.: "Atomic Energy for Military Purposes," Princeton University Press, Princeton, N.J., 1945.

Somerville, J.: "The Way of Science," Schuman, New York, 1953.

Swann, W. F. C.: "Physics," Wiley, New York, 1941.

Taylor, F. S., "A Short History of Science and Scientific Thought," Norton, New York, 1949.

Taylor, L. W.: "Physics, the Pioneer Science," Houghton Mifflin, Boston, 1941.

Thompson, J. A.: "Count Rumford of Massachusetts," Rinehart, New York, 1935.

Thomson, J. J.: "Recollections and Reflections," Macmillan, New York, 1937.

Upton, M.: "Electronics for Everyone," Devin-Adair, New York, 1954.

Weaver, W. (ed.): "The Scientists Speak," Gaer, New York, 1947.

Wendt, G.: "You and the Atom," Morrow, New York, 1956.

Westaway, F.: "The Scientific Method," Blackie, Glasgow, 1937.

Whitehead, A.: "Science and the Modern World," Mentor Books, New York, 1948.

Zworykin, V., and E. Ramberg: "Phoeoelectricity and Its Applications," Wiley, New York, 1949.

Journal Articles, Pamphlets, etc.

Various articles in the *American Journal of Physics:* Cohen, I. B., Vol. 18, No. 6, 1950; Compton, A. H., Vol. 14, No. 2, 1946; Fletcher, Harvey, Vol. 14, No. 4, 1946; Jauncey, G. E. M., Vol. 13, No. 6, 1945, and Vol. 14, No. 2, 1946; Johnson, Wendell, Vol. 15, No. 2, 1947; Watson, E. C., Vol. 14, No. 4, 1946.

In the *Scientific American:* Bozorth, R., Vol. 192, No. 1, 1955; Bethe, H., Vol. 189, No. 3, 1953; Darrow, K. K., Vol. 186, No. 3, 1952; Ingalls, A.: Vol. 186, No. 6, 1952; Pierce, J., Vol. 183, No. 4, 1950; Rush, J., Vol. 193, No. 2, 1955.

Colton, F.: *Natl. Geographic Mag.*, Vol. 105, No. 1, 1954; Hanson, N.: *Physics Today*, Vol. 8, No. 8, 1955; Herrick, C.: *Am. Scientist*, Vol. 34, No. 2, 1945; Macmillan, E.: *Am. Scientist*, Vol. 43, No. 3, 1955; *Unesco Courier*, Vol. 7, No. 10, 1955; Report of the Panel on the Peaceful Uses of Atomic Energy to the Joint Committee on Atomic Energy, Vol. I, GPO, Washington, D.C., January, 1956.

INDEX

Absolute zero and gas at constant volume, 125–128

Absorption-line spectra, 228–230

Acceleration, 58–59
  and angular speed, 140–141
  constant, motion with, 59–60
    computing distance covered in, 60–62
    examples on, 64–65
    general relations for, 62–64

Accelerators, particle, 437–440

Achromatic doublet, 223

Air resistance, effect of, on projectiles, 70–72

Alhazen, 4

Alpha rays, 376, 377

Ammeters, 298

Ampère, A. M., 288n., 315, 316

Amplifier, triode as, 348

Anderson, Carl, 427, 428, 441

Andrade, E. N., 7, 9n.

Ångström, A. J., 227

Angular motion, 139–140

Angular speed and acceleration, 140–141

Anode, 292

Antinodes, 170

Antiproton, 440

Aquinas, St. Thomas, 4

Archimedes, 2, 3, 105

Area, measurement of, 19–20

Aristotle, 2–4, 6, 67, 178, 197

Armitage, A., 11

Arrhenius, 292

Aston, F. W., 364

Atomic bomb, 458–459

Atomic-mass scale, 364–365

Atomic weights, 295

Atomicity of energy, 385

Atoms, electricity as constituent of, 268–269
  heavier, structure of, 399–401
  hydrogen, circular orbits in, 395–397
  and molecules, 113–114
  planetary, difficulties of, 394–395

Avogadro's law, 130

Balmer formula, 392–394, 398

Band spectra, 231–232, 401–402

Battery, 292

Becker, 435

Becquerel, A. H., 375

Bell, Alexander Graham, 167n.

Bernoulli, Daniel, 114
  equation of, for pressure of gas, deduction of, 478–479
  (See also Joule-Bernoulli equation)

Beta rays, 376, 377

Betatron, 368–369

Bethe, H. A., 460

Bevatron, University of California, 440

Blackett, 428, 431

Bohr, Niels, 397, 399, 412, 414, 417, 418, 454
  theory of, 394–395, 408, 409, 415
    appraisal of, 402–403
    extensions of, 398–399

Bolometer, 232

Born, 408, 414

Bothe, 435

Boyle's law, 124–125, 475

Bragg, W. H., 372–373

Bragg, W. L., 372–373

Bragg crystal spectrometer, 405

Brahe, Tycho, 5, 9

Branched circuit, equivalent resistance of, 303–305

Branching, 441

Brown, Robert, 117

Brownian motion, 117–118

Bunsen, Robert, 227

Cajori, F., 5n., 7

Capacitance, 472

Capacitors, 284

Carbon arc, 186

Cathode, 292